anatomy of the cell

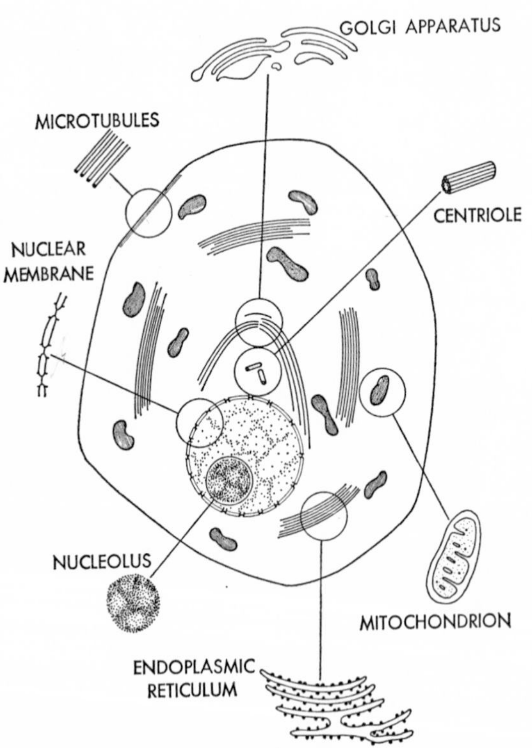
GOLGI APPARATUS
MICROTUBULES
CENTRIOLE
NUCLEAR
MEMBRANE
NUCLEOLUS
MITOCHONDRION
ENDOPLASMIC
RETICULUM

anatomy of the cell

BJÖRN AFZELIUS

translated by Birgit Satir

THE UNIVERSITY
OF CHICAGO
PRESS
CHICAGO AND LONDON

Translated by Birgit Satir from:

Cellen. © 1964 by Björn Afzelius. Published 1964 by Wahlström and Widstrand, AB, Stockholm.

Library of Congress Catalog Card Number: 66-13860

THE UNIVERSITY OF CHICAGO PRESS, CHICAGO & LONDON

The University of Toronto Press, Toronto 5, Canada

Published 1966. Printed in the United States of America

contents

1

structure and ultrastructure

In a newborn baby one finds approximately 2,000,000,000,000 cells. This figure indicates how complicated the human body is and how tiny its building units are. The weight of an average cell is about 0.00000001 (10^{-8}) g and its diameter about 0.02 mm (20 μ).[1] In spite of its minuteness, every single cell sets the frame for a microcosm, a closed world in which a multitude of cell components move according to specific laws and in which an unknown number of different units compose a minimum without which the cell would die.

This book describes some of the best-known components of the cell. Other cell elements are given a brief treatment either because of the scarcity of knowledge about the component or because the component does not play a leading role in the life of the cell. Every chapter has as its cardinal point a cell component that is specialized for one or several functions. The scientific term for a component is *organelle*. Above all, the aim of this book is to demonstrate how knowledge about the construction of an organelle can help us understand how the organelle, or even the whole cell or the entire organism, functions. The emphasis is thus placed more on the appearance of the cell machinery than on its chemical composition; therefore, this book will be easily read by those without any chemical knowledge. The few chemical terms and formulas which appear can be left out without losing the conti-

[1] Two units of measurement used in this book are μ (pronounced "mew") and Å (Ångström). 1 μ = 0.001 mm. 1 Å = 0.001μ or 0.000001 mm. 1 mm = 1,000 μ = 10,000,000 Å.

nuity of the text. This does not imply that the volume gives so simple a view of the material presented that I was forced to employ half-truths and to leave out fundamental questions. Chapters 2 and 3 especially contain questions which are not easily explained without the description of rather complicated phenomena partly in chemical, partly in structural, terms. For readers interested in a presentation of the enzyme content of different organelles, a list is included on pages 3 and 4. It has not been possible to give a complete account of the original works from which the material was drawn. The literature list found on page 115 contains, broadly speaking, three types of works: important original studies done in cell biology, excellent popularized texts (to the extent that they were found in easily accessible publications), and original studies from which were borrowed the illustrations for some of the figures in this book. Most of the illustrations, however, have not been published before.

A description of the cell machinery in its totality, picturing the manner in which the different organelles are associated in order to achieve the functioning unit, the living cell, would have been desirable in this chapter. Time, however, is not yet ripe to write such a chapter. The theory which is feasible today is either a pure description that places the organelles in relation to each other in an arbitrary cell without drawing any conclusions, or a functional general theory that introduces specific imaginary assumptions. One such assumption is the existence of a "cell skeleton"; another, that almost every organelle can be freely transformed into another organelle. Some pertinent questions relating to the study of the cell are these: Does the cell in its totality possess a specific organization inasmuch as its components have fixed positions or move in fixed patterns? Is the cell merely a collection of cell organelles or is a higher degree of organization present in the cell through which the cell organelles can fully express their capacities? Does some kind of interaction occur among the cell components by virtue of their being associated in a specific way?

It is easier to evaluate the implications of these three questions and their central role in the study of the biology of the cell if we look at the results from similar questions asked at a lower and a

TABLE 1

Cell Structures and Their Functional Enzymes

Cell Components	Occurrence	Enzyme Content	Functional Scope
Cell nucleus	Universal	Certain glycolytic enzymes. An unknown number functioning in→	DNA synthesis; formation of messenger RNA (Chap. 6)
Mitochondria	Universal	Citric acid cycle enzymes; electron-transport enzymes, etc.	Oxidative phosphorylation; terminal electron transport; breakdown of amino acids and fatty acids; synthesis of amino acids and fatty acids (Chaps. 2 and 3)
Endoplasmic reticulum	Universal	Glucose-6-phosphatase; DPNH–cytochrome c reductase; several enzymes in connection with→	Detoxification; steroid and lipid metabolism. Likely: active transport. Glycogen islets; glycogen synthesis (Chap. 1)
Ribosomes	Universal	No enzyme systems demonstrated	Participate in protein synthesis (Chap. 6)
Ground cytoplasm (the substances surrounding remaining organelles)	Universal	Multiple enzymes concerned with→	Carbohydrate synthesis; glycolysis; pentose phosphate oxidation cycle
Lysosomes	Common	Hydrolases→	Breakdown of proteins, nucleic acids (DNA, RNA), carbohydrates, and their derivatives (Chap. 8)
Microbodies	Liver cells; kidney cells	Uricase, enzyme used in→	Synthesis and breakdown of hydrogen peroxide (Chap. 7)
Golgi apparatus	Universal	Thiamine pyrophosphatase. Possibly some enzymes connected with→	Lipid synthesis (Chap. 4)

TABLE 1—*Continued*

Cell Components	Occurrence	Enzyme Content	Functional Scope
Cilia and centrioles	Common	ATP-splitting enzyme which transfers energy to movement; possibly acetylcholine esterase, electron-transport enzymes, and glycolysis enzymes	Movement; excitability. Centrioles participate in cell division (Chaps. 10 and 12)
Synaptic vesicles	Nerve and sensory cells		Impulse-transfer (Chaps. 11 and 12)
Cell membrane	Universal	Enzymes in connection with——→	Regulation of transport of substances in and out of the cell, i.e., active transport (Chap. 4)
Nuclear membrane	Universal	An ATPase	Regulation of passage between nucleus and cytoplasm (Chap. 5)

Note.—This table should not give the impression that an average cell has a specific number of different organelles, every one equipped with a specific number of enzymes. The enzymes and functional scope in the table are both limited and rather arbitrary.

higher level of organization. Let us start at the higher level–tissues, organs, and organisms. Ten years ago in the United States a cancer patient, whose case has since made medical history, died. Before her death, a few cancer cells were removed from her body and cultured in a nutrient solution in small glass jars. Descendants of these cells are alive today, not only as cultures in America, but also in nearly all scientific centers. Their total weight may reach several hundred kilograms. It is possible that there exist more living cells from this patient now than there were when she died. The question now arises: Is she still alive? No biologist will go along with this idea (except possibly in a very diffuse sense, since all organic components may be assigned some connection with all beings which are alive or have been alive on the earth). Even if 30 kg of her living muscle cells, 0.5 to 1 kg of her nerve cells,

1 kg of her liver parenchymal cells, 0.5 kg of her heart muscle cells, and so forth could be found and all these cells were mixed, this woman would not reappear. What is missing is the organization which the cells impose on each other in the live human being, as in any live animal or plant. (A small number of biologists—the vitalists—believe that, besides this, something "supernatural" is necessary, that is, something which does not follow chemical and physical laws. This viewpoint seems to stem from a lack of confidence in the different properties which the molecules can have when they are part of larger organizational units, as in the construction of a body. Anyway, vitalism seems to be a bad choice as a starting point for the registration and description of biological phenomena in chemical and physical terms.) The essential distinction between, on one hand, an organism and, on the other, the sum of its parts is apparently to be found in the fact that the organism has a specific structure, an architectural design, which elevates it to a higher level of organization than do its individual, single cells.

Similar reasoning can be applied to an organizational level below the cell. The chemical composition of some cell components is rather well known. It is also known what types and proportions of molecules are included in a specific organelle. For some organelles, the manner in which the molecules are combined is known. It is possible to study in what way the totality deviates from the summation of the single parts and to learn something about how forms, electrical charges, and other properties of the molecules create organization. Such experiments have clearly demonstrated that molecules grouped in a specific architectural pattern have properties which were not displayed when they were alone.

This implies that a sulfur atom has specific properties when it is isolated, others when built into a protein in solution, and still others when the protein is arranged in a special way in a biological structure and is surrounded by a special environment. Whatever detailed knowledge we possess about the sulfur atom in isolation, whatever knowledge about the behavior of other atoms in the protein (carbon, hydrogen, nitrogen, phosphorus), we still know only a tiny bit about the potentialities that a sulfur atom may possess. For every level of organization, matter displays different properties.

In some ways, this approach to atoms and molecules has compensated for the need of the vitalists to search for supernatural explanations of life processes and has replaced earlier vague ideas about distinctions between life and death. It is still difficult or impossible to specify the border between life and death at an organizational level corresponding to molecules. A molecule is still a molecule, whether peacefully on a shelf for chemicals or functioning in cell machinery. Only for structures of a size comparable to an organelle or larger does the term "life" begin to be understandable; only here can life be defined in a rather definite manner. An integral part of what we call "life" is the possession of organized structure. In this connection, electron microscope studies can be said to touch an important part of the nature of the living.

Similar reasoning applies to structures at the organizational level of organelles. Organelles also achieve their efficiency by the manner in which their molecules are put together in a specific organization. The more essential problems the electron microscopist is wrestling with are, or ought to be, attempts to understand the connection between cell structure and function. The pictures have to be interpreted and fitted together as in a mosaic, showing the essential feature of life: organization.

Both the organism and the organelles obtain their effectiveness and their "live qualities" by arranging their components into organizational units of distinctive form. It has been tempting to assume by analogy that a cell is a cell because its organelles are constituents of a fixed framework. Any proof of this, however, has not been found. In 1950, before detailed pictures of the cell were obtained with the electron microscope, the fine structure of the cell could be studied only by indirect methods. F. H. C. Crick (one of the 1962 Nobel laureates) and a colleague tried to answer questions about the inner organization of the cell by means of such indirect methods. They reached the conclusion that the cell lacks an inner organization, and that the arrangement can be compared to the disorder of "Mother's Workbasket." Embryologists, however, have always been more inclined to say that the cell has an inner organization. Usually they are referring to the egg cell, since much information was derived from the developmental potentialities of specific regions in the egg. Electron microscopy gave a more detailed picture of the cell, but a final answer to the question of inner organization has so far not been obtained. On the contrary, we could say that electron microscope studies have made the question even more difficult. We cannot see the forest for the trees.

In this connection, we should mention an organelle which is believed to fulfill the requirements needed to create order out of chaos in the cell. This organelle is a membrane system in the interior of the cell which every now and then behaves like a branched network. These membranes were first described in 1947 by Porter and collaborators using the electron microscope. They called the membrane system the *endoplasmic reticulum*. Since then, thousands of publications have described further details about the appearance of the endoplasmic reticulum in different cells. Porter himself has proposed the hypothesis that this is the structure that gives the cell its form and organization. The endoplasmic reticulum, in other words, should function as an inner cell skeleton; furthermore, it should be the transport system which brings different substances to different places in the cell. It might also be a system for transportation of impulses from the cell membrane into the cell. It forms a foundation to which enzymes can attach themselves; it forms walls in a system separating different liquid phases in the cell. All these are clearly important functions, but it has not yet been determined whether Porter's hypothesis that the cell really possesses such an organization is correct. It should be noted that, curiously enough, in egg cells from many animal groups, the endoplasmic reticulum is almost or completely nonexistent.

The endoplasmic reticulum is one of several organelles in the cell. When a person looks at an electron micrograph of a cell for the first time, the picture looks as confusing as an aerial photograph of an unknown area or a photograph of the surface of the moon. But a person can train himself to "read" an aerial photograph, and little by little he can gain an understanding of the light and dark areas and the edges of the surface of the moon. Likewise, interpretation of electron micrographs is partly a question of practice. A cell is as yet an unknown area where speculations are a driving force for further investigation. Among other things, this book is aimed at giving the necessary knowledge for interpretation of electron micrographs. Further, I hope that this book gives the reader some idea of what kind of problems are approachable by electron microscope analysis and what kind of reasoning is valuable within this branch of biological research. But above all, the new electron microscope findings have been used as a basis for a presentation of an actual part of biological research.

Finally, the title "structure and ultrastructure" requires an explanation. What structure is and what it implies in the cell's life has already been discussed. The word "ultrastructure" differs from the word "structure" only in its application to objects which cannot be seen with the light microscope. In other words, it deals with architecture which can be studied only with the electron microscope or with indirect methods. The word has been adopted by the electron microscopists and generally designates the elements which they have a monopoly in studying—a nomenclature which perhaps betrays some kind of exclusiveness and a professional pride.

2

mitochondria

Two observations made with the help of the electron microscope surpass in importance all others made so far. The first one is the demonstration that the cell has an extremely complicated structure. The second is the demonstration of the fundamental likeness between cell components from widely different cells. These two theses compose the theme for much of this book, but they are not universally true. They apply only as long as we deal with multicellular plants and animals and for the majority of the group protozoa. They do not apply to bacteria.

It is possible that a complex organization may be found in the interior of a bacterium, but, if so, we lack evidence of it as yet. On the other hand, it is possible that a bacterium is no more than a little sack filled with many macromolecules and macromolecular aggregates, including the long deoxyribonucleic acid (DNA) threads. Certainly bacteria do have flagella, but these are not comparable to flagella found in protozoa, plants, and multicellular animals; some people talk about counterparts of the so-called mitochondria, but these bodies do not resemble the ordinary mitochondria; an analog to the nucleus has been found, but it has no nuclear membrane and also has other differences.

What does this mean? Biochemical information has supported the "sameness" of all live material. Many enzyme reactions progress in the same way in bacteria, plants, and animals. The citric acid cycle enzymes, for example, occupy a key position in animal and higher plant metabolism; all these enzymes can be found in bacteria. Many biochemical reactions are performed in the same manner in bacteria as in higher organisms. But evidence from electron microscopy points in another direction. The bacteria do not fit into the big group composed of protozoa, higher plants, and animals. Although yeast, protozoa, and most other microorganisms have the same fundamental construction as the higher animals, the bacterium is much simpler. This means that the logical classification of plants and animals should be as follows: The group *Procaryota* includes bacteria and blue-green algae and is characterized by a low organization and a primitive nuclear equivalent without a surrounding membrane. The group *Eucaryota* includes living organisms which have a higher degree of organization and a nucleus with a nuclear membrane. To this second group belong unicellular and multicellular plants and animals. The connection between *Procaryota* and *Eucaryota* will be discussed further in Chapter 3. The refinements that biology thus is forced to introduce on behalf of this division can perhaps best be illustrated by the following question: Are bacteria cells? Plates 1 and 2 demonstrate the differences between a procaryotic cell (if it can be called a cell) and a eucaryotic cell. They show a *Proteus* bacterium and a cell from a rat's liver. The bacterial cell is cut longitudinally and shows as much or as little as can be seen with an electron micrograph of a bacterium. The liver cell is also shown in an electron micrograph, but, in spite of a lower magnification, only part of the cross-sectioned cell can be seen. The round cell nucleus is a good structure for orientation in the labyrinths of the liver cell.

As befitting a eucaryote, the nucleus is surrounded by a membrane, which at higher magnification appears to be double and provided with tubular cylinders (Chap. 5, p. 38). The cytoplasm, which is the name for all the cell substance outside the nucleus, contains many different structures. Among other things seen in the picture, there are darker round or oval spots which are called mitochondria. Every mitochondrion is almost as big as a bacterium and seems to possess a higher degree of structural complexity than a bacterium. For several reasons the mitochondria have been the aim of very intensive studies. The intention is both to study the enzyme reactions occurring in the mitochondria and to understand how the different enzymes are bound to each other and to a foundation in a way that makes the work of the mitochondria both effective and expedient. The manner in which a mitochondrion works can no longer be expressed by merely a mass of chemical formulas without consideration of the mitochondrial structure. At this point the electron micrographs are valuable, because they represent the meeting place for the anatomical studies giving a detailed picture of the body and the new requirements of biochemical science—consideration of enzyme aggregates and their mutual assembly and movements.

In order to get an idea of the effectiveness of mitochondria as generators of energy-rich chemical bonds, the following calculation can be made: A horse produces with the muscles of its four legs a quantity of work per time unit which corresponds to at least one horsepower. The dry weight of the total amount of mitochondria in these muscles is between 0.5 and 1 kg. This amount of mitochondrial mass supplies the energy for the horse's work. The magnitude of the effect of the mitochondria per weight unit is the same as the one delivered by the engines in a jet plane in vertical ascent. The efficiency of the mitochondrial work is about 80 per cent, which is higher than that of the engines. In other words, the mitochondria are admirably effective machines.

The mitochondrion was one of the first parts of the cell to be described in detail and almost correctly through studies by G. E. Palade, F. Sjöstrand, and others. The pictures published by them in 1952 do not differ to any great extent from the mitochondrion shown in Plate 3. With the methods used then, which have also been used here, the edge of the mitochondrion appears as a dark double line, and in the inner part a number of mostly parallel sets of double lines are found. For the sake of simplicity, these lines, representing cross-sections of membranes, can be called the outer and inner membranes of the mitochondrion. The mitochondrion is full of a diffuse mass called the mitochondrial matrix and some dark particles. The particles have not yet received any name but have been described only as "the electron-dense particles in the matrix of mitochondria." Calling the particles dense is the same as saying that they look dark in electron micrographs.

As early as 1952, scientists were able to isolate and purify mitochondria; therefore, the enzymes that they contained were well known. Among others, there are all of the enzymes of the citric acid cycle and of cell respiration and the closely connected enzymes for the formation of adenosine triphosphate (ATP). It was tempting to propose the theory that the mitochondrial enzymes were located on the membranes of the mitochondrion. Justification can be found in both an irrational and a rational approach. The irrational approach is that a membrane is something much more obvious to think about than the diffuse substance, perhaps liquid, perhaps solid, which the mitochondrial matrix represents. The rational approach is that a membrane offers the enzymes a foundation for their operations—like stamps have a foundation in the pages of a collector's scrapbook. This arrangement into a definite pattern should enable the enzymes to function in coordination and thereby endow the mitochondrion with an enzymatic character which differs from that of free enzymes. In other words, through structural organization, the enzymes should gain a higher degree of effectiveness. These were the theories starting to mature in 1952. Today a great deal more is known about this organization, and the answers have been obtained not so much from further speculation as from experiment.

In order to explain the directions that have been taken in the study of the function of mitochondria, we must look closer at the mitochondrial enzymes. Mitochondrial work consists of, among other things, the action upon the compounds which have to be oxidized by the cell. The mitochondrion does this by a chemical disintegration process called the citric acid cycle. Oxidation of a substrate in the citric acid cycle implies that the compound is oxidized in tiny steps, while simultaneously another compound, diphosphopyridine nucleotide (DPN), is reduced to what is called DPNH.[1] Malic acid is oxidized to oxaloacetic acid at the

[1] The abbreviations DPN, DPNH, TPN, and TPNH shall, according to an international agreement, now be replaced by NAD, NADH, NADP, and NADPH. The first four abbreviations mean *d*iphospho*p*yridine *n*ucleotide, oxidized and reduced form, respectively, and *t*riphospho*p*yridine *n*ucleotide, oxidized and reduced form, respectively. The second four abbreviations are synonyms of the first and stand for *n*icotinamide *a*denine *d*inucleotide (oxidized and reduced) and *n*icotinamide *a*denine *d*inucleotide *p*hosphate (oxidized and reduced).

same time that DPN is reduced to DPNH. This DPNH is bound to a series of enzymes called the electron-transport chain (or respiratory chain). Similar to the DPNH–DPN system, the other substances of the electron-transport chain can oscillate between a reduced and an oxidized state. The last member of the electron-transport chain is able to bind free oxygen. Participating in the electron transportation are enzymes responsible for the conversion of the energy freed by the oxidation into a form useful for the cell; these are the so-called oxidative phosphorylating or energy-transferring enzymes. In chemical terms, the task of the oxidative phosphorylating enzymes is to form the compound ATP from adenosine diphosphate (ADP) and inorganic phosphate, which, as mentioned, they are able to do by channeling energy released from oxidation into the electron-transport chain. ATP can be called the currency of biological energy transport. A given amount of muscular work or osmotic work can be said to cost specified units of ATP.

In the citric acid cycle and the electron-transport chain and its adherent energy-transfer chain more than twenty different enzymes are found. The mitochondria contain an additional fifty or so other enzymes involved in the degradation or synthesis of biological substances. It is possible to find out which of these enzymes are found joined to the membrane and which are in the matrix of the mitochondria. Some tools used to do this are rotating knives, ultracentrifuges, and sonicators. It is also necessary to have an electron microscope determination of the purity of the isolated samples to decide, among other things, whether the preparation consists of mitochondrial membranes or mitochondrial matrix. Without electron microscopy much of this would be guesswork.

The first step in this type of study is to obtain material very rich in mitochondria (for example, beef heart). This tissue is minced and the mitochondria isolated from this mass. The appearance of such mitochondria is shown in Plate 4. We can see that these isolated mitochondria, when compared to the mitochondria from the intact sectioned tissue, have a well-preserved structure and on the whole have maintained their size. The space between the two parallel borders of the inner membrane is somewhat widened and the corresponding space for the mitochondrial matrix has shrunk. We can also see that the mitochondria are a pure population, free of contaminants from other cell constituents.

The next step is separation of the membranes and the mitochondrial matrix. We must burst the outer membrane of the mitochondrion in order to release the matrix and the inner membrane. This can be done by sound or ultrasound. Plate 5 illustrates such isolated inner membranes. The inner membranes have not retained their form, but they are approximately the same size as in the intact mitochondrion and have a wall that appears as a dark line. The enlargement in Plate 5 is three times that of Plate 4.

The swelling which has apparently started widening the inner membrane during the isolation of mitochondria has at this point reached an extreme degree. Every isolated inner membrane in Plate 5 behaves like an inflated balloon. It is apparent that the inner membranes, broken during sonication, have formed closed vesicles by fusion of the membrane edges. In order to imagine this collection of round, cut vesicles as a whole mitochondrion, we must visualize every single vesicle pressed together to form a flat plate with a top, bottom, and closed sides. A collection of these flat plates must be arranged on top of one another with matrix between them, and finally the whole arrangement must be surrounded by a double outer membrane into which the plates open. Of major interest, perhaps, is that the prepared fraction of mitochondrial membrane is uniform and that biochemical studies have shown that it contains the oxidative phosphorylating enzymes. The vesicles are capable of oxidative phosphorylation; that is, they can make ATP if they are exposed to ADP, inorganic phosphate, and fuel in the form of DPNH. They are unable to use compounds such as glucose or compounds from the citric acid cycle for fuel, since they lack the enzymes of the citric acid cycle. Everything indicates that most enzymes of the citric acid cycle either float freely in the matrix of the mitochondria or are loosely bound to the inner membrane. The different enzymes of the citric acid cycle have no mutual order-inducing collaboration at a higher level of effectiveness than they do in a free solution. It is only in textbooks that the ten enzymes of the citric acid cycle are depicted as a closed ring with a fixed order. The chemical progress of oxidation in the citric acid cycle does occur in decisive steps, but the participating enzymes do not have a fixed position in relation to one another. It has further been established that several of the other mitochondrial enzymes behave as if they were free in the matrix of the mitochondrion. On the other hand, enzymes from the electron-transport chain and the phosphorylating enzymes do have chemical reactions which progress not only according to a certain scheme, but also show a strict arrangement which constitutes the secret of their high efficiency. This connection between a structure and a biological function makes the inner membrane of the mitochondrion a difficult but a fascinating and important object to study.

The classical manner for studying the structure of mitochondria with the electron microscope has been to fix the tissues, the cells, or the isolated mitochondria in one of several possible ways, embed them in a transparent material that can be cut into thin sections, and take electron micrographs of the sections. This method has been employed since 1952, which justifies the usage of the word "classical." In later years, a variant of this technique has appeared. Here neither fixation nor embedding, as they are normally understood, is necessary and sectioning can also be omitted. Isolated mitochondrial membranes are thin enough to be penetrated by an electron beam; therefore, all that is needed is to immerse them in a contrasting medium that makes them visible against the background. The contrasting medium is dense and appears dark. The particles are less dense and therefore appear as light islands. This method is as productive as it is simple. What one gains is a clear picture of the whole surface of the mitochondrial membrane, which is not the case with sectioning. This seems to be the ideal method for finding out whether or not the enzymes form some kind of organized pattern on the outside of the membrane. It might be expected that the enzyme chains would stand out against the background of the membrane itself, almost as the electrical circuits which are printed on plastic in a transistor radio.

The first to show the mitochondrial membrane in this manner

was the electron microscopist H. Fernández-Morán, who worked with the biochemist D. Green. They found that the mitochondrial membranes could be visualized as circular plates of the same size as the cut vesicles. The walls, however, do not appear as smooth surfaces, but are covered with bumps. Each bump looks like a small ball about 70 to 90 Å and is connected to the membrane by a shaft about 50 Å in length and thickness. These balls were simply taken to be carriers of the enzymes of the electron-transport chain and of those of the phosphorylating factors. This implies that the quintessence of the function of the mitochondrial membrane should be connected to these balls and thus the balls received the pretentious name: *elementary particles.* It was assumed that the ATP molecules were formed near an elementary particle and with the help of enzymes found in a single elementary particle. An electron micrograph of the mitochondrial membranes with elementary particles similar to the ones described by Fernández-Morán is shown in Plate 6.

Since this theory was put forward in 1962, the originators of the term "elementary particles" have tried to prove that one particle contains a complete supply of the enzymes which are responsible for oxidative phosphorylation. This has been difficult, and, from the start, critical voices have stressed the point that the particles are too small to contain all the necessary enzymes. A way to save both the term and the idea of elementary particles has been to assume that not only the balls but the shaft and the base on the membrane itself compose the functional unit of electron transport. These three areas together are big enough to house all the enzymes which are part of the electron-transport chain. Only through experimental evidence can it be determined whether or not the elementary particles do contain these enzymes. One method is to try to remove as many balls as possible from the mitochondrial membrane and to examine the isolated elementary particles and the relatively clean-shaven membranes for their enzymatic activity. To a limited extent this shaving process has been technically possible by means of vibrations from a sonicator. Experiments done independently in several laboratories indicate that it is the membrane itself rather than the balls that contains most of the electron-transport chain and the phosphorylating factors. What the balls actually contain is not yet clear, but the fact that they can be isolated indicates that they can hardly be meaningless, disorderly bound units of the membrane or artifacts generated during the procedure.

With different methods it has been possible to isolate the proteins which seem to compose the supporting skeleton of the mitochondria. These proteins apparently lack enzymatic functions, but they support enzymes and divide the mitochondrial space into different parts. This structural protein constitutes at least half of the protein in the mitochondria. A distinction is thus made here between walls, floor, and roof of the mitochondrial warehouse and the machines which make the warehouse into a factory. We cannot say unconditionally that the membrane as such forms the working, functional cell organelle. The essential factors are that the membrane is equipped with enzymes, that the enzymes collaborate, and that the membrane creates a suitable milieu and good functional conditions for the enzymes and enzyme aggregates.

3

more on mitochondria

Biochemists working with mitochondria have usually used rat liver or beef heart. They have, therefore, unconsciously considered these mitochondria as normal—standard mitochondria—and mitochondria deviating very much from these standards are automatically looked upon with suspicion.

The same reasoning applies to electron microscopists. The mitochondrion should have a standard appearance in order to be considered a mitochondrion. This is in reality a not-to-be-permitted although practical assumption. One ought to accept the idea that all cells do not have the same duties and, accordingly, their tools may be of different shapes and efficiencies. By searching both for variation in the appearance of mitochondria and for distinctive functional features, we would expect to find some regular, parallel differences which would make it possible to understand the structure from a functional viewpoint or, vice versa, to understand how function is dependent on structure—in other words, a correlation between structure and function.

From a biochemical viewpoint, it has become clear in what respect mitochondria from the brain differ from those of the liver or muscles. These differences are of great interest when they become important in understanding the body's reaction to particular sleeping pills or in understanding the origin of some forms of idiocy which have been shown to come from specific enzyme defects. Although it has been possible to disclose the associated general alterations in structure of mitochondria from brain cells, it is still impossible to pinpoint any special details with which to correlate the metabolic abnormalities. So far we have obtained results concerning only some properties but have been unable to explain why certain mitochondria show increased sensitivity toward barbiturates or greater ability to oxidize the amino acid glutamic acid.

The first correlation to be made is between the number of mitochondria present in a tissue or organ and the degree of metabolic activity. A measure of the metabolic activity is the consumption of oxygen in the tissue, which can be calculated relatively simply by measuring oxygen concentration in the blood entering and leaving the tissue in question. The larger organs in the body, the kidneys, the salivary glands, the heart, and the liver, use the most oxygen per unit weight.

A study of these organs with the electron microscope has revealed that they are exceptionally rich in mitochondria and that each single mitochondrion is large and tightly packed with inner membranes. The correlation between numbers of mitochondria and oxygen consumption seems to be simple and easy to understand. Perhaps it seems surprising to find the salivary glands among the organs which consume the most oxygen. The electron microscope has revealed a reasonable explanation for this. The salivary gland close to the ear (parotid) contains mainly three types of cells, and one cell type alone is responsible for the high concentration of mitochondria. These cells do not resemble those of the heart or other muscles and probably have nothing to do with contraction. On the other hand, their structure is very similar to the resorbing cells of the kidneys. Presumably then, they function osmotically, more specifically by resorbing salt and water. This resorption function starts with "primary saliva" and gives a final salt-poor saliva.

Mitochondria have been counted in many cell types. Usually a good correlation exists between the number and the metabolic activity of the cells; therefore, an electron micrograph allows us a view of the relative activity of the tissues. The rather inactive loin muscle (musculus psoas) has only one five-hundredth as many mitochondria as the heart. The red muscles of the body contain more mitochondria than the faster-acting but more easily exhaustible white muscles. Muscles from the ground squirrel have been examined during hibernation and during summer activities. More mitochondria were found in the cells during hibernation, which suggests that hibernation is not a passive state for the animals but is a struggle against death from cold, with all cell ovens being mobilized to keep the animal alive.

These studies apparently fit the interpretation that a cell's respiration is directly proportional to its number of mitochondria. In experiments trying to prove this hypothesis, normal rats and rats whose thyroid gland did not function were examined. Abnormal rats showed a definitely lower oxygen consumption than normal rats. As the oxygen consumption of a mammal normally reflects the respiration of the muscles (the muscles are the largest organs), we would expect, in direct proportionality, fewer or smaller mitochondria in the muscles of the abnormal animals. The study showed, however, that the number of mitochondria had increased. We conclude that the new mitochondria which appeared in the experimental conditions do not have the same ability to consume oxygen as do normal mitochondria. Apparently they are partially defective.

The diversity of living conditions and even of cell structure of the invertebrates is greater than that of the more uniform vertebrates. Invertebrate cells are sometimes found without mitochondria, or at any rate structures that look like mitochondria. This has been described for the following cell types: muscle cells of the sea cucumber; two parasitic amoebas from the genus *Endamoeba;* certain protozoa in the stomachs of ruminants; the food digestion organ of termites; yeast under specific conditions; and the gas-secreting glandular cells of the blue manet, the Portuguese man-of-war (a jellyfish-like organism belonging to the order Siphonophora and the genus *Physalia*).

What are the physiological conditions of these cell types which enable them to live without mitochondria? ATP is needed by all cells. The sea cucumber lives in the very oxygen-poor muddy bottoms of the sea, and the *Endamoeba* lives in an almost oxygen-free milieu in the digestive tract of mammals as do the protozoa in the ruminant stomach. These animals are, to a very high degree, dependent on glycolysis instead of respiration for obtaining their ATP. The enzymes for glycolysis are located in the cytoplasm outside the mitochondria and are not dependent on the electron-transport chain. One wonders where other enzymes which are normally described as typical mitochondrial enzymes are located. For example, where are the enzymes of the citric acid cycle and those which take part in the degradation or synthesis of other essential compounds in these animals?

The siphonophore *Physalia* does not live in an oxygen-poor milieu; on the contrary, it floats on the surface of the sea. The floats, which characterize the siphonophores and keep them on an even keel, are called pneumatophores, a term which can be translated as "air carriers." The pneumatophores have, however, nothing to do with air, for the float contains carbon monoxide, a respiratory poison. Carbon monoxide blocks, among other things, the enzyme cytochrome oxidase, which occupies the terminal place on the electron-transport chain. The production of a mitochondrial poison and the reduction of mitochondria in the ordinary sense have apparently progressed simultaneously.

Finally, the yeast *Torulopsis* can be cultivated and grown in both the presence and absence of oxygen. From an electron microscope viewpoint, the same cell types behave quite differently, according to how they are cultivated. In the absence of oxygen, the mitochondria are missing according to the electron microscope definition. On the other hand, long membrane fragments, which are suspected to have taken over some of the functions of the mitochondria, are apparent. Within minutes after such mitochondria-free cells have been transferred to an oxygen-saturated medium, these membranes have disappeared and mitochondria of the normal type have appeared. In other words, this experiment indicates that mitochondria can arise from structures which an electron microscopist cannot recognize as mitochondria. Similar observations will be discussed in more detail later in this chapter.

Several classically mitochondrial enzymes are lacking in yeast cells where membranes with a simple configuration have replaced the characteristic mitochondria. The enzymes of the electron-transport chain are gone, but some from the citric acid cycle still linger.

In sperm from several animal groups another modification of the mitochondrial structure has taken place. Sperm, generally speaking, can be said to be constructed to achieve the highest degree of motility. All excess ballast has been removed, although some mitochondria, either of the normal shape or of some altered structure, can almost always be found. The modification consists of a successive reduction of matrix material, which in mammalian sperm has brought about a distortion of the structure of the mitochondrion, although it is still recognizable. In several insects, scorpions, and snails, the reduction has gone a step further. During sperm formation, the mitochondrial matrix gradually shrinks while the membranous part increases. The final state is a mitochondrial derivative without a membrane and with an almost crystalline arrangement of particles. These particles are approximately the same order of magnitude as the elementary particles from Fernández-Morán's preparations—whatever this might infer. No regular analysis of these sperm has yet been done, but the fact that they stain with Janus-green B, which shows great specificity for respiration-chain enzymes, is in good agreement with the hypothesis that the sperm contain a compact collection of these chains. The sperm represent, in a sense, the opposite pole from the mitochondria-free yeast cells. The electron-transport chains have superseded the citric acid cycle enzymes rather than the reverse. In both sperm and yeast cells, the result is that the normal structure cannot be maintained.

A comparison between cells in which mitochondria take part in a number of different chemical reactions and cells in which the mitochondrial function is more one-sided, that is, directed toward production and usage of ATP, might also be of interest. Cells from the first group contain mitochondria with a matrix which occupies a relatively large space. Cells from the other group show mitochondria tightly packed with inner membranes and a matrix of a more limited extent. These facts are in agreement with the interpretation that not all mitochondrial enzymes are located on the membrane but that several are found free in the matrix.

A unique opportunity to study the structure and function of mitochondria was provided by a patient suffering from an unusual metabolic disturbance. Because this case was unique, the disease has not been given a special name but can be called "hypermetabolism, without thyroid disturbance and of unknown origin." Hypermetabolism indicates that the person consumes nourishment at an abnormally great rate which results in an increased oxygen consumption of two to three times the normal. The qualification "without thyroid disturbance" means that the thyroid functions normally, which is not true for Basedow's disease, the most common cause of hypermetabolism. "Of unknown origin" indicates that it is not known whether this is a hereditary or an acquired disease. On the other hand, the cause is known insofar as it seems certain that the disease is caused by malformed mitochondria that lack respiration control.

Respiration control means that the cell consumes nourishment only in connection with the utilization of energy. With failing respiration control, the mitochondria respire without a corresponding withdrawal of energy and without formation of energy-rich bonds (for example, ATP). The work of mitochondria with failing respiration control results, for the most part, in a direct heat production and is, as such, work of low efficiency.

Biochemical studies of the patient with "hypermetabolism of unknown origin" have shown that the mitochondria behave normally—apart from the failing respiration control. All the studied enzyme steps are present, even if their structural coupling does not seem to be normal. This organizational defect means that the mitochondria can work whether there exists a demand for ATP production or not.

The electron microscope analysis of the same muscles has shown, among other things, the following: The number of mitochondria is several times greater than normal; the amount of inner membrane per unit volume of mitochondria is similarly increased; and some of the individual mitochondria are relative giants. Plate 3 shows a mitochondrion from this study. The electron-dense particles in the matrix of the mitochondrion are completely lacking. These particles have been interpreted as depots for energy-rich phosphate complexes. In this disease, the mitochondria are without these depots; furthermore, several different types of altered mitochondria can be found which are normally never present in muscle.

These variations in the structure of the mitochondria are much greater than in earlier observations in other cells and represent something quite new. On the other hand, neither the biochemical nor the electron microscope studies nor the more traditional clinical studies give any clue for suitable medical treatment. It is not clear why the great variation in the structure of the mitochondria leads to a failure in respiration control or why defective mitochondria bring about the appearance of many different mitochondrial types. We can assume that the understanding of this problem might progress a step further if it were possible to imitate this unique disease in animals. Further, some knowledge of how mitochondria arise and how long they exist would be of great value in this problem.

Among the innumerable theories on how mitochondria arise, we can discern two main groups: (*1*) mitochondria are formed from older mitochondria by division or by budding and (*2*) they arise from some other cell component (nuclear membrane, cell membrane, ground cytoplasm). One of the stronger pieces of evidence supporting the theory that mitochondria arise from something else came from experiments using centrifuged sea urchin eggs. (Sea urchin eggs are cells which from many viewpoints are extremely adaptable to experimental studies since, among other things, they form a very uniform cell material.) During centrifugation, the sea urchin eggs elongate as the heavier cell components are pressed against the centrifugal pole of the egg and the lighter components are led upward to the opposite pole. Then the egg is broken into two halves, and observations with the light microscope indicate that only one half contains the mitochondria. When the two halves of the egg are fertilized with sperm, both parts develop rather normally and form larvae with the normal number of mitochondria. This would seem to favor the theory that mitochondria arise from something other than mitochondria, but the experimental error here is such that the migration of mitochondria from one part of the egg to the other during centrifugation is not complete. This can be shown with the electron microscope. In whatever way the centrifugation is done, there is a concentration of mitochondria toward only one egg pole; still, many mitochondria remain in the other part of the egg.

The problem of how mitochondria arise has been approached in another way in a study by David Luck, who employed a more elegant technique. Using the mold *Neurospora,* he has worked in parallel fashion with both biochemical and autoradiographic methods in conjunction with electron microscopy. The mold *Neurospora* can be grown under such conditions that the number of mitochondria increases uniformly over a long period of time. If the compound choline is added to the culture, it is taken up by the cells and built into the structure of the mitochondria. Choline is incorporated solely into the mitochondria. This, of course, holds true for choline with and without radioactive isotopes (labeled and unlabeled choline). Luck's experiment was performed in the following way: For ten minutes at the beginning of the growth phase, during which the mitochondria grow in number, radioactive choline was present. Every mitochondrion in the cell then contained the radioactive label. Then the cells were transferred to a new medium with unlabeled choline. The number of mitochondria increased approximately ten times and the radioactive label was divided evenly among all mitochondria. This result must be interpreted in the following way: The newly formed mitochondria have been made from the older ones. If this was not true and the new mitochondria instead arose from some other cell component, then the original mitochondria would have kept all the radioactivity and the new ones would have none at all. Luck's experiment gave an unequivocal result.

In this respect, the mitochondria resemble independent living organisms, for example, bacteria, which they also resemble in both magnitude and form. It is tempting to create a new biological thesis: Every mitochondrion arises from another mitochondrion. This statement is analogous to the hundred-year-old thesis, "Every cell arises from another cell." But some reservations must be introduced. First, only one single type of cell has been studied with this technique, and it is therefore not known if the results can be generally applied. The closely related yeast, *Torulopsis,* already presents some complications in this scheme, as was mentioned at the beginning of the chapter. Second, the results are valid for only one mitochondrial component, namely choline. Isolated mitochondria in the pure state have been examined for their ability to form proteins, especially those proteins which participate in the construction of mitochondria. The only newly formed proteins which have been shown in such experiments are the structural proteins, and not even here does everyone agree on whether the whole protein can be built under the given experimental conditions or whether only some amino acid end-groups can be coupled to existing mitochondrial proteins. The mitochondrial enzymes themselves, however, seem to be made outside the mitochondrion, from where they are secondarily taken up by the mitochondrion.

The average lifetime of a mitochondrion is a more problematic question. This does not stem from a lack of experiments and calculations. On the contrary, there is a great deal of available information about the average mitochondrial lifetime, based on different calculations from a variety of cell types, but it yields quite diverse results. It seems, however, as if the majority of the calculations give an average lifetime ranging from hours to weeks.

Anyone who has studied a great number of micrographs of mitochondria could hardly have missed noticing that the matrix of the mitochondrion is uneven. In most, a heterogeneity is found in the form of light patches in an otherwise gray mass. These "empty" patches apparently worried many electron microscopists, not so much because they did not know what the patches contained, but rather because they wished to conceal any holes. It seems to have been the prevalent opinion that the matrix of the mitochondrion ought to be homogeneous and that heterogeneity meant bad preparatory techniques.

Lately many different methods have been used to increase contrast in the thin sections and thus make structures visible which do not normally stand out in electron micrographs. Some of these contrast methods also give a clue to the chemical properties of the structures. In this way, it has been shown that the empty islands in the matrix of the mitochondrion contain a number of thin fibers and that these fibers behave as if they are nucleic acids. Plate 7 shows these fibers in a few mitochondria. It has been shown by means of different specific enzymes that the fibers contain DNA. This result is surprising and, for many, even shocking. It is more or less axiomatic that DNA belongs in the nucleus and only in the nucleus. It has been demonstrated that the DNA molecule is the actual hereditary substance. With the discovery of a mitochondrial DNA we ought to be able to explain the fact that the cytoplasm, as well as the nucleus, may carry specific hereditary factors; furthermore, we can speculate more confidently on how mitochondria are produced from other mitochondria. Nevertheless, the idea that DNA fibers exist in mitochondria strongly opposes all earlier experience, and it probably will be years before this interpretation is completely accepted. We can question why the mitochondria are equipped with DNA fibers and what consequences this may have, for example, in explaining some types of cancer that are characterized by a disturbed mitochondrial metabolism, a cytoplasmic mutation, or the appearance of a nucleic acid–containing cancer virus. It seems here as if these three hypotheses on the origin of cancer cells go together. We can also draw the analogy between mitochondria and bacteria a step further than was possible earlier. Both the DNA of bacteria and that of mitochondria are more "naked" than that found in the nucleus of the eucaryotes. In the cell nucleus the DNA is bound to proteins, but in bacteria and mitochondria it is free. In many ways the similarities between a bacterium and a mitochondrion are greater than between a bacterium and a cell from a eucaryote. Are bacteria really cells?

4

what is a cell membrane?

It is difficult or impossible to give an unequivocal and exhaustive definition of biological structures. If we want to define the concept "cell membrane" (or its synonym "plasma membrane"), perhaps the following will do. The cell membrane is the limiting surface of the living cell. It is that structure which has the main responsibility for the segregation of substances in the cell from those substances outside the cell, and it follows that it also is the site where osmotic gradient and electrical potential originate. It is the layer, which according to electron microscope technique, is depicted as a double line of about 100 Å.

This definition is one of many possible, and as with other biological definitions, every single item in it can be torn to pieces.

Some pictures reveal this dilemma. Plate 8 shows a cross-section of the top of a cell. The only part of the cell included in the section are some finger-like projections stretching toward the free medium. The projections are called microvilli, a term chosen because of the similarity of these projections to the finger-like projections, fluff or villi, of the intestine. The microvilli, like the entire cell, are covered by the cell membrane, which is shown here as the double line about 100 Å thick.

But another component is found close to this dark double line. This is a layer of fine fibrils, seemingly starting from the cell membrane, that gives it a hairy appearance. The question now is: What function do these fibrils have? And further: Do they belong to the cell membrane or are they outside the cell membrane? The answer to the first question is still very uncertain, and the second seems to be an open question which every scientist can answer to his own satisfaction. If we assume that the function of the fibrils is very closely interwoven with the function of the cell surface itself, we should be free to include these fibers in the definition of the cell membrane. If we consider it terminologically easier to use a term placing the fibrils outside the genuine cell membrane, this is also justifiable. In other words, anyone working with biological structures should be ruler of the terminology and not vice versa. Definitions are man-made inventions and should describe what one wants them to describe. Definitions should be given their own life and be allowed to expand and to incorporate new meanings with time. The drawback to this freedom is that different scientists use the same definition in various ways in order to describe different components or different functional fields. We cannot be certain what a scientist is referring to without knowing his special definition. This has resulted in a long list of misunderstandings and forms the background for many unnecessary polemic debates. It takes time to adapt to the fact that a biological term does not have an absolute value but rather can be regarded as a reflection of every single scientist's philosophy.

Another observation leads to still another digression. In biological tissues the cells are, as a rule, tightly packed together, but in the micrographs it does not look as if cell is lying against cell, membrane against membrane. It looks as if there is a space which has a constant width of about 150 or 200 Å between two adjacent 100 Å membranes. This is shown in Plate 9. How can we interpret this space? In accord with the definition given above, it is apparently an "extracellular space" (an area outside the cell), but that is not the only conceivable definition. It could be said that the cell membrane includes both the 100 Å-thick double layer (or why not only its outer unit?) and a layer outside of this about 100 Å wide which looks empty in electron micrographs but whose occurrence can be assumed because of the constant width between the dense lines. In this interpretation, the cells touch one another and there is no space between them. This choice of definition makes it more difficult to think about or to believe in the existence of an extracellular space in which different substances can pass or be stored.

With the first definition, it is possible to believe in the existence of such a space. Such is the power of words over thought. The important thing, of course, is to construct an experiment which can answer the question whether or not there exists an extracellular space.

There are two reasons why the definition given here only includes the dark-appearing double line. First, we can explain the occurrence of a constant cell interspace in a different way than by assuming that the cell membranes lie closely against each other or, alternatively, that they are stuck together with a plaster of an even thickness. Forces exist in the cell surface that push the cells apart (electrostatic forces; the cells are positively charged at their surfaces). Many types of forces are also known to drive cells together. It seems possible that the repelling and attracting forces can counterbalance each other in such a way that a constant cell interspace is created.

The second reason for choosing this definition is that every so often cells are found lying against each other, seemingly without an empty column between them. Such close contact between cells has been observed in nerve tissues and in the majority of tissues where cells surround a lumen. The region of close contact can be long (for example, in myelin in myelinated nerves), but more usually it is limited to a short section near the lumen. Plate 10 shows the border between two cells which have several regions of close contact. It looks as if the cells are locked together to prevent the passage of liquid from the lumen to other parts of the tissue. Such a hypothesis can be tested, and experiments along these lines were done by Farquhar and Palade. They examined, among other things, the kidney tubule of animals that were injected with a protein that is excreted through the kidneys. The micrographs clearly demonstrate that the protein molecules from the lumen of the kidney tubule extend to the constricted point but pass no further. For theoretical reasons, these scientists assume that the cell contact is too close for water molecules, salt molecules, and large molecules to pass but that these compounds have free passage in regions where cells are separated by an interspace.

The mode of cell membrane formation is connected with its

functions. We would expect dividing cells, in which the surface of the cell membrane also doubles, to be an excellent material to study. The classical material for study of cell division is the sea urchin egg, and electron microscope studies have been done to elucidate this formative process. These studies, however, have yielded a meager profit. Quite unexpectedly, the sea urchin eggs have happened to be an extraordinarily suitable object for this study at another and earlier developmental stage, namely, fertilization. After fertilization, the cell membrane is totally re-formed. A moment before fertilization, the surface of the spherical egg is rather even and smooth with only a few short microvilli. Below the cell membrane a single layer of round particles called cortical granules is found. The word "cortical" implies that they are found in the cortex, that is, the outer zone, the bark, of the cell. Every cortical granule is formed in the interior of the egg cell during the growth period and migrates toward the surface as the egg becomes fertilizable. The cortical granules have a different appearance in different species of sea urchins, but one feature is common to all: the surface of the granule is a double membrane about 100 Å thick.

The fertilized egg is not spherical. All the cortical granules burst and their contents are released outside the cell. What once was the cell membrane of the unfertilized egg has been lifted above the remnants of the escaped cortical granules, and a new cell membrane has been formed. The cell surface after fertilization resembles the excavated appearance of an eaten ear of corn. It is apparent that major parts of the cell membrane are newly formed and are derived from the membranes of the cortical granules. In dimensions and appearance these membrane systems are similar. The conversion of the cell surface takes place within a few minutes and is a revolutionizing reorganization with formation of a new cell surface. Plate 11 shows the surface of the sea urchin egg before fertilization, and Plate 12 shows another egg a few minutes after fertilization.

This fertilization process in the sea urchin egg demonstrates for the first time that the formation site for the cell membrane is in the interior of the cell and that major parts of the cell membrane can be exchanged in a short time without the cell losing its vital properties. Similar processes have since been described in a number of secretory cells.

A secretory cell is, in a more limited sense, synonymous with a glandular cell secreting a specific cell product; in a broader sense, every cell secreting a product is a secretory cell, if the product is not considered an unessential waste product.

In the latter sense, both the sea urchin egg and the sea urchin sperm can be considered secretory cells. It has been shown in the secretory cells of the pancreas, for example, that the secretory granules are transported to the cell surface during the secretory phase and that the contents of the granules are released into the glandular tract at the same time the granule membranes are left behind at the secretion site and apparently become part of the mosaic that composes the cell membrane. Some differences, however, have been found between the secretory granule and the cortical granule opening at the cell surface. In the pancreas, only a very minor part of the cell surface faces a free glandular tract and also accepts membrane material from the secretory granules. In the pancreas, the membrane is not renewed once and for all as it is in the egg. Surely the pancreas cell has so long a lifetime and so great an activity that its cell membrane could be multiplied to many times the original surface with all membranes supplied by secretory granules.

There is actually nothing to suggest that the surface of the pancreatic cells increases in magnitude simultaneously with secretion. As a mechanism must exist for supplying the cell membrane material, a mechanism must exist to dispose of superfluous membrane material. Nothing is known about this latter process.

Glandular cells are usually characterized by a large *Golgi apparatus.* This is an organelle with a specific appearance and with characteristic staining properties. It got its name from its discoverer, Camillo Golgi, in 1898. Plate 15 shows a Golgi apparatus from a sea urchin egg. Since the function or functions of the Golgi apparatus are uncertain, the field has been open to speculation. Much has been written about its appearance and assumed significance, but most of this literature is of very little value. It seems reasonable to assume that one of the functions of the Golgi apparatus is to act as a reservoir for cell membrane material. On their way between the production site in the cell and the deposit site in the form of secretory granules, the secretory substances pass the Golgi apparatus and are apparently provided with a surrounding membrane which is destined to become a component of the surface membrane. A Golgi apparatus is found not only in glandular cells but in almost all cell types. In the majority of cases, however, the Golgi apparatus is of smaller size.

It is tempting to generalize from these observations on the secretion of cortical granules and of pancreatic granules and say that secretion involves surrounding the substance to be secreted by a membrane that opens to the cell surface. But it is these dramatic minutes at the moment of fertilization of the sea urchin egg that show that this generalization is not justifiable. It is not only the egg that functions as a secretory cell at time of fertilization but also the sperm. In spite of the fact that the sperm is a tiny cell with no unnecessary equipment, it does have a small secretory granule at its very front, in the so-called acrosome ("point" is *akros* in Greek). It is, in other words, situated in the part that first meets the egg. The secretory granule in the acrosome lies inside the cell membrane (as does the nucleus, mitochondria, and sperm tail) but does not seem to be surrounded by a membrane of its own. This is true in spite of the fact that the acrosome granule, similar to other secretory granules, arises within the Golgi apparatus. At the moment that the sperm reaches the egg, a change takes place in the acrosome region of the sperm and the acrosome suddenly finds itself on the outside of the cell membrane. Because this whole series of events takes place on such a diminutive scale, it cannot be observed in living material with the light microscope, but has to be reconstructed from electron micrographs of dead, fixed sperm. Thus it is difficult to get a clear picture of how the passage occurs. It certainly looks as if the acrosome granule has gone through closed doors. Compare the acrosome in Plate 13 (a normal sperm) and Plate 14 (a sperm at an egg surface). Whether the cell membrane has opened for the granule and closed behind it or whether the granule has filtered through a "porous" membrane cannot be determined.

In reverse, what happens to the cell membrane in secretion is the question of how particles or dissolved substances are taken into the cell. It is natural that all proposed hypotheses will be greatly influenced by theories of secretion and vice versa. In other words, we assume that two different methods exist for the uptake of substances into the cell. Either a particle (or a dissolved substance) can sink into the cell membrane without any visible effect, or the cell membrane can receive a particle (solution droplet) by surrounding it with a cell membrane fragment and taking it into the cell. A great deal of electron microscope evidence has been found in favor of the last mechanism, both when dissolved substances and when particles are taken up. Two technical terms have been invented to describe these phenomena: *phagocytosis,* which can be translated as cell-eating, meaning that a solid particle is taken into the cell by being surrounded by a piece of cell membrane; and *pinocytosis,* which can be translated as cell-drinking, meaning that small droplets can be taken up by being surrounded by cell membrane. Drawing a clear line of distinction between the two terms, we arrive at the same difficulties encountered when drawing a limit between food and drink.

One of the first electron microscopic studies of this problem was made by Palade and dealt with the appearance of the capillaries. In these, the wall between the blood stream and the outside tissues is very thin. It is a wall, nevertheless, and is composed of living cells whose flattened cytoplasm and cell membranes form a tube. Near the nucleus are found mitochondria and other relatively large organelles, but in the other parts of the cytoplasm, such components are missing. Here Palade found instead many small vesicles, which he interpreted as a visible sign that transport takes place between the blood and the tissues and vice versa and that it occurs within closed vesicles. At the time that this report was written, 1953, any speculation about such a transport was unusual, and there was no reason to assume that any substance was transported via the capillaries in the form of a quantum, that is, in equal packets.

The uncertainty about what kind of errors could arise owing to the electron microscope technique was much greater at that time. It is, therefore, not too surprising that the work was received with a mixture of sharp criticism and complete astonishment. Only much later did Palade's idea receive general favor. Plate 16 illustrates what a capillary looks like in cross-section. As Palade showed, it looks as if the cell membranes on both the outside and inside of the capillary are involved in the formation of vesicles. This would seem to indicate that something is transported from the blood to the tissues or the reverse. The micrographs do not give any indication of transport direction.

Later studies have attacked the question of particle transfer through capillary cells with a simple experiment. An iron-containing sugar was injected into the blood stream of animals, and at specified time intervals the tissues were removed for study of the capillary wall. The experiment confirmed the theory that transport takes place in the vesicles, insofar as the dense iron-containing sugar could be found in the blood, the vesicles, and outside the capillary cells. But this is not a case of true pinocytosis, since the cells apparently do not take up the substances but let them pass across the cell. Plate 17 shows phagocytosis as it appears in an intestinal cell from a polyp which was fed carbon particles.

The experiment shows that formation of pinocytotic vesicles does not necessarily mean that substances are incorporated into the cell mass. In order to say definitely that the substances are inside the cytoplasm, we have to assume another step. Either there is a dissolution and disappearance of the membranes of the pinocytotic vesicles, the substances being released into the cytoplasm in this way, or the substances, after being confined in the vesicles for some time, are changed and can now pass through the walls of the vesicles. If desirable, we could say that the formation of the pinocytotic vesicles merely enlarges the cell membrane and that their content has not penetrated the cell cytoplasm until it has passed the membrane of the pinocytotic vesicle or until the vesicle has dissolved. This way of looking at the mechanism of the pinocytotic vesicle implies that the wall of the vesicle is part of the cell membrane, an enlargement of the surface of the cell membrane, and an expansion of the definition of cell membrane.

These relatively new concepts of pinocytosis and phagocytosis have become very popular after several years of only limited acceptance. One of the reasons for its popularity today is probably the fact that the pinocytosis mechanism obviously works and gives an explanation of how the cell regulates its metabolism in relation to its outer milieu. But if we consider the pinocytotic vesicles as small, broken-off and reclosed cell membrane elements, we realize that nothing has been gained when it comes to explaining how the cell can regulate the uptake of substances from the outside. A surface enlargement does not in itself explain the specificity with which the cell membrane works; neither does it explain the selectivity which the membrane possesses when it comes to the incorporation of substances.

The foregoing must not give the impression that the contents of the pinocytotic vesicles is necessarily identical in composition with the surrounding fluid. It has actually been shown that the substance of the pinocytotic vesicles is considerably enriched with respect to some constituents. Proteins are taken up to a very much higher degree than the water in which they are dissolved. Pinocytosis is thus a selective and active process to a much higher degree than the term "cell drinking" would imply.

In the pinocytosis theory, and with other theories, it is customary to consider the cell membrane a membrane of a constant thickness, constant structure, and constant chemical composition that is able to form invaginations or folds but is a relatively passive layer. Some recent experiments, however, have been performed indicating a more active role in the life of the cell for regions of the cell membrane where its structure oscillates between an "open" and a "closed" state. These states seem to make it possible to explain many problems in dealing with the conduction of nerve impulses, selective permeability, and even protoplasmic streaming. This new hypothesis of dynamic membrane construction is supposed to hold not only for the limiting membrane of the cell but for the inner membrane system in mitochondria and elsewhere as well. The hypothesis has been worked out by Kavanau and rests partially on some experiments by Sjöstrand.

This chapter has shown that it is difficult to define the term "cell membrane." For one of the simplest definitions, we can assume that the cell membrane is the living cell's limits. Everything which is outside the cell membrane is the dead extracellular milieu. The cell membrane and most of what is inside should in turn be living substance able to regulate its metabolism as new conditions arise. But in using such definitions, we jump "from the frying pan into the fire." Two new terms have to be defined now: living and dead. In spite of the importance of these terms, it cannot be said that any human being has succeeded in giving a clear distinction between what is living and what is dead (Chap. 1). Why should the function of the extracellular fibrils be downgraded, as would be the case if these definitions were accepted? Much can be said to support the theory that these diffuse hairs on the outside of the cell membrane are a constant cell component equal in importance and specificity to many ingredients of the cytoplasm.

5

the cell nucleus and the nuclear membrane

Normally, there should not be any difficulty in establishing what the membrane of the cell nucleus is, and it can be said that there is general agreement as to what the main function of the nuclear membrane is. The *nuclear membrane* separates the contents of the nucleus from that of the cytoplasm and this is apparently its major function. Because the nucleus and the cytoplasm have different compositions in, among other things, their ion content, and because cell divisions normally involve some degree of mixing between the contents of the nucleus and the cytoplasm, it is difficult to imagine that the nuclear membrane can function either as a hermetically sealed wall or as a passive sieve. It is better to assume that the nuclear membrane, like the mitochondrion, can regulate its behavior with regard to the cell substances in a way that seems appropriate. As is true for the cell membrane, the purpose of the nuclear membrane seems to be to let some substances through and keep others out.

The structure of the nuclear membrane has been known for many years (many in the compressed time scale of the electron microscope). In low-power electron microscope magnifications, the nuclear membrane appears as a series of little rings. These rings can be seen in Plate 18, which shows an oblique cut through the membrane. This picture is of an immature sea urchin egg. Not every cell has such a clear structure of tightly packed rings as the sea urchin egg. The reasons for the special suitability of the sea urchin egg for electron microscope study of the nuclear membrane are partly its relative lack of internal cell organelles, and partly its very large size. It may seem strange that the nuclear membrane can be assumed to disclose its secrets better in a large cell than in a small one, but the explanation is as follows:

To have any effect on the cytoplasm, the nucleus must be able to send substances through its membrane to the cytoplasm. In a cell with a large amount of cytoplasm, a greater amount of these substances is needed than in a cell with less cytoplasm. Furthermore, if a cell grows uniformly, the surface of the nucleus (the nuclear membrane) increases with the square of the enlargement, while the cytoplasm increases its volume with the cube of the enlargement. In other words, if a cell increases uniformly in size, the ratio between the surface of the nuclear membrane (through which passage of matter is supposed to take place) and the amount of cytoplasm (which is the acceptor) will increase. For growing cells to maintain their geometry, the nuclear membrane must do more work. The transport capacity must be greater per surface unit of nuclear membrane. These relationships are based on the assumption that the cell and the nucleus increase while maintaining their geometry. In reality, however, it is rare to find a uniform increase. Normally the nuclear surface increases more than that of the cell. It is characteristic of especially big cells to have a nucleus with an irregular shape with numerous invaginations and buckles rather than a spherical shape. In some of these cells, the nucleus is greatly branched and penetrates the whole cell, sometimes in the form of a fine mesh network. This can be looked upon as a modification that serves to maintain the ratio between the surface of the nuclear membrane and the cell volume.

In other giant cells the nucleus is rather spherical. It is in these cells that one might expect the most extensive exploitation of the nuclear membrane for passage of substances. The sea urchin egg is one of these cell types. From this viewpoint it is interesting that the nuclear membrane of the immature sea urchin egg has an extraordinarily high concentration of "rings," about 80 per square micron. In the mature sea urchin egg the ratio between the surface area of the nuclear membrane and the cytoplasmic volume is lower, but this cell behaves in several aspects as an abnormal cell. It is a cell in a resting or sleeping stage which is not disturbed until the moment of entrance of the sperm. We do not find the concentration of rings per surface unit greater here than in normal, smaller tissue cells.

The rings of the nuclear membrane seem to be a detail in nuclear membrane construction that varies with nuclear membrane activity and whose finer structure should be worthwhile to explore for several reasons. Plate 19 and Figure 1 show how the

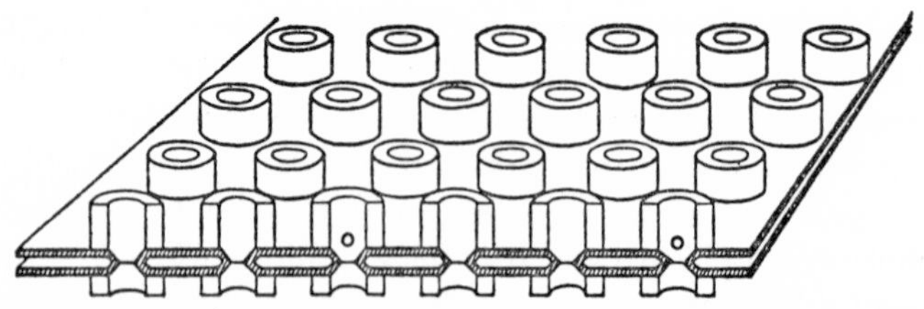

FIG. 1.—Somewhat schematic reconstruction of the structure of the nuclear membrane in which the relationship between the cylinders and the other components has been especially emphasized.

nuclear membrane and its rings are constructed. The rings can be regarded as cylinders perpendicular to the border between the nucleus and the cytoplasm. The cylinders penetrate two dense layers and the layer, which has an empty appearance in the micrographs, between them. These layers and the cylinders together form a structural unit in such a way that the different components come together in a structure of constant appearance and give the effect of being joined. They probably also form a functional unit. There ought to be no doubt left that this complex unit should be called the nuclear membrane.

In one particular cell the nuclear membrane has a structure deviating from that described above. This is in another very large cell, namely, one of the large luminescent unicellular organisms of the sea, *Noctiluca scintillans.* This protozoan belongs to a group called the dinoflagellates, and a distinctive feature, among others, of the group is that throughout the greater part of the cell's life the chromosomes are clearly visible and in a state which reminds us of prophase chromosomes. Plate 20 shows the chromosomes of another dinoflagellate. In *Noctiluca* the division of the nucleus takes place inside a closed nuclear membrane, which implies that the two chromosome sets at division migrate in different directions within the long stretched nucleus that constricts after division of the chromosomes and forms two daughter nuclei. The organism can thus divide for generations without breakdown of the nuclear membrane and therefore without any mixing of the nuclear substance and the cytoplasm, although it is not quite reasonable to believe that they are completely separated. If the nucleus and the cytoplasm could exist side by side without any exchange of substances, the cytoplasm might as well exist without the nucleus and the nucleus without the cytoplasm. Chapter 6 will deal with the nature of the substances which are exchanged between the nucleus and the cytoplasm.

Electron micrographs of the nucleus of the dinoflagellates show the large chromosomes as convoluted threads in a nuclear substance of a more homogeneous nature. Between the nuclear substance and the true nuclear membrane (in the sense of a border between the nucleus and the cytoplasm), a layer of vesicles is found whose walls have a complex structure. These walls are like the nuclear membrane of ordinary cells—that is, they are characterized by cylinders that penetrate two dense and one less dense layer. The true nuclear membrane that lies outside this row of vesicles, on the contrary, lacks perforating cylinders. The true nuclear membrane and the vesicles below it form a layer between the nucleus and the cytoplasm which presents a structural complexity that is a degree higher than that of other nuclear membranes. In explaining the functions of this layer, we must assume the presence of mechanisms which are a step more complicated than those of normal cell nuclei. In other words, there seems to exist a transport of substances from the nucleus into the vesicles. After this transport has occurred, the filled vesicles can be brought to the surface of the nucleus, open at the true nuclear membrane, and empty their contents into the cytoplasm.

All the transition stages which must occur in such an emptying process can be watched in electron micrographs. The vesicles are round when they are in the nuclear substance, ellipsoid when they are flattened against the nuclear membrane, and pear-shaped when the nuclear membrane has started to give in. Other vesicles have melted into the wall of the nuclear membrane and seem to have a degenerate structure. Plate 21 shows some of these stages.

Some consequences of this theory are worth consideration. This mechanism implies that a structure as complicated as the nuclear membrane can be synthesized inside a closed nucleus. In other words, the membrane does not have to be formed alongside the other membranes in the cytoplasm; a nuclear membrane can be built within the fine fibrillar network inside a nucleus. Perhaps we have here a model of how genes can govern directly the construction of a complex structure, which, transferred to the cytoplasm, can influence the machinery of the cell. In *Noctiluca* it appears that the production of big nuclear products, including membranes, takes place during the major part of the cell cycle. The phenomenon is probably not limited to this species but is probably generally valid. In normal cell division (not that of *Noctiluca*), the nuclear membrane fragments and disappears into the cytoplasm, apparently to be part of the cell's general storage of membranes.

Another consequence is that particles or aggregates of particles that are larger than the cylinders in the nuclear membrane can be pushed through the membrane without causing any wound. This is, in other words, a mechanism by which particles as big as nucleoli (particles—some microns in size which are part of most cell nuclei) can leave the nucleus with a minimum of harm to the membrane. For some cells, the expelling of nucleoli has been described. Among these are egg cells, for instance, the sea urchin egg. A study of the nuclear membrane of this cell has shown that there really exist stages corresponding to the nuclear membrane vesicles of the *Noctiluca*. Large packages of particles (the size of nucleoli) lie against a protruding part of the nuclear membrane. A "wound-healing membrane" is formed under the particles within the closed nucleus, and only in later stages, when the wound-healing membrane has grown together with the original nuclear membrane, is the package of particles ready to be expelled into the cytoplasm. This is, in principle, the same complicated mechanism found in *Noctiluca,* a mechanism that involves a great amount of substance leaving the nucleus without necessarily disturbing the ion balance between nucleus and cytoplasm.

The mechanism can, so to speak, be compared to the pinocytosis mechanism of the cell membrane. It is a question of new formation of membrane material in both. This mechanism for transporting substances from the nucleus to the cytoplasm is hardly, however, the most significant one. The most normal and important path is probably directly through an uninterrupted membrane. A number of theories consider how such a transport through a nuclear membrane may take place. The simplest hypothesis is that substances pass through the cylinders that can be thought of as little chimneys through which substances smoke from the nucleus. The cylinders would be open tubes through which the smoke would pass freely. But from a structural viewpoint, this assumption is false. In the nuclear membrane there are dampers on the chimneys; or, more scientifically, the cylinders are equipped with a demarcated diaphragm at the level of the less dense of the three layers of the nuclear membrane. It does not seem likely, therefore, that the tubes are open between the nucleus and the cytoplasm, either from a structural or a functional viewpoint.

Loewenstein and his associates succeeded in introducing electrodes into a large cell and measured specific electrical properties of the cell membrane and even of the nuclear membrane. They found that these two different types of membranes have different properties from an electrophysiological viewpoint and, further, that the nuclear membrane can maintain an electrical potential and have a measurable electrical resistance. It therefore cannot be an open sieve.

In spite of these experiments and in spite of micrographs of closed cylinders, the researcher still wants to say that the primary transport is through these cylinders. This is based on proofs of a direct and indirect nature. Among the indirect ones, the researcher can point to the fact that the nuclear membranes of large cells have proportionally more cylinders than the less active nuclear membranes of the majority of smaller cells. The probable role of the nuclear membrane vesicles of the *Noctiluca* nucleus is also indirect proof. The direct proof comes from an experiment done by Feldherr, who injected colloidal gold (gold grains about 100 Å or 0.01 μ) into the cytoplasm of amoeba. After designated time intervals, the amoebas were fixed for electron microscopy. The amoebas fixed earlier had only a few gold grains in the nucleus, but many grains were apparently on their way through the nuclear membrane. These grains were in the cylinders but not between the cylinders in the less dense layer between the two dense layers. This is good proof that the cylinders take part in passage through the nuclear membrane. The direction of particle transport in this experiment was from the outside to the inside. It is not as easy to perform the experiment to check if the particles take the same route from the nucleus to the cytoplasm. We cannot inject a substance into the nucleus and then withdraw the needle without puncturing or disturbing the membrane. A torn nuclear membrane cannot heal as quickly as a cell membrane.

6

ribosomal hieroglyphics

A cell component which has been intensively studied in recent years is composed of little particles of uniform appearance and about 150Å in size. The arrangement of these particles is, however, anything but constant. In different cell types or in the same cell in different functional stages, these cell components occur in what seems to be a random distribution of free particles in groups of a definite size. They can be connected to membranes in the cells to form rings or whorls, they can be tightly packed without any detectable pattern, or they can sit in rows on the membrane. Plates 22 through 25 demonstrate some of these patterns.

The first person to call attention to these particles and their general occurrence and varying patterns was George Palade. In a report in 1958, he formulated the problem in the following way: "Sometimes, while looking at these intriguing patterns, I believe that I feel very much like the French explorers who, during Napoleon's expedition to Egypt, found themselves face to face with hieroglyphs. Like some of them, I am recording the patterns, and I am waiting hopefully for a biochemical Champollion to decipher their meaning."

Although we are still waiting for a Rosetta stone, I believe that the picture is now much clearer than in 1958, thanks to intensive deciphering work in many of the leading biological laboratories of the world. The picture which seems to emerge from the interplay between Palade's particles and other cell components is more complicated than we would have expected earlier, even though we can be sure that we are not at the bottom of the problem yet. The picture that is emerging is, however, attractive because of its logical development.

The clarifying contributions have arisen from biological detective work in different scientific fields, and their agreement inspires confidence in our understanding of the ribosome.

The electron microscope contribution was the demonstration that the particles were distinct units. Whether or not they occur in living cells as distinct particles 150 Å in size or as diffuse clouds is of no importance in this connection for the same reasons that it does not worry the electron microscopist if the electron is shaped like a ball, or like a cloud, or perhaps has no shape whatsoever. The important thing here is that Palade's particles can exist as units which can be seen and counted and whose arrangement can be recorded.

Chemical analysis of pure preparations of the isolated particles established that they contain almost equal amounts of RNA and protein. The particles can be assumed to be a combination of these two substances and can now be given a descriptive name: *ribonucleic acid-containing granules* or *ribosomes.* But even in 1958 some experimental details were known that could not be explained. With one technique it was possible to obtain preparations with a higher RNA concentration than that of pure ribosomes. These preparations were shown, with the electron microscope, to consist of ribosomes mixed with some very fine threads. We might interpret this to mean that there exist ribosomes which, in addition to protein and RNA, contain threads with a high concentration of RNA—perhaps pure RNA.

Much earlier, several other methods had been used to prove the existence of a relationship between ribonucleic acid content and the degree of protein synthesis (or sometimes the degree of ability to synthesize protein; a cell can have the potentiality for a process without making use of it). This relationship was determined, for example, in the pioneering experiments in the thirties by Caspersson using ultraviolet microscopy.

While electron microscopy developed from the production of the first blurred pictures of ribosomes to detailed micrographs, a technically parallel important development was taking place in another biological method—namely, X-ray diffraction analysis. With this technique, the DNA of the nucleus, the compound that above all is the hereditary substance, could be analyzed. Wilkins succeeded in getting extraordinarily detailed X-ray diffraction diagrams of pure crystalline DNA. Mainly on the basis of these pictures and Chargaff's chemical data, Watson and Crick succeeded in presenting the very elegant interpretation of DNA structure, now called the Watson-Crick helix. For this, Wilkins, Watson, and Crick received the Nobel Prize in 1962. The chemical, structural explanation of what the Watson-Crick helix implies can be conveyed thus:

Two long continuously intertwining chains of DNA are wound around each other into a regular double helix. On each level of the helix, a nucleotide from one chain meets a complementary nucleotide from the other chain. Four nucleotides (the name for the building blocks of nucleic acids) are known. The importance of this scheme is that the double helix through its chemical configuration seems to offer an explanation of how the DNA structure can double and the genetic material increase while maintaining its chemical identity. Figure 2 shows how the DNA doubles, forming two identical double helixes from only one double helix. The structure also allows for formation of other substances which can leave the nucleus and affect the development of the cytoplasm.

On the basis of biochemical experiments and calculations of a more theoretical nature, we can now say that the substance made by the DNA of the nucleus is RNA. One kind of RNA is made with a special nucleotide sequence and therefore with a specificity corresponding to that of its DNA model. In order to direct the cell machinery to produce a specific protein, the RNA should have easy access to this machinery situated in the cytoplasm. It could creep through the cylinders of the nuclear membrane and later flake into the cytoplasm, or it could leave the nucleus in some other way. It also seems as if the *nucleoli* are in some way involved in this interplay between nucleus and cytoplasm, for example, by acting as a depot for ribosomes. The RNA, which is assumed to have maintained the specificity (information) of the

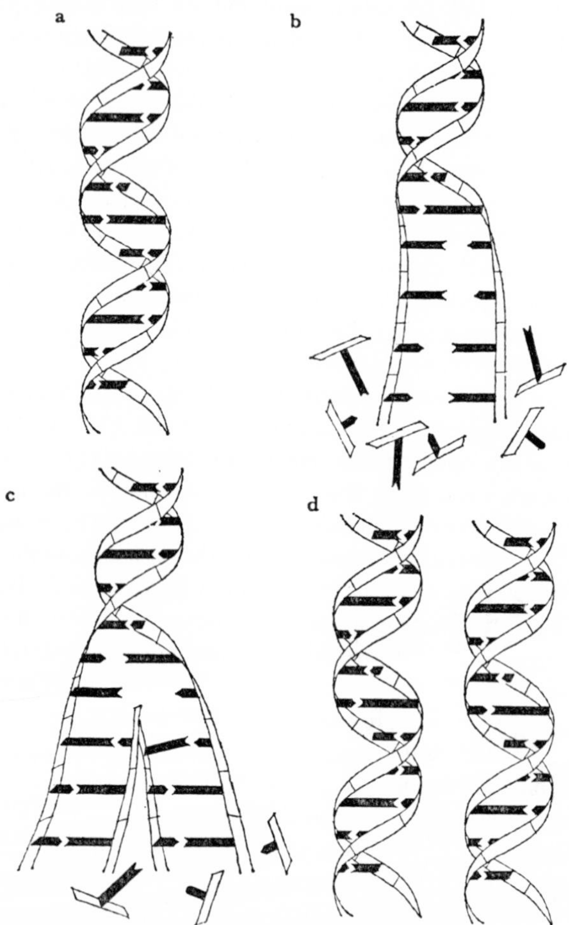

FIG. 2.—A scheme for imagining how the DNA molecule divides and gives rise to two molecules identical to the original molecule. *a*. Double helix with paired nucleotides. *b*. The helix starts to unwind. *c*. Loose nucleotides find their places on the complementary nucleotides along the helical chains. *d*. Two newly-formed double helixes which have maintained the nucleotide sequence of the original molecule, its genetic code.

DNA molecules and be able to intervene in the machinery of the cytoplasm after leaving the nucleus, has been named *messenger RNA.*

We can predict that the messenger-RNA molecules will appear as single threads (not double helixes) and therefore be easily breakable and thin, about 15 Å. Further, we can predict that the messenger RNA forming the mold for the production of a large and complicated protein will be a longer molecule than the messenger RNA directing production of a smaller protein. Is it possible to calculate exactly how long a messenger-RNA molecule must be in order to transcribe the information concerning construction of a specific protein (for example, hemoglobin)? Such a calculation can be performed with some assumptions. There are four different building units (nucleotides) for RNA, and there are twenty building units (amino acids) for the proteins. For every amino acid in the protein thread, there should be three nucleotides in the RNA thread by analogy to the Morse code alphabet which is poor in symbols (short, long) and requires more strokes for one word than is necessary on a typewriter with the usual twenty-six–letter alphabet. (One nucleotide per amino acid would only make a code for four different amino acids. A combination of two nucleotides will code for sixteen amino acids.) For hemoglobin, the total number of amino acids in the four chains of the molecule has been determined. Knowing there is a constant distance between two adjacent nucleotides in the RNA chain and knowing three nucleotides make one amino acid, we can predict that the messenger RNA for the hemoglobin chains must be 1500 Å long. The hemoglobin-dictating part of the chromosomal DNA should have exactly the same length if it is to be responsible for the blueprint of the hemoglobin molecule. 1500Å equals 0.15μ, which is a great distance in the world of the cell, and it cannot be expected that these 0.15μ threads are completely stretched. They appear as helixes and as superhelixes. This calculation is founded on the assumption that every amino acid built into a protein is coded by a nucleotide triplet, that is, three adjacent nucleotides in the messenger-RNA molecule. Nothing, so far, challenges this assumption, but a great deal favors it. Experimenters have even succeeded in determining which (one or several) nucleotide triplet corresponds to any one specific amino acid.

The theory about messenger RNA implies that the chromosomal DNA directs the building of long or short messenger-RNA threads, according to whether these are designed to direct production of protein chains of high or low molecular weight. When the messenger RNA reaches the cytoplasm, it has to find the production site in order to direct protein synthesis. The production site is the ribosomes, which perhaps can be shown most directly with ribosomes isolated from cells. The ribosomes can be visualized as spheres 150 Å in diameter; the thickness of the messenger-RNA thread is only 15 Å, but it is several thousand Ångstroms long. The meeting is between two ill-matched partners. Their proportions to each other are as a pearl to the string in a necklace. In a necklace there are many pearls and the pearls are threaded on the string. What is the situation with the ribosomes? Do they go together in groups? This indeed seems to be the situation, as can be demonstrated both in broken cells which have been centrifuged in order to compare size of the ribosomes with ribosome aggregates and in intact cell structures studied with the electron microscope.

Ribosome chains form the mysterious pattern with which Palade was confronted. With new methods, it has now been possible to obtain higher contrast and sharper micrographs of the ribosome chains than in 1958. These pictures show a very thin thread running between the ribosomes, a thread seemingly connecting them, but still leaving them about a ribosome-width apart. In other words, we see not only the pearls but also the string of the necklace. Now the deciphering of the ribosomal hieroglyphs can begin. The short chains with a few ribosomes should imply the presence of a short messenger-RNA molecule and thus a building site for low-molecular-weight proteins. The large ribosomal spirals likewise should be fabrication sites for high-molecular-weight proteins. Also, it should be possible to detect from a ribosomal pattern whether a population of equal-sized or different-sized proteins is being formed. The ribosomal pattern within the cell can be assumed then to reflect the work of the cell in regard to its protein production.

This assumption can be tested by studying cells which are specialized in synthesizing only one specific protein, if the molecular weight of the protein is known. A suitable cell for analysis of this kind is the one that forms red blood cells. This cell type synthesizes mainly hemoglobin, whose corresponding messenger RNA should be 1500 Å long (calculated from the molecular weight of hemoglobin). If every ribosome has a diameter of 150 Å and these are normally arranged–that is, have 150 Å between them–then there will be space for five ribosomes on each messenger-RNA molecule. The ribosomes in this cell type should appear as a necklace with five pearls. Both centrifugation and the electron microscope have been used to show that aggregates of five ribosomes are in the majority.

The ribosomes are not tied together on a pearl strand messenger-RNA string in all cell types. In the unfertilized sea urchin egg, for example, the ribosomes in centrifugation experiments behave as isolated particles, and even electron micrographs show them as free particles (Plate 25). But this cell is in a resting stage with regard to its degree of protein synthesis activity.

Is it legitimate to ask why ribosomes have to be threaded on messenger RNA in order to start working and what lies behind this complicated machinery? Part of the explanation is probably that it is advantageous to the cell for the machinery of protein synthesis to be attached only when there is demand for synthesis of the specific protein. Another important reason is that the system is flexible; the same ribosomes can be used for the production of different proteins, depending on what instruction they receive in the form of messenger RNA.

When ribosomes have been removed from cells, their protein production stops within a few minutes, if new messenger RNA is not provided. The simplest explanation for this and other experimental results is that messenger-RNA molecules have a short functional lifetime, although the ribosomes themselves are long-lived and can function through several cell generations. The result is that the ribosomes are supplied with messenger RNA continuously in an actively protein-synthesizing cell; incoming messenger RNA can carry the same message or a new one. A cell nucleus can switch the cell's production to new proteins relatively quickly by producing new messenger RNA.

The similarity between ribosomes, which only work when so instructed by a messenger RNA, and some automated and programmed machines enables us to adopt a similar terminology. The ribosomes work when programmed and can be reprogrammed by a new messenger RNA. In the same way that a programmed tape is fed into a computer and works its way through in order to make the machine read the instructions, we can imagine that the messenger-RNA thread passes through the ribosome or, which in practice is the same, that the ribosome moves down the messenger-RNA thread and reads its information. When the ribosome has reached the end of the messenger-RNA molecule, it has finished the reading and the complete protein should then have been synthesized. This means that the ribosomes, which are threaded along the messenger-RNA strand, are asynchronous in their protein synthesis: they are at different steps in the synthesis of identical protein chains. At one end we have the newly threaded ribosome starting the synthesis; at the other end the synthesis is complete and the ribosome can free its finished product and leave the thread. Figure 3 illustrates this hypothesis. The figure is on the whole in accordance with an illustration from Watson's Nobel lecture. The illustration has been changed only in such a way as to leave out a third class of ribonucleic acids. These play a role in protein synthesis which in this shortened presentation can be omitted without being misleading.

The schematic picture shows the ribosomes as complex particles rather than as single balls. They are illustrated in this manner specifically because this is the way ribosomes (especially those of bacteria, which differ from ribosomes of the eucaryote) have appeared in some micrographs and also because of the analogy to programmed computers; we want to see a slot through which the program passes. The ribosomes which have passed the major part of the messenger-RNA molecule and which therefore have read more of the information are depicted with a longer protein thread compatible with the hypothesis, but this is something which has not been observed directly as yet.

It is of interest to study what type of protein could be made if ribosomes from one kind of animal (or plant or bacterium) were mixed with messenger-RNA strands of another. If the theory is correct, the ribosomes should produce proteins characteristic of the origin of the messenger RNA rather than their own specific proteins. Experiments performed to answer this question seem to

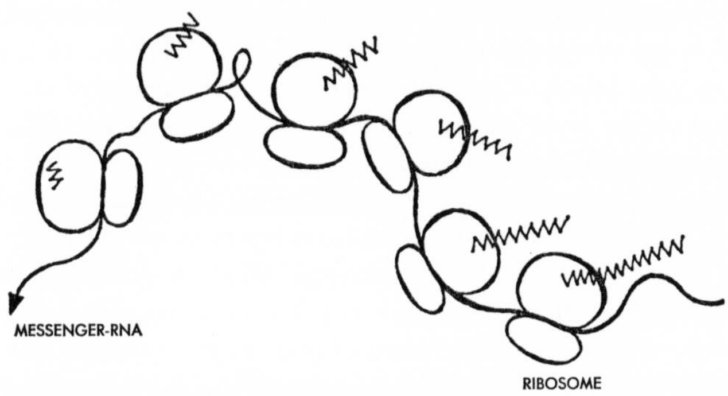

FIG. 3.—Schematic drawing of messenger RNA with ribosomes. The ribosomes on the far right are assumed to have followed a greater portion of the RNA strand and the protein thread produced is longer there.

support the hypothesis. The ribosomes can synthesize different proteins, but the specificity of the synthesis is in the chromosomal DNA and the messenger RNA.

The experiments can be expanded to include completely non-biological messenger RNA—that is, RNA chains synthesized in test tubes and having no biological counterpart whatsoever. The question can be phrased in this manner: Are the ribosomes able to follow instructions from an artificial programming tape, a test-tube RNA? A messenger RNA that has been made synthetically has the form of a monotonous repetition of the same nucleotide. It has been possible to make the ribosomes produce a protein with this test-tube RNA which, in accordance with expectation, was a long chain of one amino acid.

From the above description we might get the impression that the biological study of this problem has built an unacceptably tall house of cards of hypothesis—one theory on top of the other with facts and hypotheses intertwined. It must be added that the extent of the solidarity of these theories cannot be given here and that much support exists which has not been presented at all.

In reality, this house of cards of theories seems to be so stable that researchers have ventured to add even more stories, a superstructure of hypothesis concerning the mode of operation of hormones. In the study of the biochemical effects of hormones, one question has remained unanswered and has given rise to a great deal of speculation. This question refers to the cause of the slow onset of action of, at any rate, the majority of hormones. The hormones represent a heterogeneous group but for many of them, perhaps the majority, the rule seems to be that the observed effects of a hormone first appear several hours or even twenty-four hours after release. Some biochemical effects occur immediately in a test tube—for example, when a hormone is added to mitochondria or other cell components. Such effects, however, are produced only if the dosage of the hormone is much greater than that normally found in the cell. It does not seem that the hormone has a direct effect on the mitochondria or any other isolated cell component. For a hormone to perform its physiological effects, it must do its work in a whole cell. The effects seem to be indirect.

The first experiment which seems to give some kind of clue to the events taking place when a hormone affects a cell was done by Peter Karlson. He studied fly larvae and observed the cells after addition of the hormone which induces pupation. The first changes that could be observed with the microscope took place in the nucleus in the chromosomes. Only several hours later did chemical and structural changes take place in the cytoplasm. From these experiments, he concluded that the mode of operation of the hormone occurs via the nucleus (which seems to be true also with thyroxine, cortisone, and many other hormones). The hormone penetrates the nucleus and there induces a segment of chromosome to start the production of one or several messenger RNA's; these are transported to the cytoplasm and switch on synthesis of new proteins. There are several ways to test this theory. One is to apply a specific poison which seems to have a very specific effect—namely, blocking formation of messenger RNA. If this compound, atinomycin, is injected into animals, the hormones lose their effects: the fly larva does not enter pupation, the basal metabolism of the rat goes down, the animal's thyroxin becomes ineffective, and so forth.

A consequence of this theory about messenger RNA is that the nucleus is assigned a much more active role in the cell's life than earlier interpreters of cell function had been willing to admit. The nucleus is no longer a mere spectator to the events taking place in the cell or a stockroom for genes which participate in the cell machinery every now and then. It is true that these ideas about a continuous interplay between the nucleus and the cytoplasm will greatly influence many other biological fields. Questions about how cells affect each other during embryological development, or about enzyme induction, or perhaps about the existence of directed mutations will affect additional biological disciplines.

The developments described in this chapter represent a very active part of physiological science. What perhaps has characterized the working methods of this science more than anything else has been the progress that has arisen when results from quite different fields—biochemistry, electron microscopy, X-ray diffraction analysis, endocrinology, microbiology, genetics—have been pooled. If a researcher wants to work in modern biology, he cannot limit himself to the development of only one field.

Progress takes place through contact between the different fields of biology. After all, not completely separate things are being explored in the different fields. Everything that is being debated with various methods deals with the process of life.

7

microbodies in mice and men

It is safe to predict that the normal ultrastructural anatomy of the animal body will never be fully explored. There will always be another new technique for exploring the cell, and the electron microscopist will always find himself presented with new questions which arise as a consequence of the expansion of the entire biological field.

This chapter deals with recent studies on a heretofore enigmatic organelle, the microbody. The investigation of this organelle was evoked by new questions posed to the electron microscopist rather than by a new technical approach. In the next chapter, findings will be presented which are more the product of improvements of the electron microscope technique.

The term microbody is noncommittal. Micro in Greek means small, and body is, of course, the English word. The structure of the microbody is simple. It is an oval body about 0.5μ in size. In contrast to the mitochondrion, it is delimited by a single membrane and its interior is homogeneous except for a rod with a distinctive fine structure, apparently crystalline. Microbodies have been found in liver and kidney tissue. Some liver microbodies are shown in Plate 26.

The enigma of the microbody is its role in the life of the cell. We would also like to know how it is formed and what connections it may have with other organelles.

One suggestion for the role of the microbody emanates from studies by a group of biochemists headed by De Duve. Using standard biochemical methods, they minced rat liver to obtain a suspension of organelles free from any cytoplasmic framework. They transferred the suspension to a centrifuge tube which contained a sugar solution prepared so that the concentration of the sugar, and thereby the density of the solution, was greater at the bottom of the tube than at the top. During centrifugation, the various cell components moved to levels in the centrifuge tube corresponding to their respective densities. A great number of enzymes were localized at levels of different densities; that is, the mitochondrial enzymes were at a different level from those of the nuclear enzymes. Three enzymes did not fit into the level of any known organelle, and either seemed to belong to three separate particles showing very similar density properties or were associated in different proportions with a single group of particles. The enzymes were uricase, D-amino acid oxidase, and catalase.

It was suggested that the microbody was the organelle associated with these three enzymes. This was tested by examining samples in the electron microscope. Man, orangutan, and the chimpanzee were found to differ from other examined mammals in that they lack uricase and therefore excrete uric acid in the urine, rather than allantoin, as the final product in the metabolism of substances called purines. Birds and terrestrial reptiles similarly lack uricase and excrete large amounts of uric acid. The specific question to be put to the electron microscopist was this: Do liver microbodies from these reptiles, birds, orangutans, chimpanzees, and man differ from those of other mammals? The question has been attacked and gives an affirmative answer. Typical microbodies appear only in the other mammals—that is, where uricase is also present. In man as well as in the chicken, there are certainly bodies resembling the microbodies, but these bodies invariably lack the crystalline inclusion.

This supports the concept that the microbody contains one or all three of the enzymes mentioned. Another inference is that the rod in the microbody must consist specifically of the enzyme uricase and that this enzyme must appear in the liver cell as crystals, which are separated from the cytoplasm by a membrane. This is a somewhat surprising conclusion, since it is difficult to see the advantage of compressing an enzyme into a crystalline state in an organelle. In the economy of the cell, the enzymes are usually in solution or are spread out in a monomolecular layer in order to be reactive. The molecules of the inner layers of a crystal are, on the other hand, hidden from other substances.

Hruban has recently shown that a sectioned crystal of uricase enzyme has the same appearance as the rod in a microbody. This is perhaps not too surprising, since the uricase enzyme is obtained by isolation from the pig liver, but the demonstration by Hruban still gives very direct evidence for the theory that the microbodies contain uricase, perhaps even pure crystalline uricase. The possibility still exists that the examined preparation of uricase was not a crystal or a pure protein but a structure of mixed composition.

Three enzymes were found by De Duve and his collaborators to come to approximately the same level of the centrifuge tube and were therefore supposed to be associated with a single group of particles. Do all three enzymes appear together in the same organelle? There are some facts which favor this supposition. In the enzymatic reaction by uricase, the breakdown product of uric acid is formed and, as a by-product, hydrogen peroxide. The latter compound is reactive and of no particular use to the cell, and the presence of the enzyme catalase in the same organelle would seem advantageous. Catalase is the enzyme which breaks down hydrogen peroxide. Similarly, D-amino acid oxidase is an enzyme which forms hydrogen peroxide as a by-product. The main function of D-amino acid oxidase is to break down non-biological amino acids with the wrong steric configurations, that is, which rotate polarized light to the right rather than to the left.

It was said that man, orangutan, and the chimpanzee differ from the other mammals examined by lacking uricase. What is actually stated in most textbooks is that man and the primates lack uricase and excrete uric acid. Sometimes it is added that, in addition, one particular breed of dog excretes uric acid and lacks uricase. In the original publications from which these statements are quoted, it is mentioned that twenty-two mammalian species were examined, among them one monkey, one chimpanzee, one orangutan, and man. It is stated that the chimpanzee and "possibly of course the other anthropoids form a class of themselves characterized by the practically entire absence of uriocolytic enzymes." This generalization might have been too hasty. Four primates (man, apes, and one monkey); only eighteen other mammalian species were examined.

Since the uric acid has a relatively low solubility, the improper excretion of uric acid causes disorders of the kidney. It has therefore been of interest to examine other mammals with this type of urine excretion. The particular breed of dog referred to above, the Dalmatian, has become famous for the excretion of uric acid. It has been called "the dog that urinates like a man," and it has been kept in special kennels connected to biochemical laboratories where purine metabolism is studied. The Dalmatian has, however, not been found as useful in this respect as was expected. Although its urine contains a rather high concentration of uric acid, the Dalmatian has been known for 150 years to suffer from "the disease of drinking water," and this uric acid excretion occurs because its kidneys are "leaky" to uric acid. Its liver, on the other hand, contains a uricase and perfectly normal microbodies.

When it comes to an ultrastructural examination of the liver, about twenty different mammalian species have been examined. It is therefore possible to examine electron micrographs to find out whether the microbodies in any animal species other than the chimpanzee have the same appearance as those in man, and whether, with respect to uric acid excretion, there thus might be "an animal that urinates like a man."

Such examination has revealed that man and the chimpanzee are not alone among the mammals in having this type of purine metabolism. The Syrian hamster (also called the golden hamster) is similar to man in this respect. By means of electron microscopy it thus seems possible to find a suitable small laboratory animal, the study of which may throw light on the purine metabolism of man.

8

lysosomes; bags of digestive enzymes

The term lysosome has been constructed from Greek word roots and means "digestive body."

The concept behind the term, not to mention the reality behind the concept, is much debated. De Duve, who coined the term, gave it a concrete biochemical meaning: a cytoplasmic particle containing several digestive enzymes which are prevented from acting on the cell machinery by some kind of barrier, presumably a limiting membrane.

A lysosome can thus be regarded as an organelle which performs much the same functions in the cell as do the digestive organs in the body of a higher organism. Since a cell is simpler than an entire organism, the analogy cannot be expected to be very close. The lysosome has many abilities which a stomach lacks and *vice versa.*

De Duve used the distribution of many enzymes among various cytoplasmic fractions obtained by density centrifugation as an experimental basis for the lysosome concept. As mentioned in Chapter 7, he found catalase, uricase, and D-amino acid oxidase to be localized at a specific level which was later found to contain the particles which had been called microbodies. In another fraction there were several enzymes with common properties: they catalyzed reactions in which compounds were split with simultaneous addition of water and had maximal enzymatic activity at an acid pH value. Such enzymes are called acid hydrolases, and De Duve conceived the idea that the cytoplasmic fraction contains bags of acid hydrolases. These bags he called lysosomes.

The concept was based on some assumptions. One assumption was that a single lysosome contains not one, but several, enzyme species. This was not supported by any direct observation but seemed likely from various lines of reasoning. The particular attraction of this assumption is that the lysosome would then be a complete digestive bag. Whatever fragment of a cell should come into the digestive bags, the chances are that it would be degraded into its smaller components. A complete digestion could not be performed if there were as many lysosomal species as there are lysosomal enzymes.

Another assumption was that the hydrolases are all in an active state in the bag and are kept from digesting the cell only by their limiting membrane and perhaps an unsuitable pH value. But why don't they digest each other? The enzymes are proteins, and some enzymes in the lysosome are protein-digesting (proteolytic) enzymes and can thus be dangerous to the neighboring enyzmes in the lysosomes. The problem of how the enzymes are protected from each other in a lysosome is not an easy one. Perhaps the pH value in a resting lysosome is far from the optimal value for a proteolytic enzyme; perhaps the enzymes of the lysosomes are unusually resistant to the action of proteolytic enzymes. There is also the possibility that the lysosomes do degrade themselves slowly and have to be formed anew continuously. The latter possibility is not likely, however, since the average lifetime of a lysosome from the rat liver has been found to be 15 to 30 days, which is about twice the calculated value for a mitochondrion from the same tissue.

Today, more than ten years after the creation of the lysosome concept, there is nothing in the original concept that has had to be changed. Not only the lifetime of the lysosome, but also the lifetime of the lysosome concept is quite respectable.

Yet there have been attempts to redefine the lysosome. The electron microscopists in particular have been tempted to apply the term lysosome to particles which probably, but not necessarily, are identical with lysosomes as identified by biochemical criteria.

The electron microscopist has the advantage over the biochemist in that he can examine the particles one by one, but he is far less well equipped with methods which enable him to detect the enzymatic properties of the particles. Some lysosomal enzymes can, however, be detected with methods which can be used in electron microscopy, the easiest among them being for the enzyme acid phosphatase. There has therefore been a tendency to create a new definition of lysosomes for electron microscopy: A lysosome is a particle, with a single limiting membrane, in which acid phosphatase is demonstrable.

Much discussion is at present devoted to the question of how far the electron microscope lysosomes are identical with the biochemically defined lysosomes. They would be the same if every lysosome contains acid phosphatase which can be demonstrated by the electron microscopist and if every particle containing acid phosphatase is also equipped with the other dozen lysosomal enzymes. According to present evidence, the first condition is always found to be true, but the second condition is not. The term lysosome is likely to cover more structures when used in connection with electron microscope studies than when used with biochemical work.

It is important to elaborate methods for localizing the other lysosomal enzymes in electron microscope sections. Much ingenuity is now being devoted to these problems, and it is likely that in the near future it will be known whether a single particle contains the full set of lysosomal enzymes, whether there are lysosomes of different kinds, and whether lysosomes are a general cell component.

What then does a lysosome look like? Plate 27 shows a dog's liver cell with some mitochondria, two particles which probably are microbodies, elements of the endoplasmic reticulum, glycogen granules, and one particle which looks like a liver lysosome. It should be noted that in this micrograph the technique for demonstrating acid phosphatase has not been applied, and that not even this criterion of a lysosome can be used. It is not possible to conclude that the particle is a lysosome, but it resembles lysosomes as identified by other means. The two zones of the membrane, an outer dark one, an inner light one, and the heterogeneous contents are features which are indicative of liver lysosomes but certainly not conclusive evidence. There is no standard appearance for a lysosome. Lysosomes are known to differ in size and shape from one cell type to another and within the same cell type under various functional conditions or at various developmental stages during the life of the lysosome.

The lysosomes start functioning when the cell takes up substances either by phagocytosis or by pinocytosis. The lysosomes then fuse with the packages of ingested material, and the digestive enzymes of the lysosomes attack the digestible material. The uptake of the material by pinocytosis or phagocytosis may last from a few minutes to a few hours; and the digestion within the fused bags may require a few hours to a few days, depending on the nature of the ingested material. It seems that the cell shows no discrimination in this process: The same complement of enzymes are released into the bags of ingested material regardless of whether the bags contain a more protein-rich or a more carbohydrate-rich material, or whether the cell was fooled into ingesting a completely insoluble fluid or particle. In this respect the cell machinery is relatively automatic with a low degree of flexibility and inferior to the digestive organ of a higher animal.

Digestion within a lysosome, or a lysosome fused with an ingested vacuole, normally gives rise to amino acids, sugars, and simple organic compounds which might be useful building blocks in the synthetic machinery of the cell. It is therefore somewhat surprising that some cell types do not use the building blocks formed in the process themselves but expel them from the cell. Other cell types, however, such as the protozoans, rely entirely on this mechanism for their metabolic needs.

Insoluble remnants usually stay within the lysosome, which in this way becomes packed with different inclusions. Lipids often become inclusions because they are not digestible by the lysosome which may lack lipid-degrading enzymes. Fatty substances accumulating in the lysosomes are often colored and are sometimes called wear-and-tear pigment. The lysosomes containing them are called lipofuscin granules. They characterize, above all, cells which have lived and functioned during a long period, for instance, those in the muscle or other tissues of aged people or animals. In the protozoans, which are given the gift of eternal life, the cells are capable of getting rid of the bags of insoluble matter by a defecation-like process. The same is also true of the cells of the kidney and some other organs.

The processes described above have the uptake of material from the outside as a starting point. This is not necessarily the only impetus for the formation of a functioning lysosome. There are a few cases described in which the lysosomes start to digest the cell in which they reside. In one particular case, only a limited region of the cell is encapsulated and a lysosome is formed around this region or out of this region in an hitherto obscure manner. This may, for instance, happen when an animal is starved. The mechanism gives the impression of serving the purpose of sacrificing one part of the cell in order to give nutritive substances to the rest. There are also cases in which the lysosomes open their bags of digestive enzymes and kill and digest the cell. This may happen when an embryonic organ, for example, the oviduct in a male chick embryo, is to be resorbed.

One wonders whether the lysosome bags might open accidentally and thereby damage the cell. This may occur upon exposure to several poisonous substances. There may also be a difference between the action of substances which induce the lysosomes to burst and thereby lose their enzymes and substances which only slightly change the membrane of the lysosomes so that they remain relatively intact but allow their content of digestive enzymes to leak out slowly. The membrane of the lysosome can also become more stable when it is treated with a substance, for example, with the hormone cortisone, which includes among its actions a direct one upon this cell organelle. Finally, there may be inborn defects of the lysosomes—which has been suggested for at least three diseases.

One of the main revolutions in biological thinking was the abolition of the old humoral pathology and its replacement by cellular pathology. Today it is possible to carry the revolution one or two steps further and to seek the cause of disease in disorder at an organelle, or even a molecular, level.

9

muscle contraction

The study of muscle contraction belongs to a branch of physiology to which electron microscopy has made a decisive contribution. It might seem paradoxical that this contribution turned out to be superfluous. A new theory on the nature of muscle contraction was illustrated with electron micrographs, but the more or less binding proofs of its veracity have been obtained from phase-contrast microscopy of living muscle tissue, from X-ray diffraction studies, and from chemical experiments with differently treated or isolated parts of muscles. Together, the results of all these investigations provide such strong support to the theory that the contribution of electron microscopists seems negligible; nevertheless, the micrographs were of great importance at the time the theory was introduced. It is easy to become convinced by something you can see with your eyes.

The theory of muscle contraction to be presented here was put forward by H. E. Huxley and J. Hanson. Accordingly, it has been called the *Huxley-Hanson model of muscle contraction* or the "sliding model for muscular contraction," which can be shortened to the *sliding-filament theory*.

Both founders of this theory are distinguished electron microscopists and are well informed about possibilities of misinterpretations and artifacts from electron microscopy. They have, therefore, strongly emphasized that their theory can be supported on other grounds as well and that conflicting micrographs, if they should be found, cannot overturn the theory. They have set an example that shows how good electron microscopists build a theory. The electron microscope results gave rise to a working hypothesis, for which much support was collected from other grounds, until the validity of the hypothesis, strictly speaking, was independent of the electron microscope evidence.

A description of what muscle cells are and how they work, can be given more compactly in structural rather than in chemi-

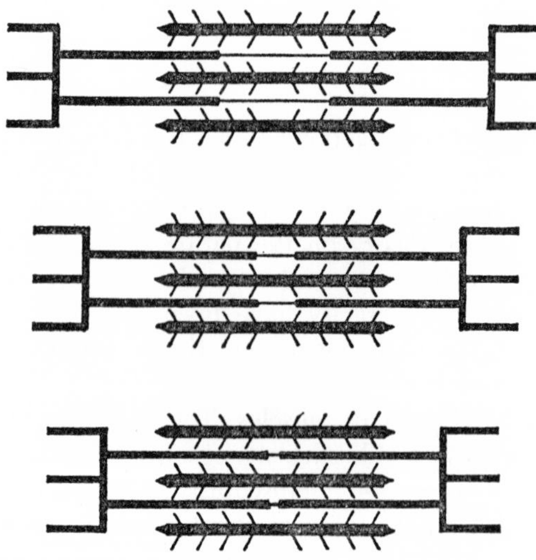

Fig. 4.—Muscle contraction according to the sliding-filament theory. In the lowest picture, the thin filaments have slid into the interspaces between the thicker filaments and the muscle has contracted.

cal terms. The most compressed diagram of muscle contraction, seen from an electron microscope viewpoint, is the one shown in Figure 4. A striated muscle appears as alternating dark and light bands; in the figure, one dark band and one-half of each of two light bands are seen. Both the light and the dark bands consist of filaments called *myofilaments*. The myofilaments are very short and do not reach from one dark band to another or from one light band to another. The light bands consist solely of thin (about 50 Å) filaments. The dark bands have thicker filaments (about 110 Å). The thin filaments stretch from the light bands into the dark bands. Contraction implies that the two types of filaments are displaced in relation to each other so that the thin filaments slide, thereby shortening the length of the light bands or causing them to disappear altogether. This is the essence of the Huxley-Hanson theory of muscle contraction—a sliding-filament theory.

In this hypothesis, in contrast to the majority of theories postulated earlier, the individual filaments are not capable of contracting. The theory implies rather that the filaments maintain their length and that they slide past each other. They, of course, cannot do this and at the same time develop force unless, during the sliding, they "brace their feet" against each other. Contact points, where the force that pulls the filaments together develops, must exist between the two kinds of filaments. It is natural that electron microscopists have been looking for these contact points, and such points have been found in electron micrographs. The thick filaments do have protrusions extending toward the thin filaments at regular intervals. We could compare these filaments to a row of men with outstretched hands. The thin filaments are the rope that these hands have to catch and pull in order to get forward.

The myofilaments are bound together in clusters of several hundred filaments per bundle (varying from approximately ten to ten thousand). The scientific name for a bundle is *myofibril,* which consequently is characterized as consisting entirely of filaments. The myofibril is surrounded by other cell components, namely, mitochondria and a system of channels normally called the *sarcoplasmic reticulum* or, shorter, *sarcotubules.* (The word sarcotubulus is from the Greek *sarx* for flesh and the Latin *tubulus* for small tube.) The arrangement of the sarcotubules is regular, with sections of the system running parallel to the myofibrils and with other transverse sarcotubules running perpendicular from the cell surface inward toward the myofibrils. The transverse sarcotubules enter at specific levels of the myofibrils, either in the middle of the light band or, in other muscle types, at the border between the light and dark bands. It has recently been found that these transverse sarcotubules in reality are cell membrane invaginations. Generally speaking, the faster a muscle can work (that is, the faster it can contract and relax), the more developed its system of sarcotubules. The myofibrils are especially thin and flat in very fast muscles, which implies that the distance from the sarcotubules to the middle of the myofibril is small. Plate 28 shows the relationships among myofibrils, sarcotubules (arrows), and mitochondria in a longitudinal section of a leg muscle from a rat.

It is important to try to connect the biochemical data to the information about the appearance of a muscle in a contracted and in a relaxed and lengthened stage. The first task is to localize myosin and actin, two fibrillar proteins which together make up about half the total protein of muscle.

Huxley and Hanson have determined the location of myosin and actin. The thick filaments contain mainly myosin and some other proteins, and the thin filaments consist totally, or for the most part, of actin. It is perhaps necessary to mention that a thick filament consists of not one but of several hundred myosin molecules. Every projection from a thick filament can be a reactive end of a myosin molecule.

The thin filaments, in the same way, consist of many actin molecules. A consequence of the sliding theory is that the projections of a thick filament work in one direction along half the filament and in the other direction along the other half. This postulate comes from the fact that the myosin filaments at a contraction pull actin threads from two directions toward the middle and, therefore, the "hands" on both sides around the middle of the thread pull in different directions. It is of interest to note that the thick filaments and their projections are symmetrical around the middle, which can be shown with negative-staining methods. The thick filaments look as though they are twined of very fine threads which are plaited at even intervals with loose ends sticking out and with the midregion free of projecting ends. The dimensions of these very fine threads are in agreement with those of a single myosin molecule.

The ATP used during the contraction process normally comes

from the mitochondria, which explains the close association between mitochondria and myofibrils. At the beginning of a muscle contraction, ATP combines with myosin. It is used during the continued work as the charged myosin combines with the actin filaments. Every time a myosin group reacts with an actin group, the actin filament is assumed to be pulled forward a specified unit length along the myosin thread, for example, 130 Å. In other words, the movement is not even but is assumed to take place in little jumps followed by a pause. The length of a small contraction can be calculated either from assumptions based on structural data or from chemical formulas.

When the experimenter calculates the unit distance per advance of the actin filament, he proceeds on the reasonable assumption that a specific point on the actin filament moves from one projection to the next along a myosin filament. When figuring the distance from chemical data, the experimenter starts from a calculation of the amount of ATP used to move an actin filament a specified distance and then divides the distance by the number of ATP molecules. This division implies that each advance requires a breakdown of one ATP molecule at every projection. If the experimenter assumes the consumption of two ATP molecules for pulling the actin molecule one unit distance, he has to divide the total distance by half the amount of consumed ATP molecules. It is probably more than accidental that these two different methods for calculating the unit distance have given very similar results. This can be interpreted as support for the sliding-filament theory.

Physiological studies of different types of muscle cells have indicated that the sarcotubular system functions in transmitting the signal for both contraction and relaxation. Some studies have been performed with electrophysiological techniques, that is, by the application of fine electrodes to the surface of the muscle cell. In a very important work by A. F. Huxley and R. E. Taylor, the muscle was stimulated locally to produce contraction of one single myofibril or, specifically, one single light band of the fibril. The work was published as late as 1958 but has already become a classic. A. F. Huxley (who should not be mistaken for H. E.

Huxley of the Huxley-Hanson theory, although he also is one of the proposers of the sliding-filament theory) was awarded the Nobel Prize for medicine in 1963 for his neurophysiological studies. By examining various types of muscles, he showed that different muscles behave in different ways. Some muscles are susceptible to stimulation if the electrode is applied in the middle of the light band. Other types react to stimulation on the border between the light and dark bands. An electron microscope study showed, as expected, that the distribution of the sensitive points of these two types of muscle cells coincides with the sites where the transverse sarcotubular elements enter. This indicates that the transverse sarcotubules take the impulse from the cell surface and carry it into the body of the cell during a contraction. Figure 5 shows how a muscle reacts in such an experiment.

There is a good deal of evidence that contraction is triggered by a sudden release of the calcium ion within the cell, and that relaxation may be triggered by an equally rapid pulling back of the calcium into the sarcotubules. Accordingly, it has been possible to ascribe two functions to the sarcotubular system: to transport the impulse for contraction, and to induce relaxation. Is it unreasonable that the same structure performs two opposed functions? In Aesop's fable, a satyr was frightened by a man who could blow both warm and cold air out of his mouth; but, unlike the satyr, the researcher should not be astonished at a biological structure performing two different functions. As a matter of fact, the mouth itself can do much more than blow warm or cold air, and the sarcotubular system probably can do much more besides helping in contraction and relaxation. After all, a cell has to perform many more functions in order to work and maintain its individuality than there are cell organelles.

The function of thick filaments versus thin filaments can be understood and illustrated entirely by a longitudinal cut through them. It would be unfortunate, though, to omit a description of the construction of these filaments in myofibrils cut in cross-section, because, among other things, the filaments both form an interesting pattern and pose more questions.

Two main types of striated muscles are known, classified according to their patterns as seen in cross-section. One type occurs in all striated vertebrate muscles examined to date. The other type occurs in insects and crayfish and in the totally unrelated animal, *Sagitta* (a planktonic sea animal called the arrow worm).

Vertebrate muscles have the thick filaments (or more specifically, myosin filaments) arranged in a pattern known as the

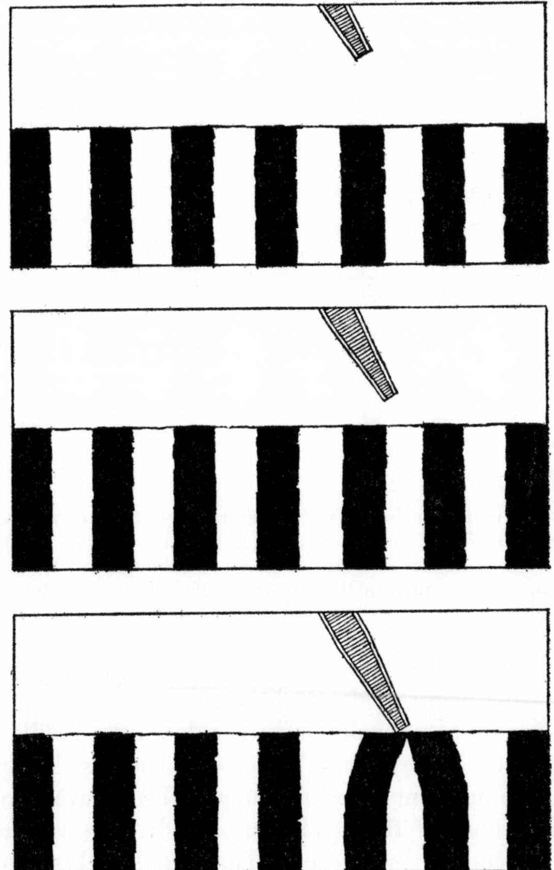

FIG. 5.—Three stages of a contraction which takes place in a very limited part of a muscle cell. The muscle cell has been stimulated to contract by a microelectrode which touches a sensitive point in the middle of a light band of the muscle cell. At contraction, the light band disappears.

hexagonal arrangement. The pattern is the most common one for closely packed biological structures and is found macroscopically in, for example, the honeycomb of a beehive. The thin filaments (actin filaments) are spaced at an equal distance from the three nearest myosin filaments. This means that the myosin threads are surrounded by six actin threads. If the myosin filaments represent the middle of every chamber in the honeycomb, then the actin filaments are placed in the six corners of every hexagonal chamber. With this way of packing, the proportion of myosin to actin threads is 1:2. This is apparent from Figure 6.

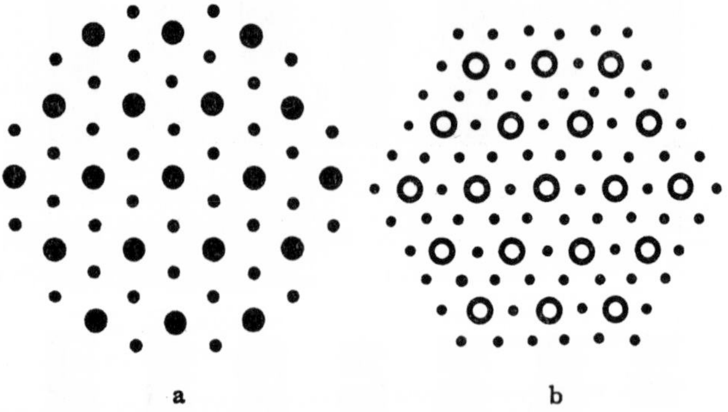

FIG. 6.—A comparison between a myofibril of vertebrate-type (*a*) and of insect-type (*b*). Every myosin thread (large solid or open circle) is surrounded by six actin threads (small circles), although in such a way that the quotient between myosin threads and actin threads is different in both cases.

The arrangement of the myofilaments in insects, the crayfish, and the arrow worm is identical with regard to the myosin filaments. They are hexagonally packed—a dot in the middle of every chamber in the honeycomb. The actin filaments, however, are between two adjacent myosin filaments. They have two nearby neighbors instead of three. This implies that every myosin filament is surrounded by six actin filaments, but these should be placed in the middles of the six walls of the honeycomb compartment. The ratio between myosin filaments and actin filaments is also different, namely, 1:3. This is illustrated in Figure 6.

As a consequence of the different filament arrangement, a diversity can be expected in the mode of action of the myosin filaments. In the insects, crayfish, and arrow worm category, every myosin molecule must be assumed to pull an average of three actin filaments, whereas the vertebrate myosin filaments pull two.

The insect type of muscle can be expected to have stronger myosin filaments or at least they must perform more work. Nor do the myosin filaments look alike in the two categories; they are both thicker (140 Å rather than 110 Å) and more tubular in the insect type. This can be seen in Plate 29.

Striated muscles have been described in a few other animal groups, but only in the groups mentioned have electron microscopists been able to show that the filaments have a regular arrangement. Striated muscles appear early in the history of animals; they are found, for example, in the jellyfish, which belongs to one of the most primitive groups among multicellular animals. Nothing has been found that suggests that smooth muscles are more primitive than striated, and nothing suggests that they are two completely different muscle types. It is reasonable to ask if the same mechanism is functioning in contraction of both smooth and striated muscles.

The difficulty in understanding the functional mechanism of smooth muscles is due partially to the fact that it has been difficult to clarify their fine structure. Some types of muscle cells have properties which in several aspects place them between smooth and striated muscles. To these belong, for example, the muscles of the majority of mollusks (that is, snails, mussels, and cuttlefish) and of leeches. These muscles are of interest partly because they resemble striated muscles, which possess both thin and thick filaments that, among other things, contain myosin. The proportion between the two kinds of filaments cannot be stated in the same way as that of regular striated muscles, since this relationship differs in contracted and relaxed muscle. There is a far greater number of fine filaments than myosin filaments, that is, more than five times as many actin filaments as myosin filaments. It seems, therefore, that every myosin filament has to pull half a dozen or more actin filaments. This has perhaps forced the myosin filaments to become much thicker than they are in other striated muscle (500 Å or more). The thick filaments can also contain another muscle protein, *paramyosin,* which apparently makes the filaments even stronger. When they contain such an inner resource, they show a regular crystalline structure.

Smooth muscles of vertebrates have constituted and perhaps still constitute something of a stumbling block for the sliding-filament theory. So far, electron microscopists have been unable to demonstrate the different types of filaments, something which the theory requires. All filaments of smooth muscles of vertebrates look alike and are of the thickness of actin filaments. This fact has been interpreted by many scientists as opposing the sliding-filament theory, and therefore the theory has been considered unable to give the correct explanation for muscle contraction—at least for smooth muscles. Such a conclusion seems to be too hasty. It might very well be that even smooth muscles of vertebrates have two kinds of filaments. It does not necessarily follow that two different filaments do not exist because they have not yet been distinguished with the present electron microscope preparatory techniques. In the same way that we should not depend only on our eyes when it comes to a newly found structure in electron micrographs, we should also not attribute too much to the absence of an expected structure in the pictures.

10

cilia; a problem of nine plus two

Cilia have always been a favorite research problem among electron microscopists. The reasons for this are simple.

First, they have a regular and aesthetically pleasing structure.

Second, they can be seen in the living organism with the light microscope and hence a great deal is known about how they move, how fast they move, and the circumstances under which they move. We would thus expect that a knowledge of their structure would make it possible to solve the problem of their beating pattern, but this has turned out to be very difficult.

Third, cilia have an extraordinarily constant structural organization; in protozoa, plants, and animals, all cilia have the same construction.

Fourth, this constancy is not absolute; small variations have been found from cell type to cell type. This stimulates the curiosity. Is the variation due to developmental coherence or is it due to different functions? Can the variations be connected to differences in the manner in which cilia work and, if so, can the structural variation help to explain the ciliary mechanism?

Fifth, cilia appear in cell types where the researcher least expects them. This keeps alive the speculations on the role of cilia.

Finally, we can maintain that cilia possess nearly all the qualities we have become accustomed to consider as special characteristics of living matter—they move, they are excitable, they show some ability for impulse conduction, they have a metabolic turnover, they can show secretion activity, they carry specificity factors, and they have a high degree of organization. In spite of all this, they are so small that they are difficult to observe with the light microscope. Their thickness of 0.2μ corresponds to the limit of resolution of the light microscope.

It is not difficult to define a cilium if we do not ask for too rigid a definition. A cilium is a cell organelle with the structure shown in Plate 30. A typical cilium has the ability to move according to an asymmetrical scheme consisting of a straight effective stroke and a more flexible recovery stroke. This is illustrated in Figure 7.

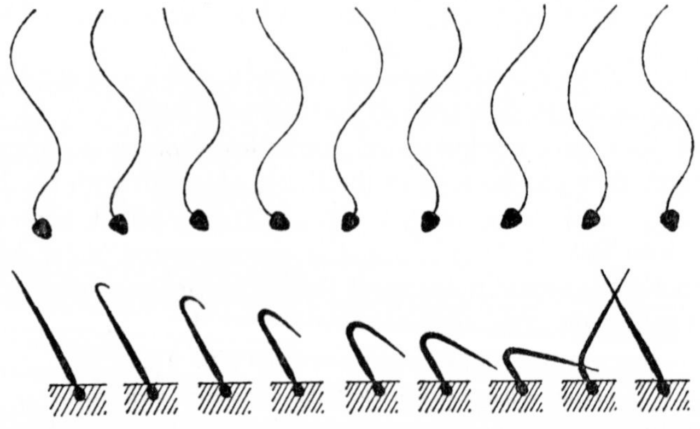

FIG. 7.—Comparison between ciliary movement and flagellar movement. The ciliary beat is characterized by a stiff effective stroke (*left*) and a slower softer recovery stroke. The flagellar beat is an eel-like motion, with a wave crest moving toward the free tip (upward in the drawing).

The difference between the curves of the effective stroke and the recovery stroke gives rise to a liquid stream, usually running parallel to the cell surface. Normally on its free surface, a ciliated cell either has many tightly packed cilia or has ridges with cilia in single or multiple rows. The cilium extends from a small body in the cytoplasm called the basal body.

The electron micrograph illustrated here is not really a picture of a cilium but of a cell organelle with the same apparent structure but a different pattern of motion. This cell organelle is called a *flagellum.* A typical flagellum moves in gentle, undulating waves like a snake. The flagellum is thus bent into symmetrical waves that move from the basal body toward the tip. The upper half of Figure 7 shows successive stages in the motion of a flagellum. The wave motion gives rise to a stream of liquid which is directed away from the flagella base in anchored cells. In free cells, the wave motion causes the cell to move forward. The wave crest of the flagellar curve utilizes the resistance of the water to move the cell forward. Normally, a cell has only one or two flagella on its surface, but exceptions to the rule have been found.

In scientific literature, flagellar motion is normally interpreted as a symmetrical wave. It has not yet been determined whether this is the normal way for a flagellum to move, but for the type of flagellum shown in Plate 30, this interpretation is correct. This flagellum, the tail of a sea urchin sperm, is one of the few which has been studied with satisfactory techniques. It has a symmetrical wave form and a motion in one plane identical to the textbook concept of a typical flagellum.

So cilia and flagella have a very similar ultrastructure, and it is not possible to distinguish between them in electron micrographs. Many electron microscopists call both cilia and flagella, cilia. Characteristically, cilia are built of eleven filaments running lengthwise, nine of which are peripheral filaments arranged in a ring and two of which are inner filaments. The nine peripheral strands appear as double tubules and the inner ones are circular in cross-section. The complex of $9 + 2$ is surrounded by a membrane which is simply the cell membrane, although often it is called the ciliary membrane. A detailed study of the nine peripheral filaments has revealed that the two units of a doublet are not alike: one unit has small projections called *arms*, the other has none. The direction of the arms is constant in every cilium and flagellum, always running clockwise if we look from the inside of the cell toward the tip. Since the arms are arranged clockwise, the flagellum or cilium does not possess a plane of symmetry. If we try to visualize a symmetrical axis through the center of the cilium, the arms on one side point downward and on the other, upward.

The fact that cilia and flagella lack a plane of symmetry makes it possible to identify all eleven filaments and to find dissimilarities among them. Figure 8 shows the system for numbering the filaments. In sea urchin sperm flagella and in some other cilia and flagella, filament number 6 differs from the others. In addition to the two arms, this filament has projections on the opposite side which apparently are in contact with the arms from filament 5. The projections and the arms form a connecting bridge between

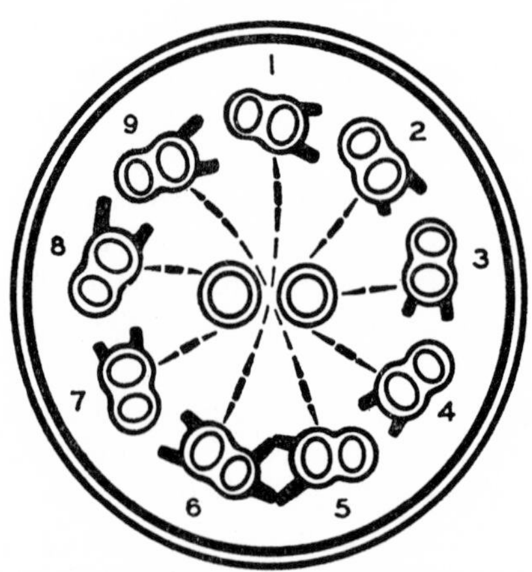

FIG. 8.—Schematic drawing of a cross-section of a cilium or flagellum. Only one of the nine peripheral filaments lies equally distant from each of the two inner filaments. It is called filament number 1; the others are numbered in sequence, from it.

filaments 5 and 6. Although the arms from the other filaments seem to end freely, the arms from filament 5 attach to something.

Further details can be discovered by careful investigation of the micrographs of cilia and flagella. The unit of the peripheral filaments that carries the arms is twisted toward the center and might be of a different size than the unit without the arms. In electron micrographs, it sometimes appears darker and connected to a radial, thin fiber running toward the center, giving the whole structure the appearance of a wheel with spokes. The partition within the peripheral filaments can have a characteristic contour. As more electron micrographs of cilia are studied, more details appear. Whether these details play a role in ciliary movement is an open question, but it gives the electron microscopist a sense of great pleasure and often astonishment when a new and unexpected detail appears in a picture already scrutinized for hours.

Why is this complicated structure so constant in both the plant and animal kingdoms? Is it an ancient type of structure which has somehow experienced genetic constancy (inability to mutate to a new form), or is the 9 + 2 pattern the best possible solution for the motion of a ciliary and flagellar type? This is an unanswered question, although the first alternative seems unlikely. Far too many variations have been discovered recently for this hypothesis to be correct.

One of the explanations proposed for the 9 + 2 complex is founded on the fact that two circles can be surrounded by nine equally large, closely spaced circles without creating big gaps between the nine outer and the two inner circles. This can be demonstrated with eleven pennies. The geometry of six circles surrounding one circle is more compact, which may be the reason for the frequent occurrence of the hexagonal array in biological structures. (To see this, only seven pennies are needed.) Perhaps some of the clues to the problem of 9 + 2 are such geometrical considerations, but they cannot be the entire story.

In order to find the solution of the 9 + 2 complex, attention should be focused on more specific questions such as: How do the 9 + 2 filaments behave during the ciliary beat? Are there eleven muscles bending the cilium (or alternatively the flagellum)? Or are the filaments relatively unessential for ciliary work, with other constituents inside or outside the cilia bringing about the bending of the cilium or flagellum?

The first task is to learn whether the forces bending the cilium are derived from the cilium itself or from a site in the cell body.

We have an answer. The cilium or flagellum moves because of a mechanism which is built into its structure. In other words, the cilium bends itself. This has been deduced and proved in several ways. The simplest of these is that the opposite alternative would be absurd—namely, that a 2-μ cell body (as the sea urchin sperm) should be able to wag a 40-μ tail. Further observations have been made on isolated cilia or flagella which have been made to move in different ways.

The other question is whether the 9 + 2 filaments are the driving force in the ciliary beat or whether they play a relatively minor role. After all, the 9 + 2 complex comprises only a small part of the total mass of the cilium. The fact that the complex is clearly visible in the electron micrographs is in itself no proof that the filaments are more important than, for example, the diffuse substance surrounding them. This question is more difficult to answer, but one approach is to determine if the exact arrangement of the 9 + 2 pattern is correlated with the direction of the ciliary beat. We must choose a material in which the direction of ciliary beat is constant. The comb jelly, which has the size and appearance of a gooseberry and has gotten part of its name, "comb," from the plates that appear in eight long rows, is a suitable organism. The combs are the structures by which the animal paddles its way through the water; they are composed of thousands of cilia which seem to have fused together to form plates. Every cilium in a comb has the eleven filaments oriented in the same way. The two inner filaments are always placed on a line perpendicular to the direction of ciliary beat and therefore, according to the laws of mechanics, are in the least effective position for pulling the cilia in the direction of the beat. If the direction of the ciliary beat could be called a forward-backward motion, the two central filaments would, in an assumed contraction, produce a lateral motion rather than a forward-backward one. Furthermore, according to the lever law, with their central position they would have to perform such heavy work in order to make the cilium bend, that it can be considered impossible for them to develop the necessary force.

The nine filaments have a constant position in a ring around the two inner filaments. In the cilia of the comb jelly, filaments 3 and 8 deviate from the others by being connected by bands that run lengthwise. It is inconceivable that either the bands or the filaments with which they are in contact can give rise to the forward-backward motion—that is, in the direction of the ciliary beat.

Figure 9 shows schematically how the cilia of the comb jelly look in cross-section.

Of the seven other peripheral filaments, three are situated on one side of the band and four on the other. The filaments are not evenly placed forward and backward, which would be impossible anyway because there is an odd number of filaments. The smaller group has filament number 1 in the middle, and it is placed in the

FIG. 9.—Schematic drawing of cilia from the combs of the comb jelly. Filaments 3 and 8 are connected by bands which run alongside them and divide the cilia into two unequal parts.

direction of the effective stroke. Filament number 1 leads the ciliary stroke.

Is it possible to relate the arrangement of the filaments to the movement of cilia and flagella from other cell types? The arrangement of the inner filaments in relation to the ciliary beat has been known for years. Even in some flagella it has been possible to determine this relationship. The inner two filaments always run perpendicular to the beat of the cilium or flagellum. No exception to this rule is known. The nine peripheral filaments seem to be arranged like those of the comb jelly—for example, as in the flagella of the sperm tail of the squid. They can also have the reversed relation to the effective stroke—that is, filaments 5 and 6, rather than filament 1, leading the stroke.

Whatever side is leading in the ciliary beat, it can be ascertained that the filaments have fixed positions in both cilia and flagella. This leads to the conclusion that the nine filaments cannot have equivalent tasks during the ciliary beat, if their job is to bend the cilium. Some filaments are less favored because of their position.

It does not seem to be so simple to reconstruct the work of a cilium or a flagellum on the basis of the 9 + 2 pattern. Part of the explanation for the cilia having filaments in a ring rather than, for example, in two opposite groups, could be that a tubular structure is a very strong construction. It is no accident that a bamboo cane is a hollow cylinder like a steel ski pole. It can be demonstrated that the ciliary structure is strong. In order to overcome the viscosity of water, the cilium must perform hard work; to keep stretched out stiffly, it must have a sturdy structure. The length of the longest cilia (the combs of the comb jelly) and flagella (the sperm tail of the *Discoglossus* frog) can be measured in millimeters. The thickness of one of the nine peripheral filaments is about 200 Å, that is, 0.00002 mm. The ratio between length and thickness of the filament can be greater than 50,000:1. It is doubtful if any man-made material could be maintained fully stretched without bending or breaking, if it had such a high ratio of length to thickness. The cilia are both stable and workable. In order to understand this, we must assume that the ciliary filaments have a stability corresponding to that of steel and, further, that the 9 + 2 filaments do not function as separate elements but as a coordinated and joined unit. If we consider the ring of the nine peripheral filaments as a unit, the ratio of length to thickness is reduced to about 5,000:1 in these long cilia, which is a more reasonable, although still very impressive, value. It is almost necessary that the filaments hook onto each other; they must hang together in order to have enough strength. The arms of the filaments must be the bridges connecting them.

At the same time it is apparent that the connections existing between the nine peripheral filaments, or between all eleven, cannot be fixed connections. If this were true, the filaments presumably would all be glued together and form a stiff and inflexible rod. The arms must be able to function almost in the same manner as the arms of a human being—be able to hold and release something. From this viewpoint, the similarity between the arms of the ciliary filaments and the bridges of the filaments of muscle cells is interesting. Gibbons recently succeeded in extracting different components from cilia. Among other things, he has been able to show that it is the arms which decompose ATP; in other words, the mechanical work is performed at the arms. The connections between the ciliary filaments—the arms—therefore play a central part in the ciliary mechanism. As the force in muscular work can be said to be concentrated in the bridges of the muscle filaments, thus can the role of the arms of cilia be said to be determined. We might expect that sliding filaments in cilia could be the cause and origin of ciliary movement, but all experiments designed to prove this have been futile so far. It is difficult to study the different stages of the ciliary beat with the present electron microscope techniques; therefore, it is difficult to study the cilia in a contracted and relaxed state corresponding to the states in muscle.

There are other stumbling blocks. The myofibril characteristically consists of separate filaments which have continuity only over a very short distance, a dark band or little more than a light band; whereas, the ciliary filaments are of the same length as the entire cilium. If we assume the cilium works according to the principle of sliding filaments, we must presuppose that the entire filament is sliding. There is no evidence to indicate that the filaments really slide in relation to each other during ciliary movement, but perhaps this merely involves technical difficulties which have yet to be overcome.

In this discussion about how the 9 + 2 filaments might assist or perform ciliary movement, attention has primarily been directed toward the nine peripheral filaments. The two central filaments have been omitted from the discussion since they do not have a strategic position for performing ciliary beat. Their central position can be better utilized for supporting the cilium and directing the beat in the right direction or for propagating the impulse for contraction to the nine peripheral filaments—if these are contractile. They have a strong resemblance to a recently discovered organelle—the *microtubule.* Plate 34 shows longitudinally sectioned microtubules; Plates 31 and 32 show many in cross-section.

If the role of the inner two filaments is primarily one of directing the ciliary beat (and likewise the wave movement of flagella) to move in one plane, it would be expected that the rare cases of flagellar movements which are clearly three-dimensional should have inner filaments of another appearance. Expressed more simply, if the center filaments are the backbone adding stability to normal flagella (but flagella are known without stability), three-dimensional movements might be the result of a defective backbone. We can study those flagella that have a three-dimensional bending motion with the electron microscope. Some of these flagella have already been studied—for example, the sperm tail of the flatworm. This structure is shown in Plates 31 and 32. Here the "magic" $9 + 2$ number is reduced to $9 + 1$. This flagellum has a radially symmetrical cylinder in the center—one of the few flagella that has a symmetrical construction; therefore, it shows ninefold symmetry. Another flagellum with these qualities is the sperm tail of a little sea animal called—in Latin—*Myzostomum.* This sperm tail is even more defective but as symmetrical as that of the flatworm, since the two inner filaments are completely absent in the major part of the tail. (Other flagella with a three-dimensional motion have a perfectly normal $9 + 2$ appearance however.)

These two sperm types are defective in their flagellar structure. We would expect such a defect to show up more drastically in the flagellar motion than merely as a failure to direct the flagellar movement in one plane. It appears, rather, that these flagella are equipped with other gifts besides the freedom to move in all planes. They possess the rare ability to form wave motions from the base to the tip or reverse. In other words, the sperm does not have to turn around in order to back out of a corner. It looks rather as if the structure of cilia and flagella in its own right has the possibility of performing a great many tricks, but that the majority of "stable" flagella and cilia do not realize more than a small part of their potentialities. In a few organisms, some barriers are gone and the flagella show more versatility. Such a conclusion can also be reached by studying flagella from the flagellates, a primitive animal group. In this group the flagella perform so many different movements that until now no good description of them has been given.

This viewpoint leads to still another question. Is the difference between a cilium and a flagellum fundamental? Or are they more or less the same? Is the cilium perhaps only a flagellum with a simplified pattern of movement? One approach to these questions is to attempt to exhaust flagella or to disturb them in their work. Another possibility is to try to analyze eventual transition stages between cilia and flagella. From both angles, the answers are clear. All transition stages between cilia and flagella have been found; they cannot be two different kinds of organelles. If a squid sperm is set free in the sea, it starts swimming by swinging its tail in strong wave motions from base to tip, a typical flagellar movement. After a few minutes, it is exhausted and gradually changes its scheme of motion, ending up by moving as a cilium.

The hypothesis which in the end will be put forth for ciliary movement also has to explain flagellar movement. If a researcher limits himself to two-dimensional flagellar movement, this will not increase the difficulty. Making a few assumptions about the time interval between the contraction of the nine filaments in cilia and flagella, he can construct a model fitting one or another of the schemes of motion. The only difference between the two movements is the interval between the work. This working model has been introduced in Sleigh's book about cilia.

One other viewpoint should be mentioned. Many electron microscopists have been almost blinded by the idea that a cilium or flagellum must contain the $9 + 2$ complex. Electron micrographs of cilia or flagella have been shown with a $9 + 1$ complex, while the text states that the flagellum follows the normal $9 + 2$ pattern. In reality, a great many cilia types deviating from the pattern are known and, besides, cilia and flagella containing too many or too few filaments exist. For practice in observation, we can study the electron micrograph shown in Plate 33.

11

construction of the nerve cell

In nerve physiology as in muscle physiology, electron microscopy has contributed essential information. Part of the explanation why the study of nerves and muscles has proved to be especially fruitful is that these two types of tissues are highly specialized and that specialization means development of some abilities at the expense of others.

If we want to study the cause of a biological event, it is almost always most profitable to use highly developed animal groups and cells or tissues specialized for a specific function. To study the same phenomenon in primitive, unspecialized organisms only makes the task harder. To find the structural foundation for such a general and primitive property as the excitability of protoplasm is a nearly impossible task. To study excitation in nerve cells is much simpler because nerves are specialized for this function. When the functions of highly specialized cells have been transformed into chemical formulas or into structural terms, the possibility exists of seeing if the same key fits other locks. Often it seems that a similar mechanism exists in both primitve and specialized cells with only one difference—the specialized cells expose the mechanism more openly. They are dominated by the mechanism; in primitive cells, a mechanism can be concealed by the myriads of other processes going on simultaneously. In other words, specialization implies not the addition of a new quality, but more often the disappearance of a majority of comparatively unessential functions.

Nerve cells in higher animals are specialized for transmitting excitation. Before defining the concept "nerve cell," we should comment on definitions in general. A definition of a biological concept does not imply the existence of a whole class of phenomena belonging to the same group in a way that makes it natural to give them the same name. The definition is rather an area marked out by specific, sometimes rather arbitrarily chosen, qualities. The phenomena which meet the definition ought to be given the definition; those falling outside the marked area ought to be given another term. The border cases, however, can be numerous, and the number of conceivable terms is limited. It is difficult to give a strict definition which is both useful and reasonable. We try, therefore, to avoid stating the exact limits of the definition and rather indicate the middle of the field we want to describe. We speak about a typical nerve cell or a typical muscle cell.

With these restrictions in mind, the definition of a typical nerve cell can be given. It is a long, extended cell and its function is to forward a signal quickly from one place in the organism to another. Normally the direction of the passage of the impulse is predetermined in the cell so that the traffic is one-way. The passage of the impulse can be registered as a transient change in electrical potential across the cell surface. The impulse can originate in one or several places on the cell because of excitation, or it can arise spontaneously.

This definition of the typical nerve cell is one of many possible. It ought to be emphasized that one part of the definition contains a rather arbitrary element: the function of the cell should be to transmit excitation. By working it in this way, every scientist can interpret the cell type he is studying as he wants. If he proceeds from the fact that a particular cell type functions primarily by transmitting impulses and the cell type otherwise fulfills the requirements, he can call this cell a nerve cell. If he chooses instead to look upon the primary function of the cell as being a supporting cell, a glandular cell, or a metabolic reservoir, then he has to find a more adequate name to describe the cell. If a researcher studies the long cells in the stems of the alga called *Nitella,* he finds that excitation in part of the cell can be forwarded to another part of the cell, thereby creating electrical potential differences that can be measured across the surface of the cell. In spite of this, nobody would think of calling this cell a nerve cell, because it is not reasonable that the primary function of this long algal cell is to conduct impulses. In principle, the difference between the conduction mechanism of the algal cell and that of the nerve cell need not be great, but it seems to be appar-

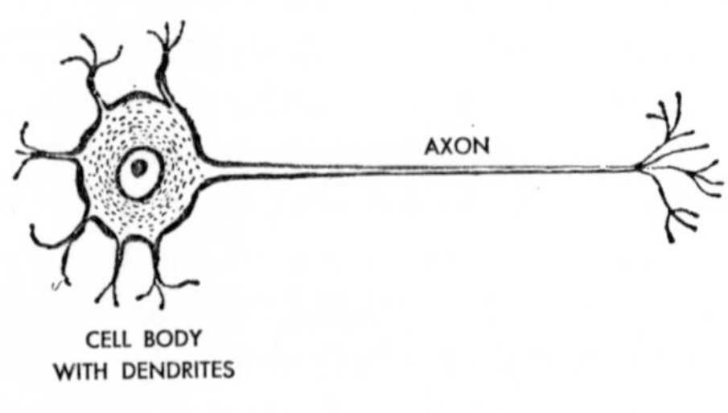

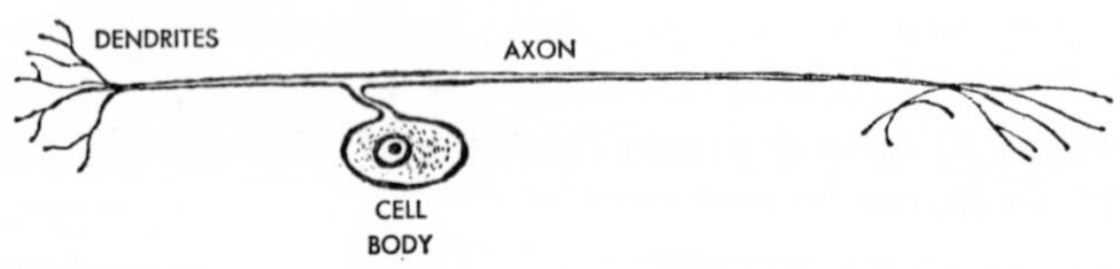

FIG. 10.—The regions of the nerve cell: cell body, dendrites, axon, and the terminal branches of the axon. The dendrites start from the cell body in the top drawing but are far from it in the bottom drawing.

ent that the main function of the algal cell is to sit in the sun, be green, and slowly be filled with starch.

A typical nerve cell can look like the cell shown in Figure 10. The nucleus is in the thick part of the cell, a section called the *cell body*, from which a number of extensions arise. Most extensions are relatively short and specialized for receiving excitation from another cell. They are called *dendrites*. Normally one extension is longer than the others, and is occasionally branched. This extension transports the excitation out of the cell and is called the *axon*. Its normally finely branched end region is simply called the end branch (terminal region). Some axons can become several meters long.

Electron microscope studies in nerve anatomy and nerve physiology have been extensive. An important contribution has been the solution of the old controversy of whether the nerve cells are adjacent but separate cells (the so-called neuron theory or nerve cell theory) or whether they are in open continuity. With very few exceptions the former concept is the right one. The functional connection between two nerve cells is a contact between two separate cells over an interspace. Contacts of this kind are called *synapses,* and the interspace between the nerve cells at the synapse is called *the synaptic gap* or *the synaptic junction.* Synapses between a nerve cell and another cell which influences or is influenced by a nerve cell can have the same appearance.

Another important relation which was shown with the electron microscope is the difference that exists between the two cells on either side of the synapse. In other words, we can see a difference between the impulse-sending and the impulse-receiving part of a nerve cell. Normally, the impulse-sending part contains more mitochondria than the receiving part, which can be taken as a sign that the sending process of impulse conduction is more energy demanding than the receiving part. Another difference is that the end branches of the axon contain a large number of vesicles of uniform size. These are so characteristic of this region that they can be used as a marker for a synapse or, more specifically, the sending part of the synapse. Usually they are called *synaptic vesicles* or, if one wants to emphasize that they are on the side of the synaptic gap that the impulse first passes, *presynaptic vesicles.* They appear likewise at the functional contacts between a nerve cell and a muscle cell or between a nerve cell and a glandular cell, and even in sensory cells (Chap. 12). Another marker for a synapse is the darker and often thickened part of the cell membrane on either side of the gap.

The synaptic vesicles vary somewhat in size, normally between 400 and 600 Å, in different nerve cells. They appear empty, but certainly are not. We can even say with some confidence what compound is in them, namely, a low-molecular-weight substance called acetylcholine. If we calculate how many molecules of acetylcholine can fit into a synaptic vesicle on the basis of the size of a vesicle and the molecular weight of acetylcholine, we get a value of a few thousand molecules. If we dissolve a few thousand molecules of acetylcholine in 1 ml (about 0.001 quarts) of water, we get a solution of acetylcholine without the slightest biological effect. If we could dissolve the same amount of acetylcholine in the amount of liquid that fills a synaptic gap, we would get a local concentration which is considerably higher and which has a measurable biological effect.

The biological effect of acetylcholine in the animal body is above all concerned with the cell membrane, and specifically with changes in its charged properties. Studies have shown that this mechanism of changing the membrane charge is especially well developed in the synaptic regions, where acetylcholine is freed from the presynaptic region in order to affect the postsynaptic zone (a dendrite of a nerve, muscle, or glandular cell). It has also been possible to evaluate the amount of acetylcholine freed during an impulse conduction. This amount is much greater than the content of a single vesicle. During impulse conduction, all of the acetylcholine has to be released in amounts corresponding to the contents of many vesicles. This freed acetylcholine apparently affects the cell membrane on the other side of the synaptic gap by changing its charged properties and thereby triggering the excitatory impulse in this cell.

Some of the strongest support for this interpretation of the role of acetylcholine and even of the role of the synaptic vesicles during impulse conduction has come from work done by Bernhard Katz. He has studied a synaptic region with very fine electrodes connected to a sensitive electronic amplifier. These microelectrodes are placed in the receiving cell near the synapse. When an impulse is transmitted through the synapse, a response can be detected with the amplifier. This has been known for a long time. When no impulse passes through the synapse, the membrane is at rest and its electrical potential is stable, that is, almost but not completely stable. At random intervals, disturbances appear in this resting potential, and it is worth noting that all these small disturbances are of about the same magnitude. The disturbances are not large enough to touch off the explosive events which lead to excitation, and therefore they do not give rise to a propagated impulse in the membrane of the receiving cell. But they do exist, and there must be an explanation for their existence.

Katz suggested that the disturbances in the resting potential of the cell membrane could be an effect of acetylcholine which in some way was released. With this assumption, he could calculate the approximate amount of acetylcholine necessary to get a disturbance in potential of this magnitude. The calculation gave a value of several thousand molecules. This was thus the same value as that derived from calculation of the number of acetylcholine molecules packed into a synaptic vesicle. Katz's conclusion was, therefore, that the synaptic vesicles in fact must be filled with acetylcholine and that, even in a resting synapse, the synaptic vesicles release their contents into the synaptic gap one at a time. The effect of a freed synaptic vesicle is enough to give rise to a potential change which can be registered but not enough to give rise to an impulse which is propagated along the nerve cell. It can therefore be said that the effect of an opened synaptic vesicle can be detected by man's electronic laboratory equipment but only to a limited extent in man's nerve cells.

For similar reasons a potential change great enough to trigger a propagated impulse can be assumed to be due to many synaptic vesicles emptying their contents simultaneously into the synaptic gap. A mechanism must thus exist which opens the presynaptic side of the cell membrane when the impulse arrives and thereby releases synaptic vesicles in great numbers. The release of these vesicles gives rise to the change in potential across the postsynaptic membrane of the receiving cell and thus triggers a new impulse.

An explanation now exists in structural terms for what takes place during the transmission of the nerve impulse from one cell to another. As we can experimentally produce variations in the number of synaptic vesicles at the end branches of the axon but hardly in their size, likewise Katz has experimentally been able to vary the frequency of the miniature disturbances in resting synapses but not the individual size of the disturbances.

Until now this chapter has dealt only with the nerve cell itself. Cells of another kind are also found in the nervous system and they are called *glia cells.* Glia is a Greek word for glue, from which one can deduce that the person introducing this term had the idea that the main function of the glia cells was to glue the nerve cells together to make an interconnected tissue or organ. In recent years the list of the functions of the glia cells has been expanded to include a great many other tasks. The ability to glue nerve cells together has not received much attention from scientists. It is a noteworthy fact that the human brain contains ten times as many glia cells as nerve cells. The glia cells are supposed, among other things, to take care of the transport of nutritional compounds from the blood to the nerve cell. The axons of the nerve cells can be covered or be naked, but with few exceptions they are surrounded by glia cells. The covered axons are called *myelinated* nerve axons and their *myelin sheaths* were once considered to be thickened nerve cell membranes. In 1954 the electron microscopist Betty Ben Geren showed that the myelin sheath by no means belongs to the nerve cell but is part of the glia cell which surrounds the nerve cell. Her interpretation of the formation of the myelin sheath is shown in Figure 11.

The interesting point in this interpretation is partly that the participation of the glia cell in the nerve impulse is greater than what was earlier anticipated, and partly that we get here an insight into how flexible a structure like the cell membrane can be. The total surface of the cell membrane of the glia cell can exceed that of the outermost surface of the glia cell by one or several powers of ten. It should also be emphasized that the physiological difference between myelinated and unmyelinated nerve fibers is a difference in excitation speed. The impulse conduction along myelinated fibers takes place in jumps. The impulse simply jumps over the myelinated regions along an axon which are very well insulated, and the potential differences only occur at the gaps between the myelinated regions where the nerve membrane is exposed. The division of the myelin sheath into several distinct sections with gaps between comes from the way the very long myelinated sheaths are formed; that is, every myelinated section is formed by a single glia cell.

The unmyelinated nerve fibers are likewise embedded in glia

cells that run parallel to them. Often several unmyelinated axons are embedded in the same glia cell in the way shown in Figure 12. Every axon is surrounded by its own section of glia cell membrane and is therefore in its own compartment inside the glia cell. The glia cells keep the axons separated from each other besides binding a great many of the axons into a bundle. The impulse in every axon runs as if it were electrically isolated from every other axon.

Several exceptions are known. Some unmyelinated axons which are not surrounded by glia cells have been described. The olfactory nerve of mammals and the nerve system of jellyfish consist of nerve fibers in which the axons are certainly surrounded by glia cell covers but in which several axons border each other inside the

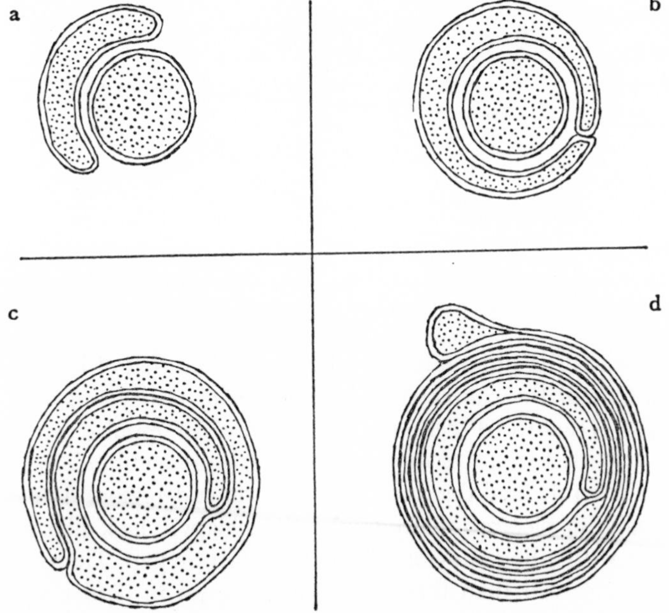

Fig. 11.—Four stages in myelination. The axon which is round in cross-section is surrounded first partially (*a*), later totally (*b*) by a glia cell. When the axon is completely immersed in the glia cell, the two sides of the glia cell meet along a borderline which first is short (*b*), later longer (*c*), and finally wound around the axon many times (*d*) in a spiral.

same compartment. There exist then possibilities for the axons to form long running contacts with each other in the glia cell. We know that an excitation along an axon in the nerves of a jellyfish normally causes an impulse excitation to be started in the adjacent axons. In the coupling scheme characteristic of the nerve system of the jellyfish, the lack of isolation of every single axon does not present any drawback. In the nerve of a jellyfish, an impulse running forward in a broad front enables the nerve cell threads to act as substitutes for each other.

The nerve net of the jellyfish has a primitive construction and is

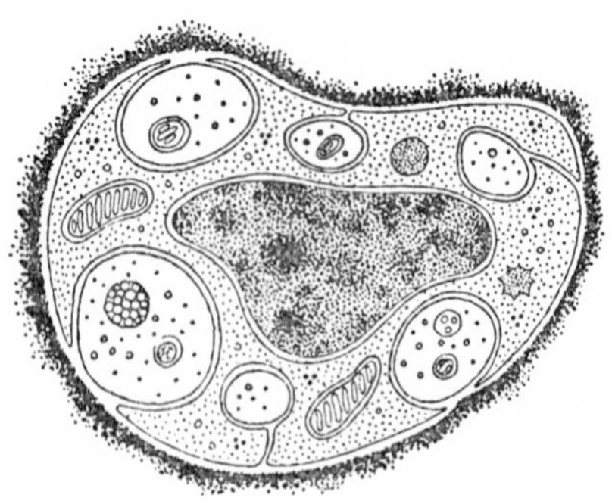

FIG. 12.—The unmyelinated axons resemble axons in an earlier stage of development of myelination (cf. Fig. 11*b*), although normally many axons are immersed in the same glia cell as shown here.

therefore rather more difficult to interpret than that of higher animals. One of the characteristic properties of the synapses of the jellyfish is that the direction is not one-way. An impulse can travel from one site to another or vice versa in the same unhindered way. There is no defined dendrite zone or axon end region. As can be expected, in electron micrographs the synapses look like mirror images with a line of symmetry in the synaptic gap. The synaptic gap is narrower than that of typical synapses in higher animals and much here suggests that the impulse conduction takes place in an electrical manner rather than by means of chemical impulse conduction (for example, acetylcholine). This does not exclude the possibility that acetylcholine or some other chemical substance participates in a subordinate role in this kind of synapse. Many little vesicles, which look like synaptic vesicles, are found at the synapses. In the jellyfish they are divided symmetrically on both sides of the narrow synaptic gap.

It is not only in a structural sense that glia cells and nerve cells are interwoven intimately. Even from a biochemical viewpoint they behave as a coordinated unit. This has most clearly been shown by H. Hydén, who with his collaborators studied this problem. They have worked out very elegant methods for separating nerve cells and glia cells in order to study their dry weight, chemical composition, enzymatic activity, oxygen consumption, and RNA production. How great a technical advance this study was can be understood by realizing that the amounts that were measured here were accurate to a few hundred micromicrograms (1 $\mu\mu$g equals 10^{-12} g, that is, a trillionth of a gram). These studies have shown that many experimental biochemical changes in the nerve system take place in one direction in the nerve cells and in the opposite in the surrounding glia cells. Nerve cells and glia cells behave, therefore, like a coupled system. RNA production and enzyme production increase in the nerve cells after different types of stimuli, while there is a corresponding decrease in these values in the glia cells. Rats trained to balance on steel wires showed an increase in the amount of RNA in the nerve cells connected with the balance sense.

It is interesting that the nerve cells synthesize RNA. That the nerve cells along with the secretory cells of the pancreas have the biggest RNA production of the whole organism is even more noteworthy. A production of RNA perhaps means, above all, synthesis of messenger RNA or that parts of the information of the genetic substance are being duplicated in order to govern formation of different proteins (Chap. 6). Which proteins are being formed, if any are formed at all, is difficult to say. A possibility is that the synthesis revolves around the formation of an enzyme that is coupled to the ion-pumping mechanism of the cell and thereby also contributes indirectly to the formation of the nerve impulse. Another possibility is that either the RNA molecules themselves or the proteins made from them are the basic material for memory.

In chemical terms the nerve impulse can be described in the following way: The electrical impulse which travels along the nerve cell axon reflects changes in the sodium and potassium ion concentrations at the cell border; the movements of these ions occur at the same rate as the impulse and give rise to the electrical changes. At each point along the axon, sodium ions first move across the membrane into the nerve cell and potassium ions pass out. This takes place within a thousandth of a second, followed by a slower recovery to normal ion concentrations. In the recupperation period, a chemical pump does active work to expel the sodium ions which have entered the nerve cell during the passage of the impulse. This pump is controlled by certain enzymes. In addition, there must be a space outside the nerve cell which can accept the expelled sodium ions. There has been extensive discussion about where this *sodium space* is. From many electron microscope studies it seems that the nervous system is a compact tissue with very narrow interspaces between the nerve cells and between nerve and glia cells. These interspaces seem to be too small to take up the amount of sodium which the sodium space ought to contain. A hypothesis has therefore been proposed that the glia cells themselves take up and bind sodium and that these cells constitute the hypothetical sodium space. This hypothesis implies that the membrane of the glia cells has a permeability to ions opposite to that of the nerve membrane and can take up sodium ions as fast as they are pumped out of the nerve cells.

The possibility for structural distortion in electron microscopy, however, was not taken into account. Nerve tissue is very difficult to fix well for electron microscopy, and glia cells are almost always found swollen or deformed. In nerve tissue which shows a minimum of fixation distortion, a space is found between the cells. Furthermore, it can be shown that this space disappears within a few minutes after isolation of nerve tissue and that swollen glia cells take the place of the sodium space.

As has been mentioned, the nerve cells produce much RNA and protein, and they also produce acetylcholine and push it out of the cell. They can, therefore, be characterized as secretory cells or at least as cells which have many properties in common with secretory cells. Some cells in the nervous system have this resemblance to an even higher degree. Cells are found which are called *neurosecretory cells.* Whether we want to characterize these cells as nerve cells or glia cells or consider them a special cell category is all a matter of taste. Their functions are the important things to know.

First, it can be said that the neurosecretory cells make a cell product which is pushed out of the cell and which affects cells situated far from the neurosecretory cells. If the product follows the blood stream in dissolved form, it can be considered a hormone or, to underline its origin in the nervous system, as a neurohormone (or the synonym, *neuroendocrine substance*). The terminology has not yet been stabilized, but generally the term *neurohormone* is used for both *neurosecretions* that are effective over long distances and for short-lived *neurohumoral* agents with short working distances, for example, acetylcholine. Many neurosecretions participate in regulating the salt content of the body; others coordinate the development of the sex organs and the maturity of the germ cells.

To release the neurosecretion into the blood, the neurosecretory cells ought to have at least one projection which ends close to the wall of a blood vessel. This is generally true, and a typical picture of such a neurosecretory projection is shown in Plate 35. The projection is full of secretory granules, and every single one of them is surrounded by a membrane.

Besides this, the cells contain structures of another category, namely, vesicles of the same appearance as the synaptic vesicles in the axon ends of typical nerve cells. This may seem strange since the projections of the neurosecretory cells do not form synapses with other cells; no receptor cell exists which has to be stimulated by the freed neurohumoral compound. A nerve impulse can run through neurosecretory cells as well as through normal nerve cells, and in both situations acetylcholine is released into the end branches. The most reasonable interpretation of the role of the freed acetylcholine at the end point of the neurosecretory cells is that the nerve impulse in these cells helps facilitate the release of the neurosecretion. The cell stimulates itself; its acetylcholine is released as a result of the impulse and affects the membrane from which it was released. When the membrane has been exposed to acetylcholine, its properties change, thus allowing the neurosecretions themselves to leave the cell. This is a rather complicated and indirect mechanism of action, and it might very well prove that the hypothesis is only good on paper. It is, however, one of the few imaginable mechanisms that explains why this cell has synaptic vesicles and releases acetylcholine.

Many contacts between a nerve cell and a muscle cell are characterized not only by their content of synaptic vesicles at the nerve end, but also by secretory granules of another kind: a dark granule with a loosely fitting membrane. In analogy to the interpretation of the end branches of the neurosecretory cells, we can interpret this picture as indicating that the nerve cell releases two products to affect the muscle cell, partly acetylcholine, partly the substance which appears in the darker granules. This nerve cell ending thus has two neurohumoral substances. Alternatively, the darker granules could contain a substance which affects the membrane of the nerve cell rather than that of the muscle cell. Much can be said for this substance being another neurohumoral substance related to adrenalin in chemical nature and in mechanism of action.

In Chapter 4 it was shown that, in principle, one can distinguish two forms of secretion (with all possible transitions), those in which the membrane of the secretory granule merges with the cell membrane and becomes part of it, and those in which the secretory products leave the secretory granule and go through the cell membrane in dissolved form. The experiments mentioned on page 91 showed that the synaptic vesicles behave as though acetylcholine belongs to the first category. Both the adrenalin-like compounds and many neurosecretions behave, on the other hand, as if they belong to the second category. Experiments are even reported in which the same adrenalin left a cell and later got back into the cell. Even after circulation in the blood over a considerable distance, adrenalin or adrenalin-like substances can be taken up by the cell types by which they are formed and stored there in secretory granules.

Calculations have been made for how much of the adrenalin of a nerve cell is bound to granules and how much is circulating freely in the cytoplasm. Even substances which have entered the body from the outside, for example, nicotine, seem to be taken up by nerve cells and transported along them as a neurosecretory substance is. These results are not only of interest for the understanding of the functions of nerve cells but also for the understanding of cells in general.

12

sensory cells

People once spoke of the five senses: sight, hearing, smell, taste, and touch. Several senses were left out—for example, the sense of balance and the sense of muscle tone. Some of the five senses are composed of several different senses, for example, touch. To try to give the real number of senses in man or in animals is a meaningless task, because it would involve far too many arbitrary decisions between what should be and what should not be considered a sense.

Two factors must be emphasized. The first is that there are many different senses, both in man and, to an even higher extent, in many other animals. The list of newly discovered senses increases yearly. The second is that most physical and chemical phenomena in the milieu of animals or man remain undetected by the animal or human organism. It is not only toward X-rays and radio waves that we are blind and deaf but also toward most of what takes place inside and outside our bodies.

Sensory impressions are received by the sense organs or, more accurately, by cells in these organs that we call the sensory cells. These are specialized for their tasks, which vary according to what kind of impressions or excitations they might have to receive and transmit to their respective nerve centers. Most of the excitations received stop at a lower nerve center, which implies that the animal or the man does not realize the existence of the excitations; a smaller number of excitations continue to the cerebral cortex or to a corresponding higher center, thereby reaching the level of consciousness.

In some sense organs the sensory cells are of a type which must be referred to as nerve cells; they are normally called primary sensory cells. In other sense organs the receptor cells are small, stubby cells and can hardly be classified as nerve cells. We would not expect to find any common features among all the different types of sensory cells, because they are highly specialized to receive quite different kinds of signals. Several common structural properties, however, have been found. Most sensory cells have one or several so-called *sensory hairs* at the free part of the cell, and all or almost all sensory cells have *synaptic vesicles* near the contact surface against the nerve cells. There is therefore every reason to take a closer look at these two regions of the sensory cell.

A sensory hair is a long, slender projection sticking into the liquid outside the sensory cell. In many sense organs, it is immovable; in others, it is bent passively by the flow of liquid; finally, in some sense organs it possesses active movement. Sensory cells from widely different animal groups and from different types of sense organs have been examined with the electron microscope. The following sense organs and sensory cells have been studied in this manner: the olfactory organs and the auditory organs from vertebrates and insects; the lateral line organs of fish; the sensory cells from crab muscles in which a muscle tone can be measured; the vibration organs of spiders; the sense organ in skates, which can register very minute differences in electrical voltage; the balance organs of many different animal groups. In all these places the sensory cells are found with sensory hairs. Cells with a kind of thickened sensory hair can be found in the visual cells of vertebrates, starfish, sea squirts, arrow worms, earthworms, a polychaete worm, sea gooseberries, jellyfish, and scallops; however, the visual cells of insects, spiders, mollusks, leeches, turbellaria, and trematodes seem to lack sensory hairs completely. Sensory cells studied in the taste buds of mammals also lack sensory hairs.

It has been surprising to find that all sensory hairs have a similar construction. Regardless of whether it is on a cell which registers mechanical, chemical, electrical, or visual excitation, the sensory hair resembles a cilium in its construction. In fact, the sensory hair of the visual cells can be assumed to be related to cilia. Sensory hairs have the 9+2 complex found in a normal cilium with or without arms. More often than in cilia, they are found to lack the two inner filaments, and the construction can then be given the code 9+0. In some sensory hairs, especially those of the visual cells, the structure is more complicated and includes a membrane and membrane invaginations in addition to the filaments. Sensory hairs are found with a very high number of inner filaments. Only the sensory hair of the vibration organ of the spider is constructed so simply that it does not betray any relationship to a cilium (the vibration organ tells the spider when it has caught something in its web).

Much speculation has been made of this unexpected agreement between different sensory hairs, or between sensory hairs and cilia. It has been asserted that most sensory hairs have the primitive (9 + 0) pattern from which cilia (9 + 2) have originated. Similarly, the opposite has been maintained—namely, that the sensory hairs have originated from the older cilia (older in the sense that they appeared earlier in the history of biological evolution). Questions such as these can rarely be answered to any degree of certainty, and discussions of this kind are normally completely fruitless. It is of interest, though, to compare the sense organs of higher animals to corresponding ones of unicellular organisms. Such counterparts could be called sense organelles.

Unicellular animals (protozoa) can react to light, electrical excitations, chemical stimuli, and mechanical excitations. Sometimes it is impossible to localize excitable regions at a specific site in the cell since the entire cell seems to have the same sensitivity to the particular excitation. In other protozoa and for other types of excitation distinct sense organelles are found. An example of this is the eyespot of the protozoan called *Euglena.* In this and even in other protozoa, the light-sensitive area has been discovered in or close to the flagellum. This parallel, with the light-sensitive and cilia-like projections of our own eye, can hardly be accidental. It seems that altered or primitive cilia were so constructed to be suited for receiving light signals and transmitting the excitation to the cell body in a pathway along the cilium.

It has also been possible to demonstrate sense organelles for mechanical excitation in certain protozoa, for example, the ciliates. Their sensory hairs project like tentacles from the cell and function as such. They are cilia with a normal 9 + 2 pattern.

It is much more difficult to decide whether cilia can function as sensory hairs for chemical excitation also—in other words, as a sense organelle for smell and taste—within the protozoan group. Several observations suggest this possibility. Freely swimming protozoa are able to "aim" themselves toward places where specific chemicals are located. This phenomenon is called *chemotaxis*, and the protozoan is said to show chemotactic motion. Chemotaxis has also been observed in the plant world in, among other things, plant sperm swimming freely.

The substances to which sperm or protozoa react are specific to such an extent that different species react to different compounds. We have been able to measure how sensitive their chemical sense is, and the calculated values have been impressive. The cells can perceive minute differences in concentration, and they can compare the concentration of a compound near their anterior part to that near their posterior part. If they could not tell the difference, they could not correct their aim. (A less plausible alternative explanation for chemotactic swimming states that initially the cells swim at random, that they remember how the water tasted a moment ago, that they compare the taste of a moment ago to that of the present, and that they direct their swimming accordingly. This alternative is very farfetched and does not agree with the observations.) Neither does the explanation seem to be correct that says that the cell makes more turns in its swimming direction when it is in taste-free surroundings than it does in taste surroundings. Such behavior does occur in larger organisms; a woodlouse zig-zags about, haphazardly changing directions, when the air is dry, while in the damp milieu in which it thrives, its course is straight. For cells in a medium in which there is a gradient in concentration, the longer a cell is, the greater is the difference in concentration between one end and the other, and the easier it should be for it to detect the actual differences. In other words, it is advantageous for a chemotactic animal to be elongated. The tentacles that wave to-and-fro in protozoan or plant sperm are normally flagella or cilia. These could be assumed to be organelles for the chemical sense, while at the same time they could function as normal, motile cilia.

This review of the sense organelles of protozoa indicates that their smell as well as their touch and visual sense organelles can be connected to their cilia, although this is not a necessary connection, since many forms of excitation can be shown to occur in cells without cilia or cilia-like organelles.

The other characteristic part of a sensory cell, again returning to multicellular animals, is the region of contact it makes with the nerve cell. Here the sensory cells contain many small vesicles which undoubtedly function in the same way as the synaptic vesicles in the synapses of nerve cells; they are the bearers of impulses to another cell. Both types of contacts, nerve cell to nerve cell or sensory cell to nerve cell serve the same end and apparently have acquired the same construction in order to do so. In both types the contact has the same name, synapse, and the vesicles, synaptic vesicles. Plate 36 shows the synapse between a sensory cell (*S*) and the terminal of a nerve cell (*N*) which occurs in a sense organ in a marine fish, the ray. This sense organ responds to weak electrical potentials in the surrounding sea water. In the nerve cell, three cross-sectioned mitochondria are seen and, in the sensory cell, a number of synaptic vesicles. Most of the synaptic vesicles are assembled along a straight ribbon running perpendicular to the cell border into a projection of the sensory cell that "plugs" into the nerve cell. The function of the ribbon is not known. It is only between the "plug" and its "socket" that the sensory cell and the nerve cell come into contact with each other; on each side is interposed a thin layer of a glia cell (*G*).

So far the interpretation of the sensory synapse is simple and indisputable: impulses flow from sensory to nerve cell. But complicating factors exist which have given rise to controversy. In some sense organs, synapses have been found in which most synaptic vesicles lie not in the sensory cell but in the terminal of the nerve cell. Pictures of such sensory cells give the impression that the nerve cells act on the sensory cells rather than accepting impulses from them. This is true for the eyes and the inner ear of mammals, according to the electron microscope. What is the explanation for little vesicles resembling synaptic vesicles occurring on "the wrong side" of the synaptic gap?

Skeptical scientists have considered that the little vesicles on the wrong side cannot be connected to impulse transport. According to them, the vesicles cannot be filled with acetylcholine (or another membrane-affecting substance) in this kind of synapse and perhaps not even in other parts of the nervous system.

Less skeptical scientists have interpreted the vesicles, whatever their location in a sense organ and nerve system, according to the hypothesis of impulse transport via synaptic vesicles. They must, therefore, draw the conclusion that at least as many impulses are going to the sensory cells as are coming from them, for example, in the eye and the ear. They also have seen the advantage of such a mechanism. The construction of sense organs introduces the possibility that a prepared report can be sent to the central parts of the nervous system. Some thinning out of sensory impressions can take place as early as the sense organ, thanks to the influences imposed on the sensory cells from projections of other cells. It can be a question of either an inhibitory or an activating influence. An inhibitory influence makes the sensory cell less inclined to send an impulse; an activating influence has the opposite effect. In electronic terms these two forms of influence on the sensory cells are called negative and positive feedbacks.

In order to understand the different mechanisms which can be thought to function in the sense organs, it is desirable to have a detailed picture of the interwoven network of sensory cells, supporting cells, and nerve cells. We need a three-dimensional reconstruction of the contacts of cell projections at a magnification where the synaptic vesicles can clearly be distinguished. The first, and until now only, detailed study of this kind was done by Sjöstrand. From the structure of the "wiring diagram," Sjöstrand has drawn certain conclusions about some retinal mechanisms, particularly those involved in the operations which are made on the report that the optic nerve conveys to the visual center in the brain. Through the side contacts that the sensory cells make, their response to a light direction can be more varied than if the cell was not affected by synapses. It is possible that these synapses between the sensory cells can explain border-contrast phenomena; that is, the ability of the eye to see not only the areas of different shades of gray but also the borders between the areas as if they were defined by an outline. A light area behaves as if it is surrounded by a darker border and a dark area by a lighter one. This optical illusion is appropriate because it increases the ability of the eye to distinguish between different shades of gray—the ability to demarcate and separate areas of similar but not identical tone. The explanation of this phenomenon can be that impulses sent along the side projections are repressive. It is, however, not clear whether the inhibition of a visual cell is due to projections from its neighbors or, as is more commonly accepted, whether the inhibition occurs at a higher level in the hierarchy of connected nerve cells in the retina.

It can be said that it is of great value to unravel the paths which nerve impulses can take in our sense organs. The construction of our senses is extremely refined even when looked upon as a mere wiring diagram. This goes for the inner ear as well as the eye, and even in the olfactory organ for example we find both ingoing and outgoing nerve fibers. It is fascinating to contemplate that the reason we can enjoy music and art depends on an intricate fabric of individual sense and nerve cells made into a functional whole by myriads of little thin-walled vesicles 400 Å in diameter.

appendix

IMPORTANT YEARS IN THE STUDY OF THE CELL

1665 Robert Hooke describes the cell walls in cork and other plant tissues. He uses the term "cell" meaning little room.

1683 Antony van Leeuwenhoek describes bacteria.

1762 Samuel Klingenstierna shows how microscopes can be built with achromatic lenses.

1827 Giovanni Battista Amici constructs a microscope with achromatic lenses.

1831 Robert Brown discovers the cell nucleus.

1838 The cell theory is proposed by Matthias Schleiden. In his first version, the cell theory implies that all plants are composed of cells.

1839 The validity of the cell theory for animals is suggested by Theodor Schwann.

1855 Rudolph Virchow expands the cell theory to: "all cells are formed from cells." "Omnis cellula e cellula."

1857–67 Louis Pasteur proves that not even microorganisms can arise spontaneously.

1870 Wilhelm His introduces the microtome in microscopical technique. A microtome is an instrument for cutting thin sections of suitably prepared tissue.

1875 Oscar Hertwig explains fertilization. By studying fertilization in sea urchin eggs, he shows that fertilization implies the melting together of a sperm nucleus and an egg nucleus.

1879 Edward Strasburger shows that every cell nucleus originates from a cell nucleus.

1884 Ilja Metschnikoff demonstrates phagocytosis.

1887 Édouard van Benenden demonstrates that chromosomes retain their individuality throughout cell divisions.

1890 Richard Altmann describes granules in the cytoplasm which he considers an expression of the metabolism of the cell.

1913 Otto Warburg develops micromethods for determining oxygen consumption and establishes that respiration of the cell is connected with specific particles (Altmann's granules; later shown to be mitochondria).

1932 Frits Zernike constructs the phase-contrast microscope.

1933–34 Ernst Ruska constructs the first electron microscope which gives a better image than the light microscope.

1935 Hans Krebs demonstrates the citric acid cycle of the mitochondria, that is, the cyclical course of degradation of carbohydrates.

1939 The first commercial electron microscopes are made in Berlin by Ernst Ruska and Budo von Borries.

1940 Albert Claude introduces a technique to separate different cell components by centrifugation.

1941 Torbjörn O. Caspersson and Jean Brachet correlate the degree of protein synthesis to cytoplasmic amounts of RNA.

1944 T. Avery, Charlotte M. MacLeod, and Maclyn McCarty show that the genes consist of DNA and not protein.

1951 The first good microtomes for electron microscopy are built.

1952 George E. Palade and Fritiof S. Sjöstrand publish the first detailed pictures of mitochondria.

1953 James D. Watson and Francis H. C. Crick suggest that the DNA molecule is a double helix with paired complementary nucleotides. The genetic heredity is assumed to be coded as a specific sequence of the nucleotides.

1954 Muscle contraction is explained as a filament displacement independently by Hugh E. Huxley and Jean Hanson and by Andrew F. Huxley.

1961 Marshall Nirenberg deciphers the first letter of the genetic code, by showing that the building of specific amino acid into a protein corresponds to a special sequence of three nucleotides in the messenger-RNA molecule.

glossary

Acetylcholine esterase—An enzyme breaking down acetylcholine to choline and acetate.

Active transport—Every passage of a substance through a membrane that requires work on the cell's part.

Amino acid—An organic compound with the formula $NH_2RCHCOOH$, where R stands for one of the twenty-four different radicals, for example, H, CH_3, SH. Proteins are chains of combined amino acids.

Artifact—An artificial product that arises, for example, during preparatory procedures.

ATPase—An enzyme which catalyzes the splitting of ATP, normally in such a way that the energy content of the ATP is freed for mechanical, synthetic, or osmotic work.

Autophagic vesicle—A portion of the cell which is segregated for lysis by lysosomal enzymes.

Autoradiography—A method in which the radioactive object is depicted on a photographic film by being placed in close association with the film.

Cancer virus—Viruses or virus-like particles which give rise to specific forms of cancer.

Cell cycle—Regular alteration of resting stages and division stages in a cell's life.

Centrifuge—Apparatus for separating lighter from heavier components of a solution.

Centriole—Organelle which resembles a short intracellular cilium. The centriole is normally near the cell nucleus; during cell divisions, however, it is found near the poles of the mitotic apparatus.

Chondriosome—Synonymous to mitochondrion.

Cytochrome—Compound formed by a protein and an iron-containing aromatic organic substance.

Cytochrome oxidase—One of the cytochromes in the electron-transport chain.

Cytoplasmic mutation—A mutation in a cytoplasmic organelle.

Cytosome—A non-specific term for any of a number of different granules in the cytoplasm. Often used more or less synonymous to lysosome.

Desmosome—Portion of the cell membrane specialized for the adhesion to a neighboring cell.

DPN—Diphosphopyridine nucleotide. Cf. footnote on p. 12.

DPNH–cytochrome c reductase—An enzyme which can be said to represent part of the electron-transport chain, but whose functions are unknown.

Dry weight—The weight of an object minus the weight of its water.

Electrical potential—The difference in electric charge between two points which is called voltage and measured in volts.

Electrode—*See* Microelectrode.

Electron micrograph—Picture of an object taken with an electron microscope.

Endocrinology—The study of hormones and the effect of hormones.

Enzyme—A protein which accelerates, enables, or controls chemical reactions in living organisms. Enzymes bind to compounds, thereby affecting their breakdown or union with other substances.

Ergastoplasm—The ribosome-carrying components of the cytoplasm.

Fatty acid—Organic acid with the formula RCOOH, where R stands for a hydrogen or a hydrocarbon radical.

Fibrils—Fine threadlike structures in or near a cell.

Filament—Very thin, threadlike structure.

Genetic code—The molecular configuration that is the hereditary substance per se and which is able to divide to form new but still identical substances and also is able to direct formation of different specific proteins.

Glucose-6-phosphatase—Enzyme splitting glucose-6-phosphate. A key enzyme in the degradation of glycogen (for example, in liver) for formation of blood sugar (glucose).

Glycocalyx—The layer of fibrous carbohydrate substances surrounding all or most cells.

Glycogen—Animal starch, a high-molecular-weight carbohydrate.

Glycolysis—Enzymatic degradation of glycogen to pyruvic acid or lactic acid without oxygen consumption.

Hydrolase—An enzyme catalyzing the degradation of a substance by water uptake.

Isotopes—Atoms with the same chemical properties but with different atomic weights. Naturally occurring or artificially produced isotopes which have spontaneous breakdown are called radioactive isotopes.

Lipid—Fat.

Macromolecule—A molecule in the cell with a high molecular weight; for example, proteins, nucleic acids, some carbohydrates.

Matrix—A mass in which something is immersed.

Metabolism—Synthesis and breakdown of compounds. The chemical processes in an organism.

Microbiology—The study of microorganisms; that is, microscopically tiny protozoa, plants, and bacteria.

Microelectrode—A fine wire or capillary which can be introduced near or into a cell to measure electrical potential.

Multivesicular body—Organelle with unknown functions and consisting of many small vesicles within an envelope.

Mutations—Relatively stable changes in the hereditary substance.

NAD, NADH, NADP, NADPH—Cf. footnote on p. 12.

Nucleotide—An association of a sugar, a nitrogen-containing base (purine or pyrimidine), and phosphoric acid. Nucleotides are the building blocks of DNA and RNA.

Osmotic work—Work performed by the cell to produce and maintain a difference in concentration of various compounds inside and outside the cell.

Pentosephosphate-oxidation cycle—One of the enzymatic pathways to break down glucose.

Peroxisome—Cytoplasmic particles in which certain peroxide reactions take place. Microbodies of vertebrate liver and kidney are peroxisomes.

Polyribosome, Polysome—The aggregate of some ribosomes and a messenger-RNA thread.

Protoplasm—The cell's contents; that is, the nucleus and the cytoplasm.

Resting Potential—A cell's electrical potential when at rest.

Sonicator—Apparatus which generates sound of high energy and high frequency.

Steroids—Complicated organic associations with ring structures, for example, cholestrin, some sex hormones, and some components in the cytoplasmic membranes.

Stimulus—A disturbance which affects the state or activity of a cell or its components.

Synthesis—Assembling of simple chemical compounds into more complicated ones.

Terminal electron transport—Final step, in which oxygen is bound, in the electron-transport chain.

Thiamine pyrophosphatase—An enzyme catalyzing the splitting of thiamine pyrophosphate, which is a factor participating in a specific step of the citric acid cycle.

Tonus—Muscle tension which is present even in resting muscles.

TPN, TPNH, triphosphopyridine nucleotide—Cf. footnote on p. 12.

Ultracentrifuge—Apparatus for separation of dissolved or suspended particles (for example, macromolecules) of different gravities; rotation increases the weight of the particles causing them to sediment.

Uricase—An enzyme catalyzing degradation of uric acid.

Uricosome—Such microbodies as have uricase.

X-ray–diffraction analysis—Technique to determine the cystalline construction of matter by means of X-rays.

bibliography

CHAPTER 1. THE STRUCTURE OF THE CELL

Bonner, J. T. *The ideas of biology.* New York: Harper and Row Publishers, Inc., 1962.

Crick, F. H. C. and Hughes, A. F. W. The physical properties of cytoplasm. *Exptl. Cell Res.* 1: 36–80, 1950.

Duve, C. de, Wattiaux, R., and Baudhuin, P. Distribution of enzymes between subcellular fractions in animal tissues. *Adv. Enzymol.* 24: 291–358, 1962.

Loewy, A. G. and Siekevitz, P. *Cell structure and function.* New York: Holt, Rinehart and Winston, Inc., 1963.

Mercer, E. H. *Cells and cell structure.* London: Hutchinson Educational, Ltd., 1961.

Porter, K. R. and Bonneville, M. A. *An introduction to the fine structure of cells.* Philadelphia: Lee and Febiger, 1963.

Rhodin, J. *An atlas of ultrastructure.* Philadelphia: W. B. Saunders Co., 1963.

Siekevitz, P. Protoplasm, endoplasmic reticulum, and microsomes. *Ann. Rev. Physiol.* 25: 15–40, 1963.

Waddington, C. H. *The nature of life.* London: George Allen and Unwin Ltd., 1960.

Porter and Bonneville's and Rhodin's works are pictorial, illustrating the structure and ultrastructure of tissues from mammals. Siekevitz and de Duve, Wattiaux, and Baudhuin have been included in Table 1. Loewy and Siekevitz's and Mercer's works are introductions to the study of the cell. Bonner's and Waddington's works are representations of the problems found in modern biology—among others, cell biological problems.

CHAPTERS 2 AND 3. MITOCHONDRIA

André, J. Contribution à la connaissance du chondriome. Étude de ses modifications ultrastructurales pendant la spermiogénèse. *Jour. Ultrastruct. Res.*, Supplement 3, 1–185, 1962.

Fernández-Morán, H., Oda, T., Blair, P. V., and Green, D. E. A macromolecular repeating unit of mitochondrial structure and function. *Jour. Cell. Biol.*, 22: 63–100, 1964.

Gibor, A. and Granick, S. Plastids and mitochondria: inheritable systems. *Science* 145: 890–97, 1964.

Lehninger, A. L. *The mitochondrion.* New York: Academic Press, 1964.

Linnane, A. W., Vitolo, E., and Nowland, P. G. Studies on the origin of yeast mitochondria. *Jour. Cell. Biol.* 13: 345–50, 1963.

Luck, D. J. L. Formation of mitochondria in *Neurospora crassa. Jour. Cell Biol.* 16: 483–99, 1963.

Luft, R., Ikkos, D., Palmieri, G., Ernster, L., and Afzelius, B. A. A case of severe hypermetabolism of non-thyroid origin, with a defect in the maintenance of mitochondrial respiratory control. A correlated clinical, biochemical, and morphological study. *Jour. Clin. Invest.* 41: 1776–1804, 1962.

Nass, M. M. K. and Nass, S. Intramitochondrial fibers with DNA characteristics. I and II. *Jour. Cell. Biol.* 19: 593–629, 1963.

Nass, M. M. K., Nass, S., and Afzelius, B. A. The general occurrence of mitochondrial DNA. *Exptl. Cell Res.* 37: 516–39, 1965.

Palade, G. E. An electron microscope study of the mitochondrial structure. *Jour. Histochem. Cytochem.* 1: 188–211, 1953.

Rutberg, U. Ultrastructure and secretory mechanism of the parotid gland. *Acta Odontol. Scand.* 19: Supplement 30, 1–69, 1961.

Sjöstrand, F. S. Electron microscopy of mitochondria and cytoplasmic double membranes. *Nature* 171: 30–32, 1953.

CHAPTER 4. THE CELL MEMBRANE

Afzelius, B. A. The ultrastructure of cortical granules and their products in the sea urchin egg as studied with the electron microscope. *Exptl. Cell Res.* 10: 257–85, 1956.

Afzelius, B. A. and Murray, A. The acrosomal reaction of spermatozoa during fertilization or treatment with egg water. *Exptl. Cell Res.* 12: 325–37, 1957.

Farquhar, M. G. and Palade, G. E. Junctional complexes in various epithelia. *Jour. Cell. Biol.* 17: 375–412, 1963.

Jennings, M. A., Marchesi, V. T., and Florey, H. The transport of particles across the walls of small blood vessels. *Proc. Roy. Soc. Ser. B.* 156: 14–19, 1962.

Kavanau, L. Structure and function of biological membranes. *Nature* 198: 525–30, 1963.

Palade, G. E. Fine structure of blood capillaries. *Jour. Appl. Phys.* 24: 1424, 1953.

CHAPTER 5. THE NUCLEAR MEMBRANE

Afzelius, B. A. The ultrastructure of the nuclear membrane of the sea urchin oocyte as studied with the electron microscope. *Exptl. Cell Res.* 8: 147–58, 1955.

Afzelius, B. A. The nucleus of *Noctiluca scintillans.* Aspects of nucleocytoplasmic exchanges and the formation of the nuclear membrane. *Jour. Cell. Biol.* 19: 229–38, 1963.

Feldherr, C. M. The nuclear annuli as pathways for nucleocytoplasmic exchanges. *Jour. Cell. Biol.* 14: 65–72, 1962.

Loewenstein, W. R. and Kanno, Y. Some electrical properties of the membrane of a cell nucleus. *Nature* 195: 462–64, 1962.

CHAPTER 6. RIBOSOMES

Karlson, P. New concepts on the mode of action of hormones. *Perspectives Biol. Med.* 6: 204–14, 1963.

Ochoa, S. Chemical basis of heredity, the genetic code. *Experientia* 20: 57–68, 1964.

Palade, G. E. A small particulate component of the cytoplasm. In *Frontiers in cytology,* S. Palay (ed.), New Haven: Yale University Press, 1958.

Watson, J. D. Involvement of RNA in the synthesis of proteins. *Science* 140: 17–26, 1963.

CHAPTER 7. MICROBODIES

Afzelius, B. A. The occurrence and structure of microbodies, *Jour. Cell. Biol.* 26: 835–43, 1965.

Baldwin, E. *An introduction to comparative biochemistry.* 4th ed. Cambridge: Cambridge University Press, 1964.

Duve, C. de, Beaufay, H., Jacques, P., Rahman-Li, Y., Sellinger, O. Z., Wattiaux, R., and Conick S. de. Intracellular localization of catalase and of some oxidases in rat liver. *Biochim. Biophys. Acta* 40: 186–91, 1960.

Hruban, Z., and Swift, H. Uricase: Localization in hepatic microbodies. *Science* 146: 1316–18, 1964.

CHAPTER 8. LYSOSOMES

Duve, C. de, Pressman, B. C., Gianetto, R., Wattiaux, R., and Appelmans, F. Tissue fractionation studies. *Biochem. Jour.* 60: 604–17, 1955.

Reuck, A. V. S. de and Cameron, M. P. (eds.). *Ciba foundation symposium on lysosomes.* London: J. & A. Churchill Ltd., 1963.

CHAPTER 9. MUSCLE CELLS

Bourne, G. H. (ed.) *The structure and function of muscle.* New York: Academic Press, 1960.

Huxley, A. F. and Taylor, R. E. Local activation of striated muscle fibers. *Jour. Physiol.* 144: 426–44, 1958.

Huxley, H. E. Muscular contraction. *Endeavour* 15: 177–88, 1956.

Huxley, H. E. The mechanism of muscular contraction. *Sci. Am.* 213 (12): 18–27, 1965.

Huxley, H. E. and Hanson, J. The molecular basis of contraction in cross-striated muscles. In *The structure and function of muscle.* I: 183–225. G. H. Bourne (ed.), New York: Academic Press, 1960.

CHAPTER 10. CILIA

Afzelius, B. A. Electron microscopy of the sperm tail. Results obtained with a new fixative. *Jour. Biophys. Biochem. Cytol.* 5: 269–78, 1959.

Afzelius, B. A. The fine structure of the cilia from ctenophore swimming plates. *Jour. Biochem. Biophys. Cytol.* 9: 383–94, 1961.

Afzelius, B. A. Cilia and flagella that do not conform to the 9 + 2 pattern. I. *Jour. Ultrastruct. Res.* 9: 381–92, 1963.

Gibbons, I. R. Studies on the protein components of cilia from *Tetrahymena pyriformis. Proc. Natl. Acad. Sci. U.S.* 50: 1002–10, 1963.

Satir, P. Cilia. *Sci. Am.* 204 (2): 108–17, 1961.

Sleigh, M. A. *The biology of cilia and flagella.* Oxford: Pergamon Press, 1963.

CHAPTER 11. NERVE CELLS

Afzelius, B. A. and Fridberg, G. The fine structure of the caudal neurosecretory system in *Raia batis*. *Z. Zellforsch.* 59: 289–308, 1963.

Geren, B. B. and Schmitt, F. O. Electron microscope studies of the Schwann cell and its constituents with particular reference to the axon. *Symp. Eighth Congr. Cell Biol. Leiden,* Leiden: P. Noordhoff Ltd., 241–60, 1954.

Horridge, G. A. and Mackay, B. Naked axons and symmetrical synapses in coelenterates. *Quart. Jour. Microscop. Sci.* 103: 531–41, 1962.

Hydén, H. The neuron and its glia—a biochemical and functional unit. *Endeavour* 21: 144–55, 1962.

Katz, B. The transmission of impulses from nerve to muscle and the subcellular unit of synaptic action. *Proc. Roy. Soc. Ser. B.* 155: 455–77, 1962.

Koelle, G. B. A proposed dual neurohumoral role of acetylcholine: its function at the pre- and post-synaptic sites. *Nature* 190: 208–11, 1961.

Robertis, E. de. *Histophysiology of synapses and neurosecretion.* Oxford: Pergamon Press, 1964.

Young, J. Z. *A model of the brain.* New York: Oxford University Press, 1964.

CHAPTER 12. SENSORY CELLS

Eakin, R. M. Lines of evolution of photoreceptors. In *The general physiology of cell specialization.* Pp. 393–425. D. Mazia and A. Tylor (eds.). New York: McGraw-Hill Book Co., Inc., 1963.

Sjöstrand, F. S. Ultrastructure of retinal rod synapses of the guinea pig eye as revealed by three-dimensional reconstructions from serial sections. *Jour. Ultrastruct. Res.* 2: 122–70, 1959.

Waltman, B. Electrical properties and fine structure of the ampullary canals of Lorenzini. *Acta Physiol. Scandinav.* 66 (Suppl. 264): 1–60, 1966.

technical explanation of plates

All plates except Plate 6 are electron micrographs of sectioned material.

PLATE 1.—Parenchymal cell from rat liver. Fixation after Millonig. Epon embedding. Lead citrate staining. Electron microscopy by Rune Gustafsson.

PLATE 2.—*Proteus vulgaris* bacterium. Fixation after Kellenberger. Epon embedding. Electron microscopy by Toshiko Mohri.

PLATE 3.—Mitochondrion from the sartorius muscle of a 35-year-old woman suffering from hypermetabolism of unknown etiology. Fixation after Zetterqvist. Epon embedding.

PLATE 4.—Mitochondria isolated from rat muscles. Fixation after Zetterqvist. Epon embedding. Electron microscopy by Birgitta af Burén.

PLATE 5.—Inner membranes obtained from burst beef heart mitochondria. Fixation after Zetterqvist. Epon embedding.

PLATE 6.—Inner membranes of the same material as in Plate 5 but prepared as intact preparations according to negative-staining method. Sodium phosphotungstate impregnation.

PLATE 7.—Mitochondria from bone marrow cell of a rat. Staining with uranyl acetate followed by lead hydroxide has made the mitochondrial thread of the DNA type visible. Fixation after Zetterqvist. Epon embedding. Electron microscopy by Margit M. K. Nass.

PLATE 8.—The free cell surface of a cell of a blue mussel gill. Fixation after Afzelius. Embedded in methacrylate.

PLATE 9.—Cell border between two ectodermal cells of a chick embryo incubated for 19 hours. Fixation after Kellenberger. Epon embedding. Electron microscopy by Margit M. K. Nass.

PLATE 10.—Cell border between two cells of the comb jelly (*Mnemiopsis leidyi*) in the apical sense organ. Fixation after Afzelius. Methacrylate embedded.

PLATE 11.—Cell cortex of the unfertilized egg of the sea urchin *Strongylocentrotus droebachiensis.* Fixation in osmium tetroxide in sea water. Methacrylate embedding.

PLATE 12.—The broken cell surface of the sea urchin egg (*Strongylocentrotus droebachiensis*) 4 minutes after fertilization. Same fixation as in Plate 11.

PLATE 13.—Longitudinal cut of sperm of the sea urchin *Strongylocentrotus droesbachiensis.* Fixation with osmium textroxide in sea water. Methacrylate embedding.

PLATE 14.—Sperm from the same species after "acrosome reaction" triggered by the sperm coming in contact with the egg. This implies that a round granule in the tip of the sperm (down in the picture) is ejected through the cell membrane. Fixation and embedding as in Plate 13.

PLATE 15.—Golgi body from an oocyte of the sea urchin *Echinus esculentus.* Fixation with osmium tetroxide in sea water. Methacrylate embedding.

PLATE 16.—Blood capillary from the sartorius muscle of a healthy person. Fixation after Zetterqvist. Methacrylate embedding.

PLATE 17.—Gastrodermal cell from a hydroid *Clava squamata* fed carbon particles. Fixation with osmium tetroxide in sea water. Epon embedding.

PLATE 18.—Immature egg from the sea urchin *Echinus esculentus.* Fixation with osmium tetroxide in sea water. Methacrylate embedding.

PLATE 19.—Tangentially cut nuclear membrane from an immature egg of the sea urchin *Brissopsis lyrifera.* Fixation and embedding as in Plate 18.

PLATE 20.—Part of the nucleus of the organism *Ceratium tripos* (Protozoa. Dinoflagellata). Fixation with osmium tetroxide in sea water. Epon embedding.

PLATE 21,—Nucleus and chromosomes from the phosphorescent planktonic organism *Noctiluca scintillans* (Protozoa. Dinoflagellata). Fixation with osmium tetroxide in sea water. Epon embedding.

PLATE 22.—Ribosomes from a rat liver parenchymal cell. Fixation after Zetterqvist. Epon embedding.

PLATE 23.—Ribosomes from the clitellar gland cell of the leech *Hae-*

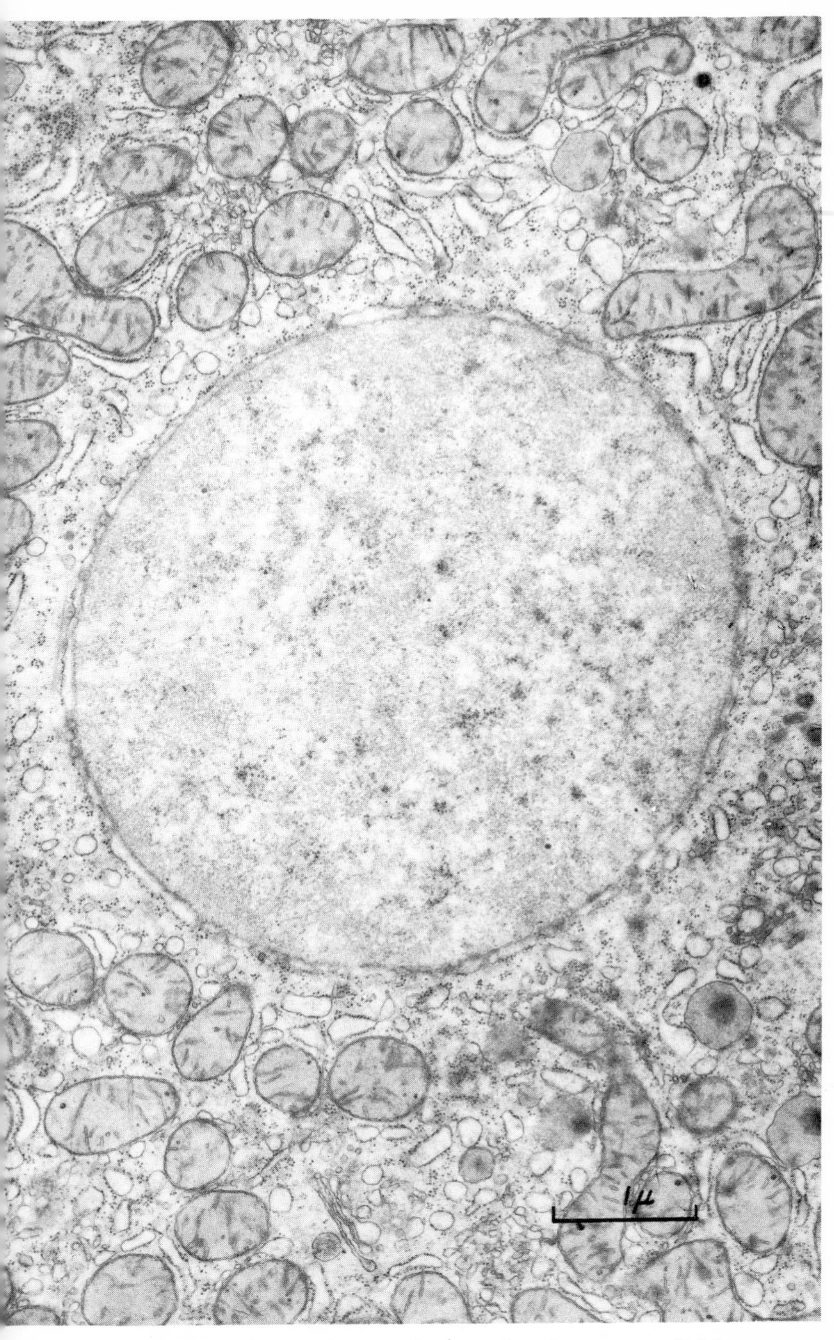

PLATE 1.—The liver cell with a big round nucleus surrounded by a membrane (cf. Plate 2).

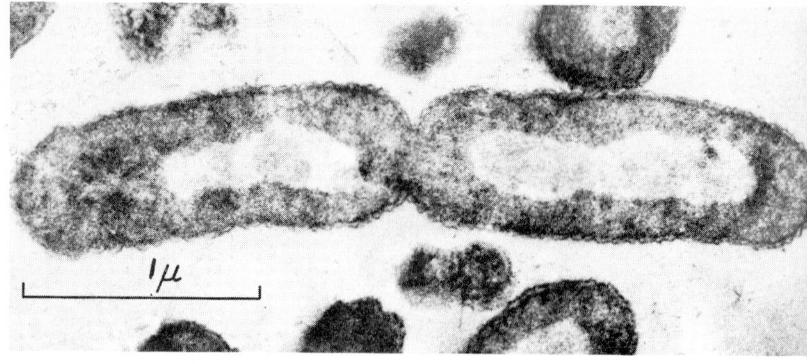

PLATE 2.—The gene material in the bacterium is free (cf. Plate 1)

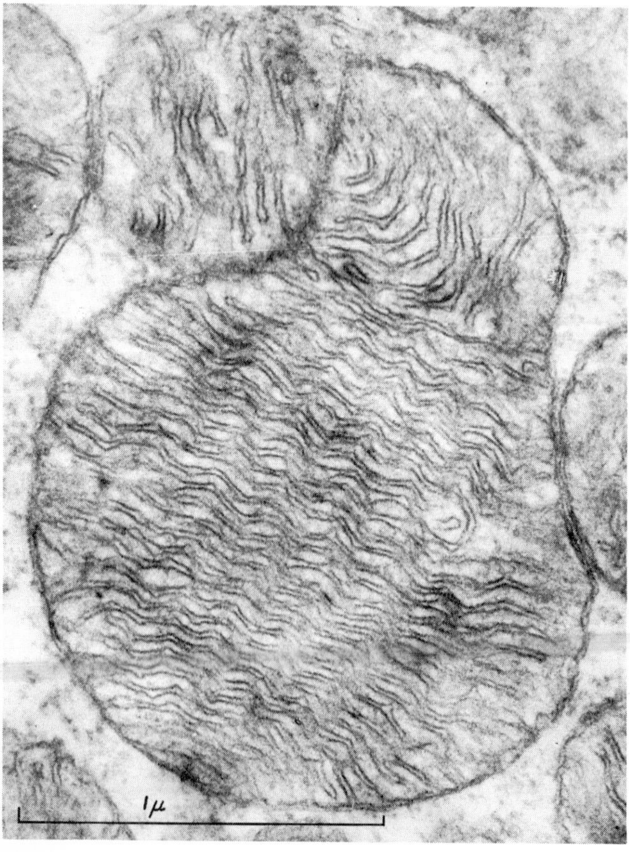

PLATE 3.—Mitochondrion from a muscle cell. The zigzag lines represent the inner membranes of the mitochondrion which are the site for many enzymes.

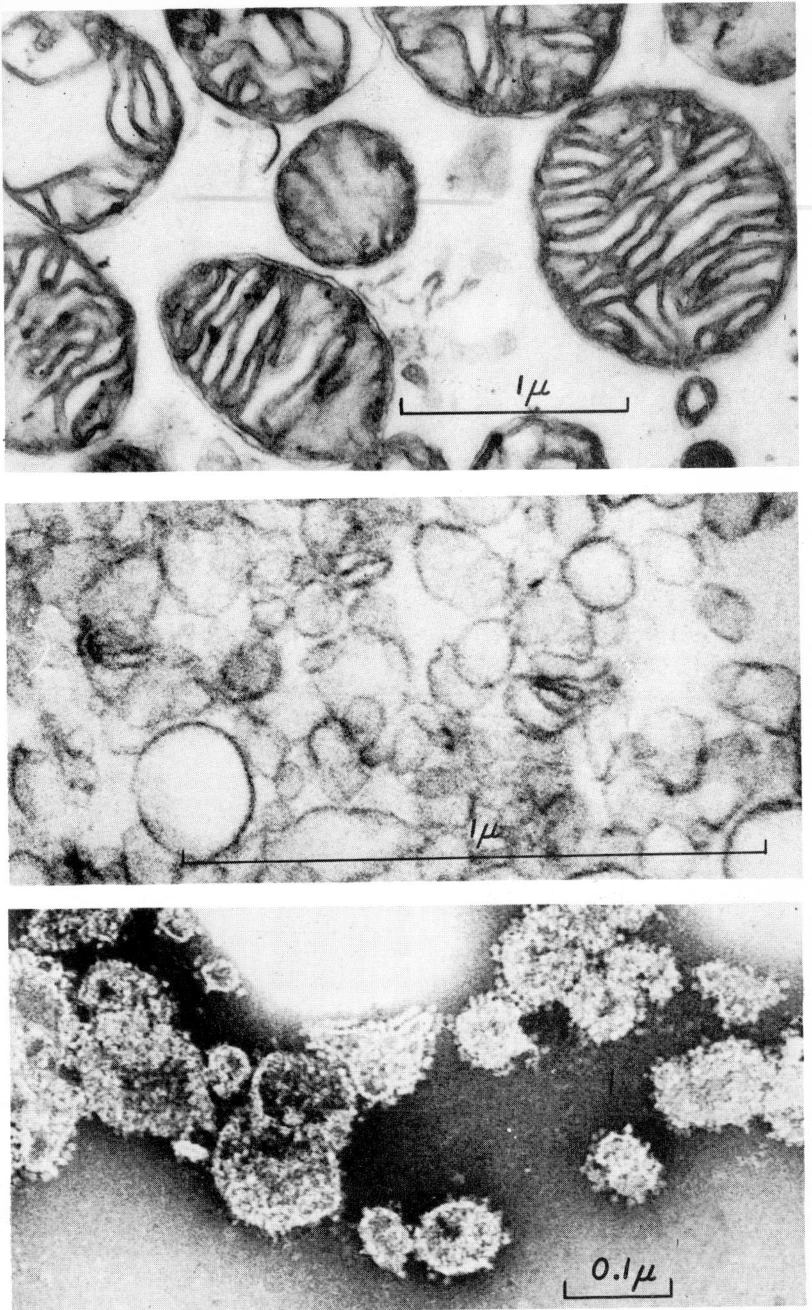

PLATES 4 through 6.—Preparatory steps in studies of mitochondria. Whole isolated mitochondria (Plate 4); isolated inner membranes (Plate 5); inner membranes with elementary particles (Plate 6).

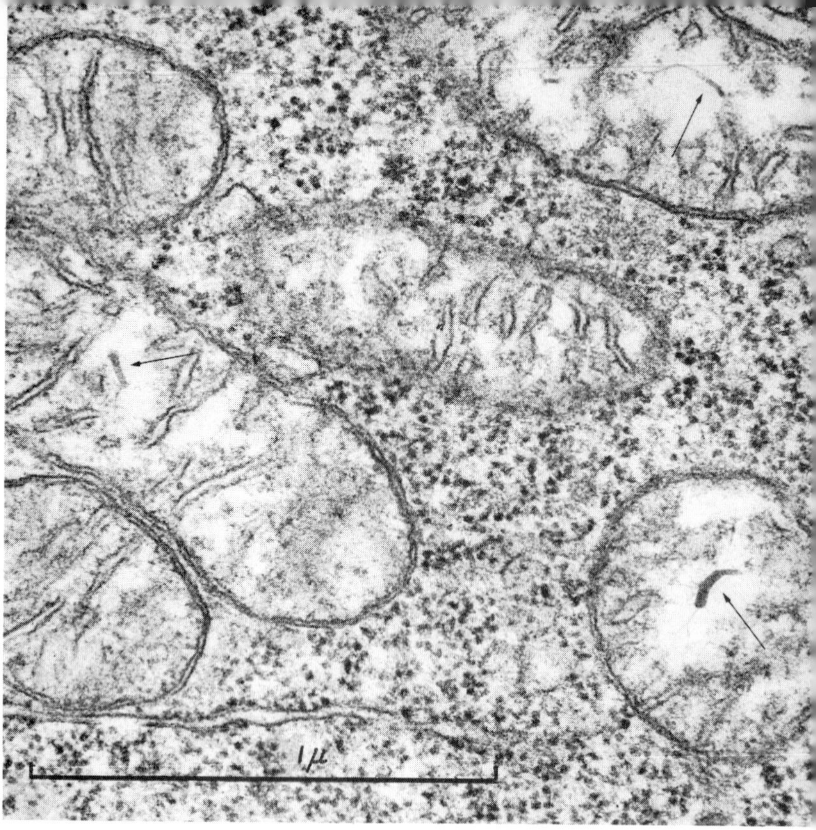

PLATE 7.—Mitochondria treated in such manner that their threads of a DNA type are made visible (*arrows*).

PLATE 8.—Cross-section of finger-like projections surrounded by the cell membrane on the free surface of the cell.

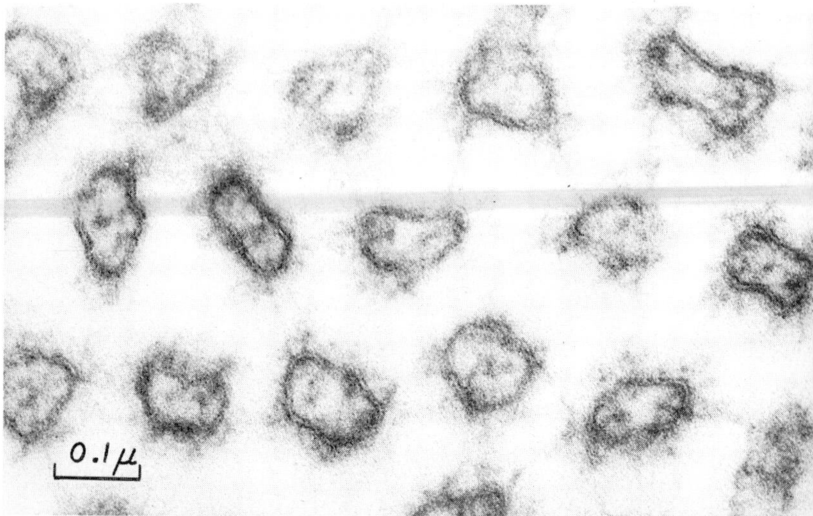

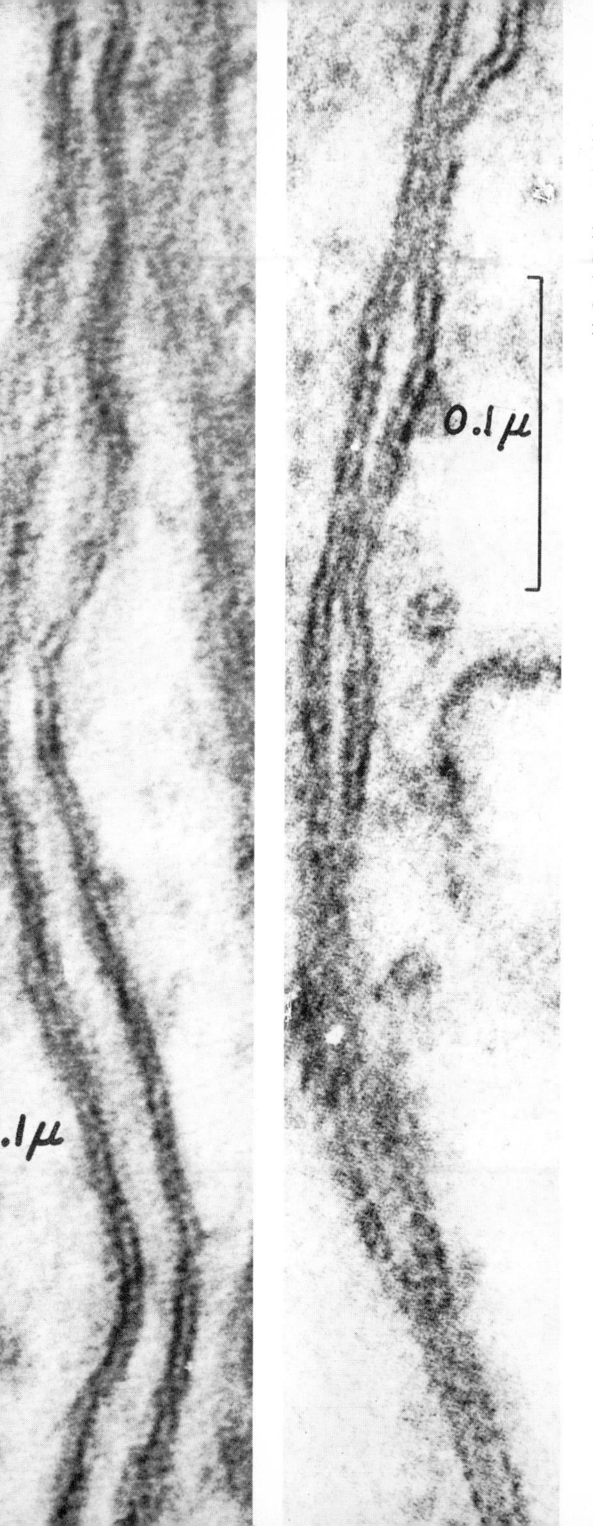

PLATES 9 and 10.—Parallel cell membranes from two cells of a chick embryo (Plate 9), and cell membranes meeting in spots (Plate 10). With this magnification the egg would be about 9 miles long.

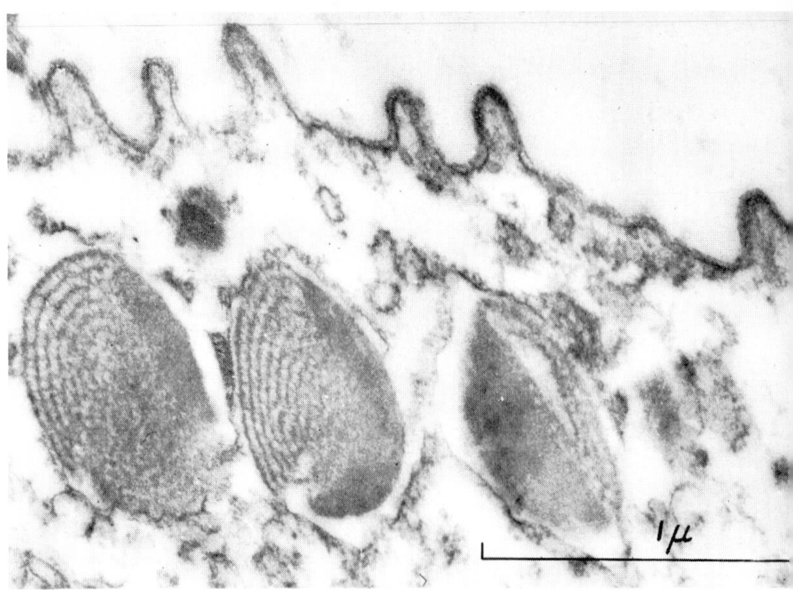

PLATE 11.—Surface layer of a sea urchin egg. The picture shows three of the cell's approximately 30,000 so-called cortical granules.

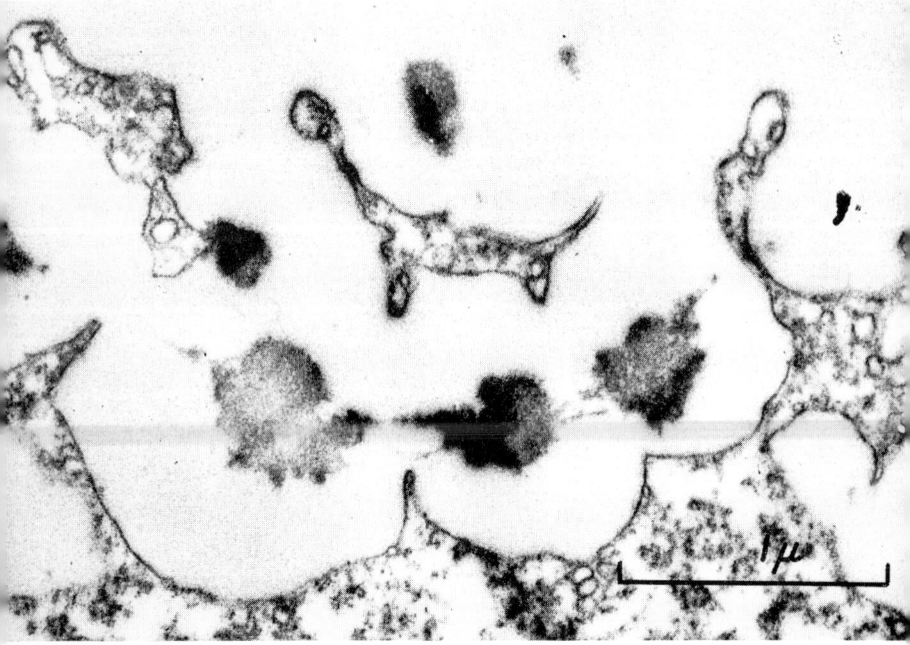

PLATE 12.—Minutes after fertilization the cortical granules burst and the egg gets a new surface formed from the membranes of the cortical granules.

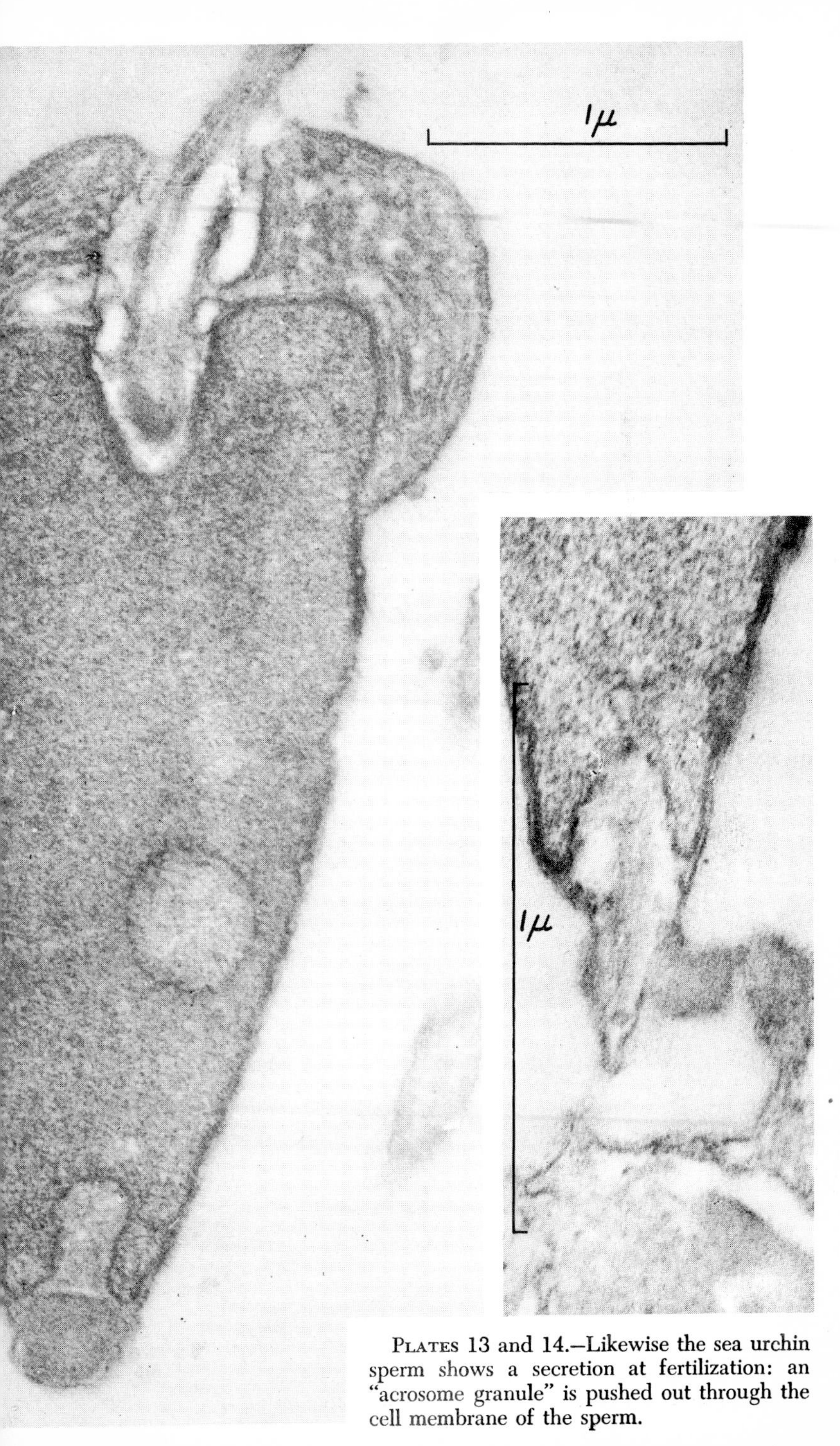

PLATES 13 and 14.—Likewise the sea urchin sperm shows a secretion at fertilization: an "acrosome granule" is pushed out through the cell membrane of the sperm.

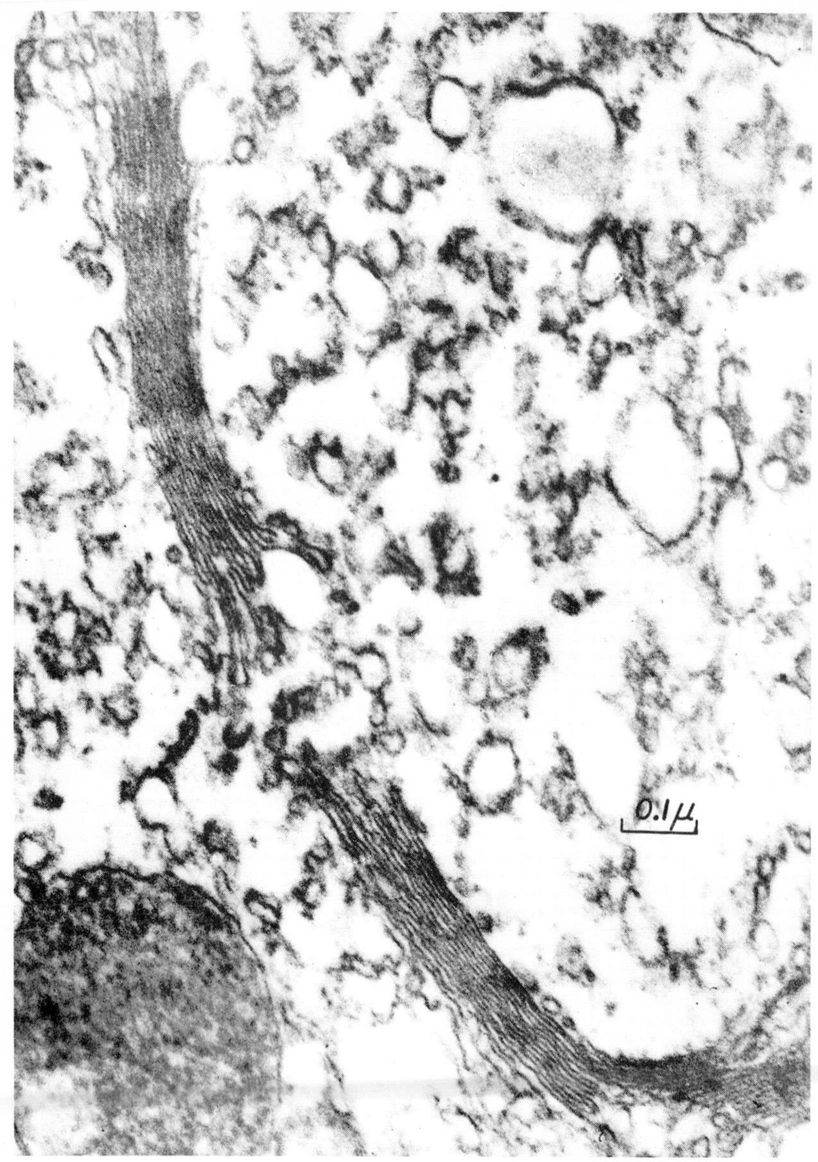

PLATE 15.—The Golgi apparatus usually appears as a stack of membranes.

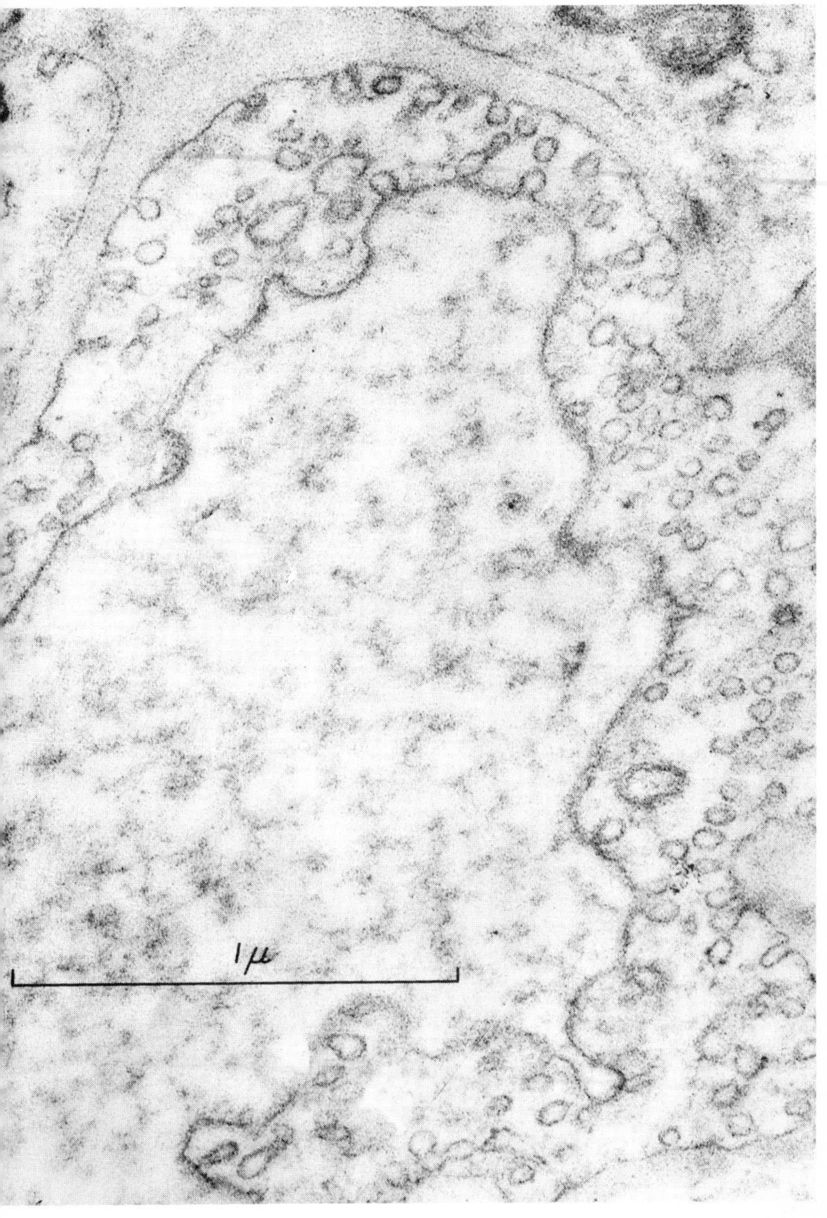

PLATE 16.—The flat cells of the capillaries contain few organelles besides the numerous small vesicles which are interpreted as a sign of pinocytosis, cell drinking. The space surrounded by the capillary cell is the blood stream, and the diffuse fluffy substance in this is serum proteins.

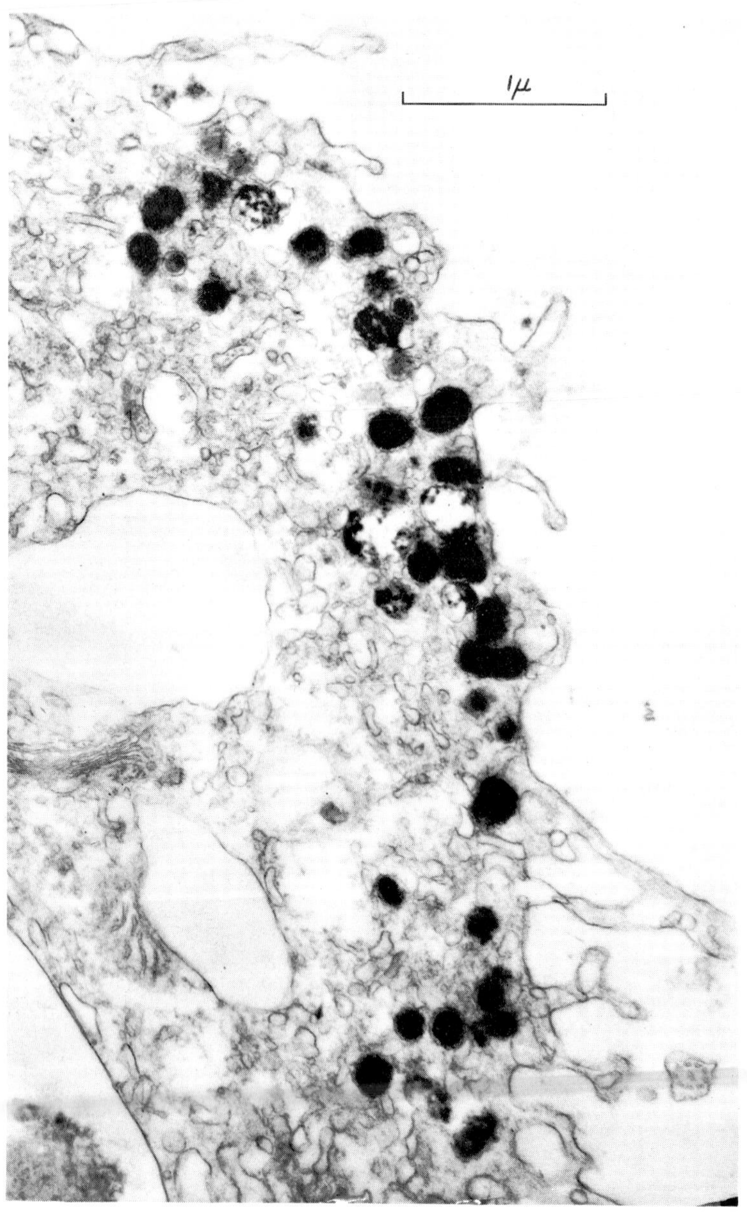

PLATE 17.—This cell has taken up many carbon particles by phagocytosis

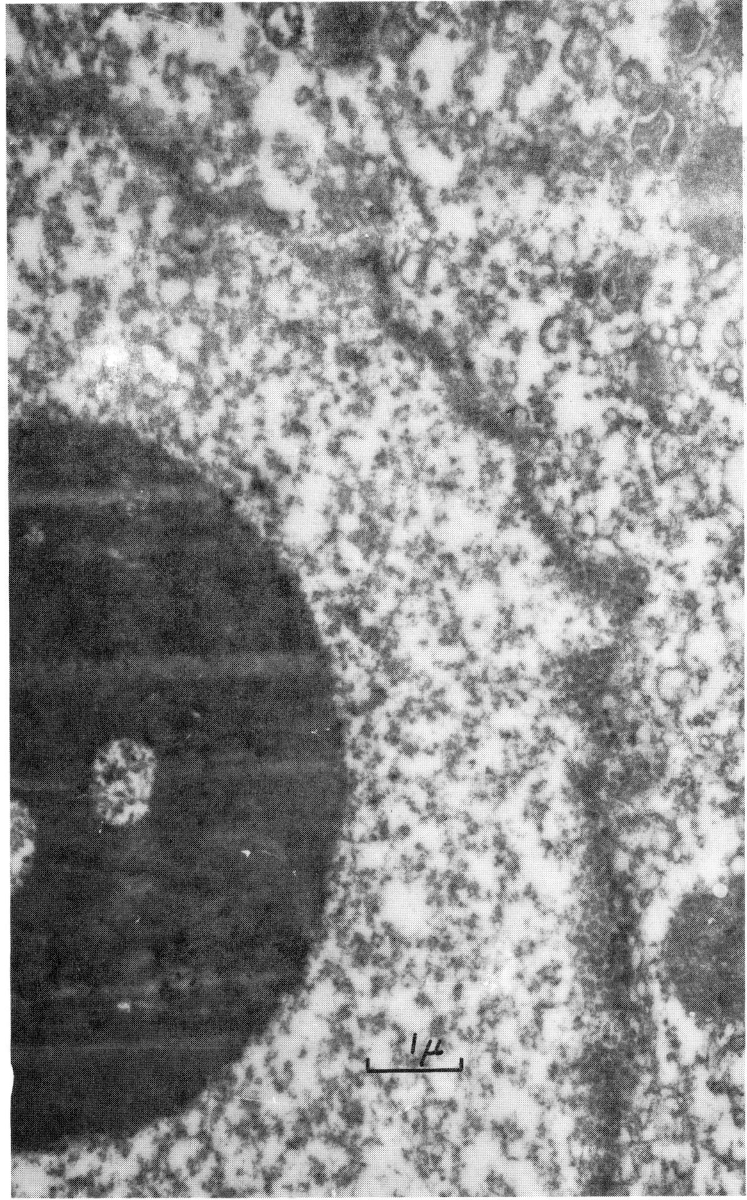

PLATE 18.—The sea urchin egg has an extensive nucleus with a big nucleolus (*the dark body on the left*). The nuclear membrane is seen cut obliquely and looks like a collection of rings.

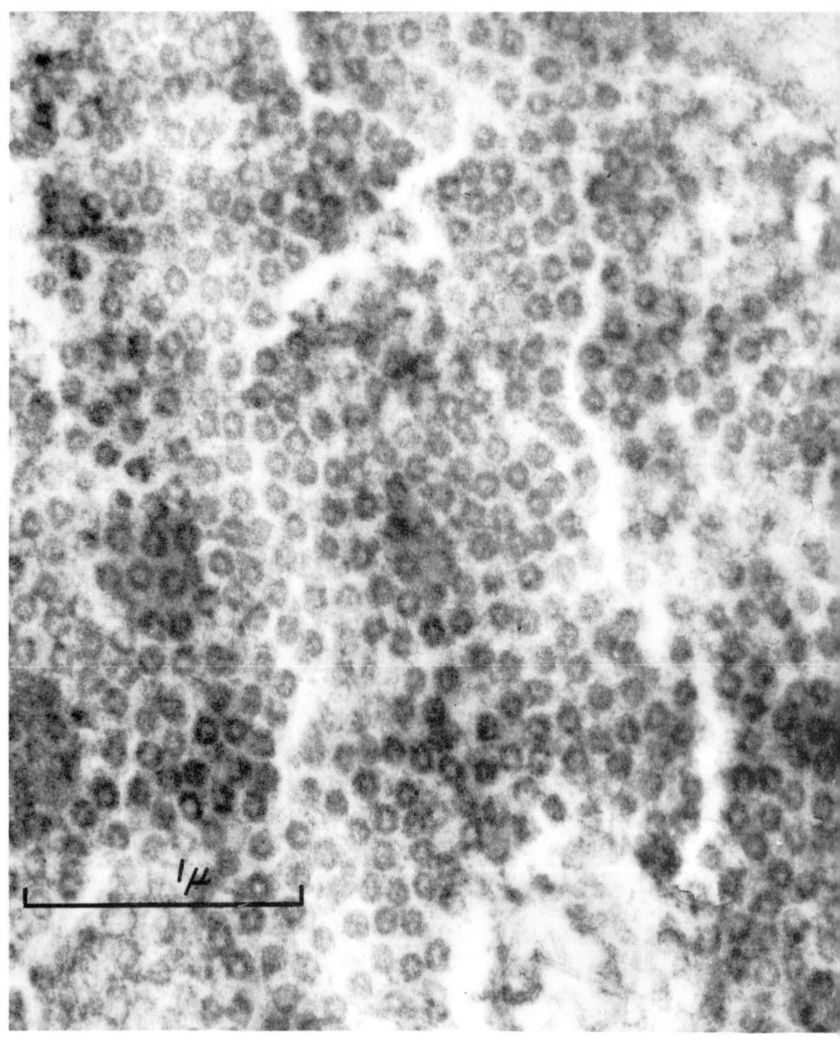

Plate 19.—In this cut a large part of the surface of the nuclear membrane has been included and a number of the approximately 100,000 cylinders of the membrane are seen in cross-section.

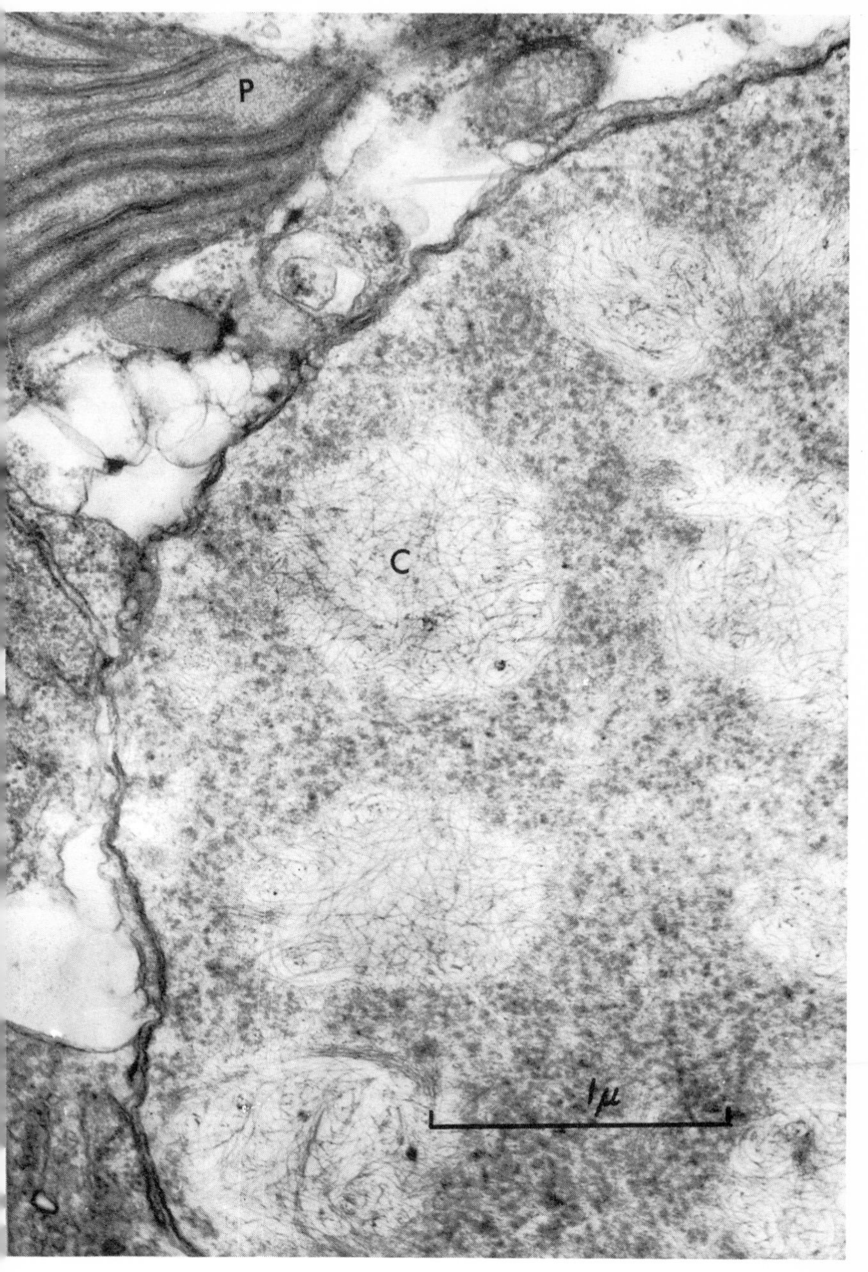

PLATE 20.—In this cell the chromosomes (*C*) have a distinct fibrillar appearance. Part of a chloroplast (*P*) at top.

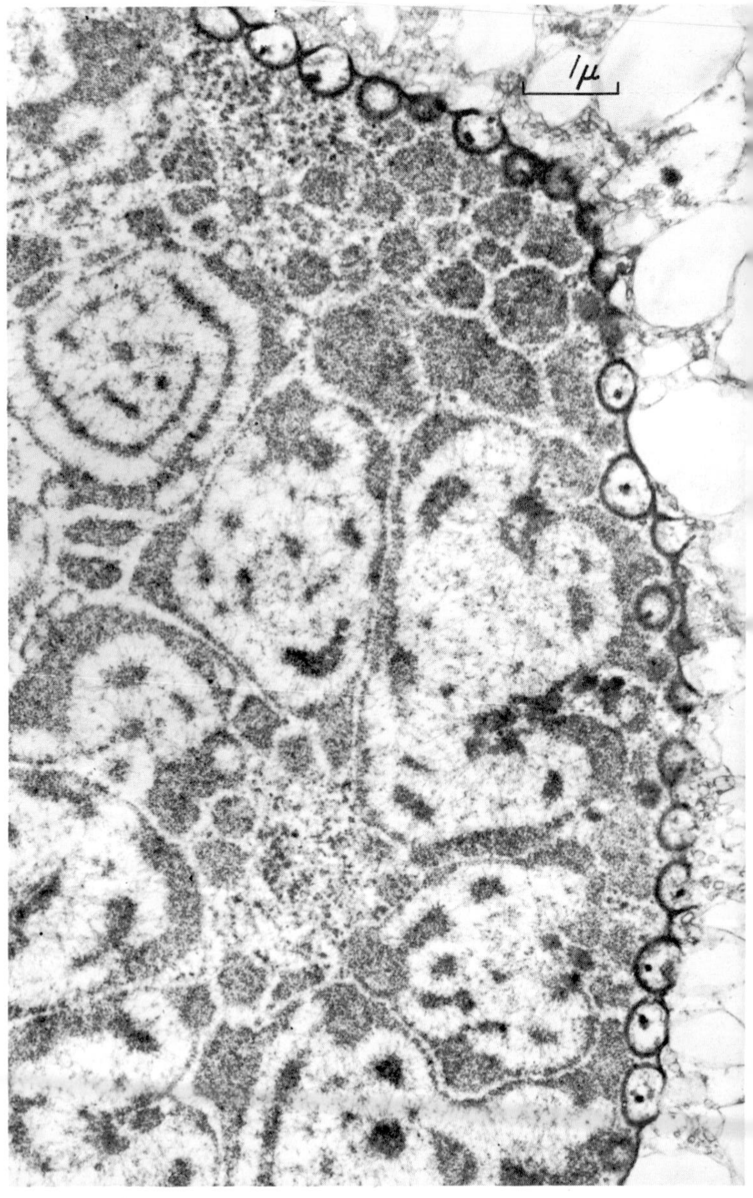

PLATE 21.—The nucleus of *Noctiluca*. The chromosome balls predominate. A row of vesicles marks the border between the nucleus and the cytoplasm.

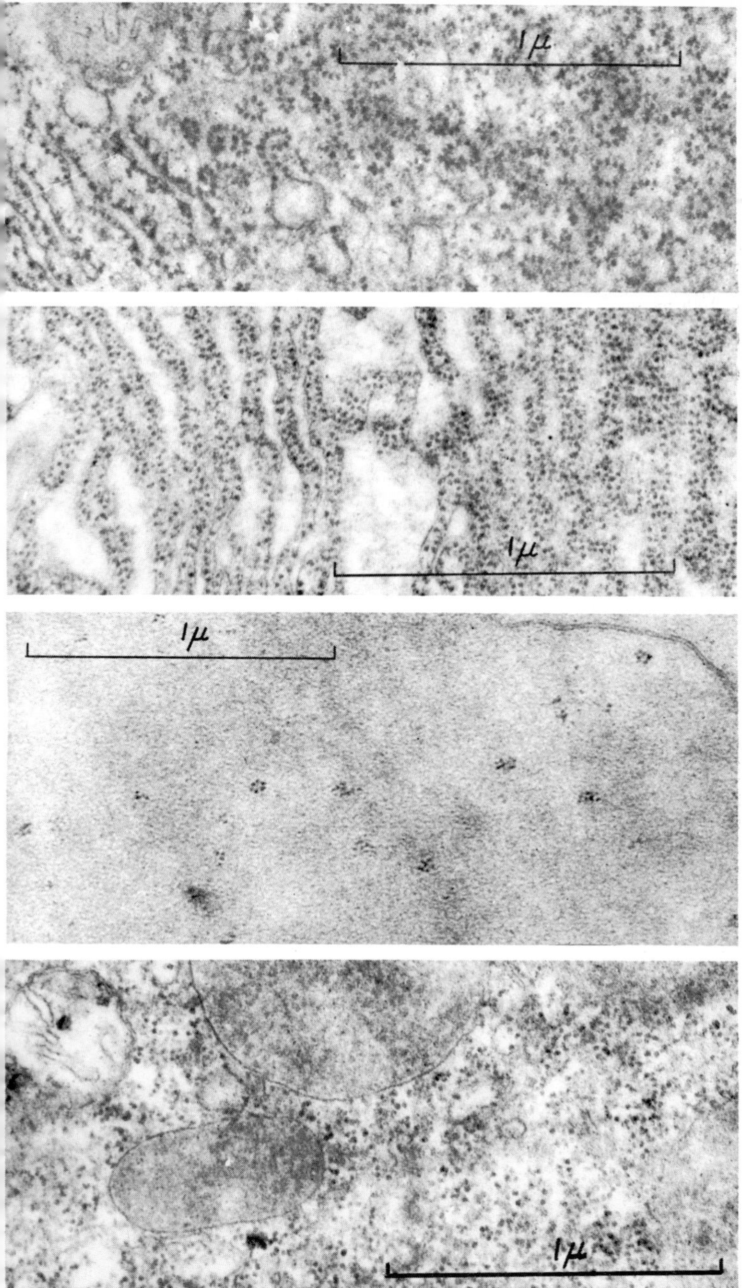

PLATES 22 through 25.—Ribosomes form different patterns in different cells, whether they are membrane-bound (Plate 22—rat liver, Plate 23—leech gland) or free (Plate 24—chick lens, Plate 25—sea urchin egg).

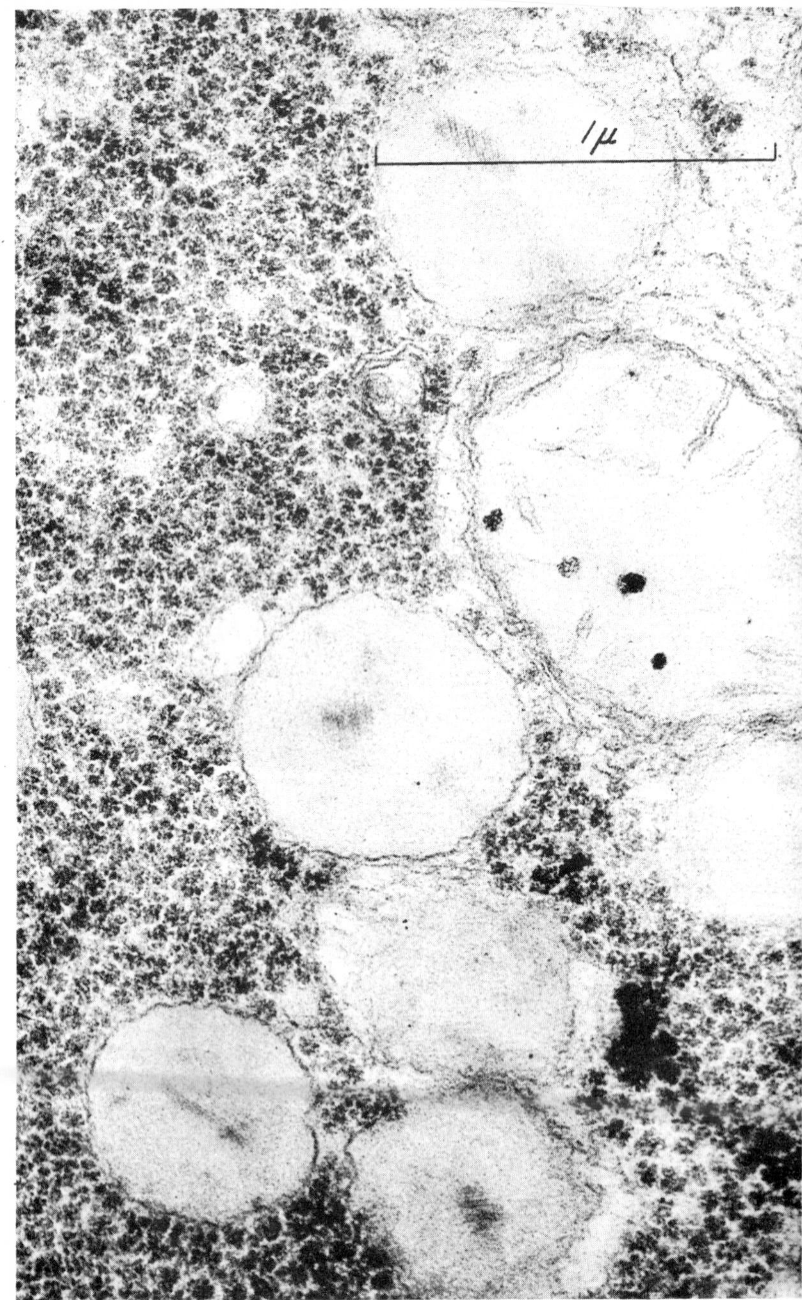

Plate 26.—Microbodies with crystalline inclusions. A mitochondrion is at the right.

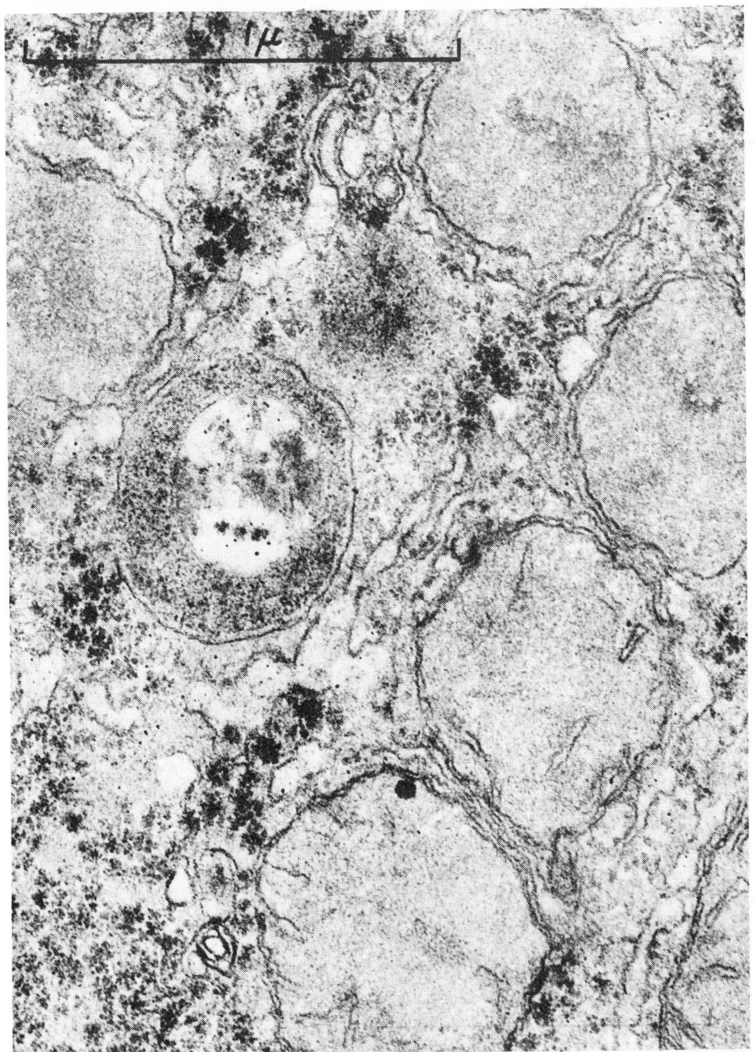

PLATE 27.—The body to the left of the center probably is a lysosome

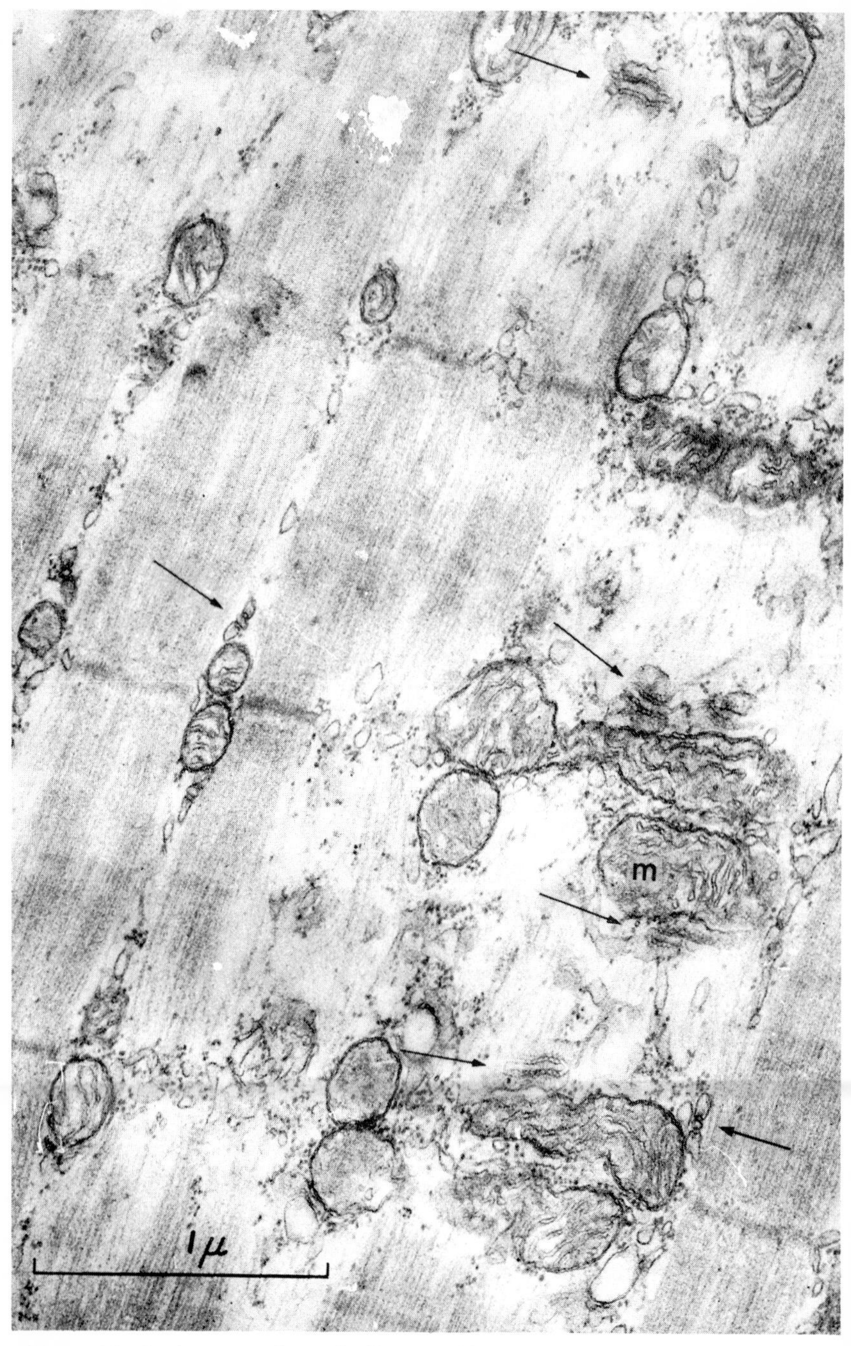

PLATE 28.—In this striated muscle fiber myofibrillar bundles, mitochondria (*m*) and sarcotubules (*arrows*) are evident.

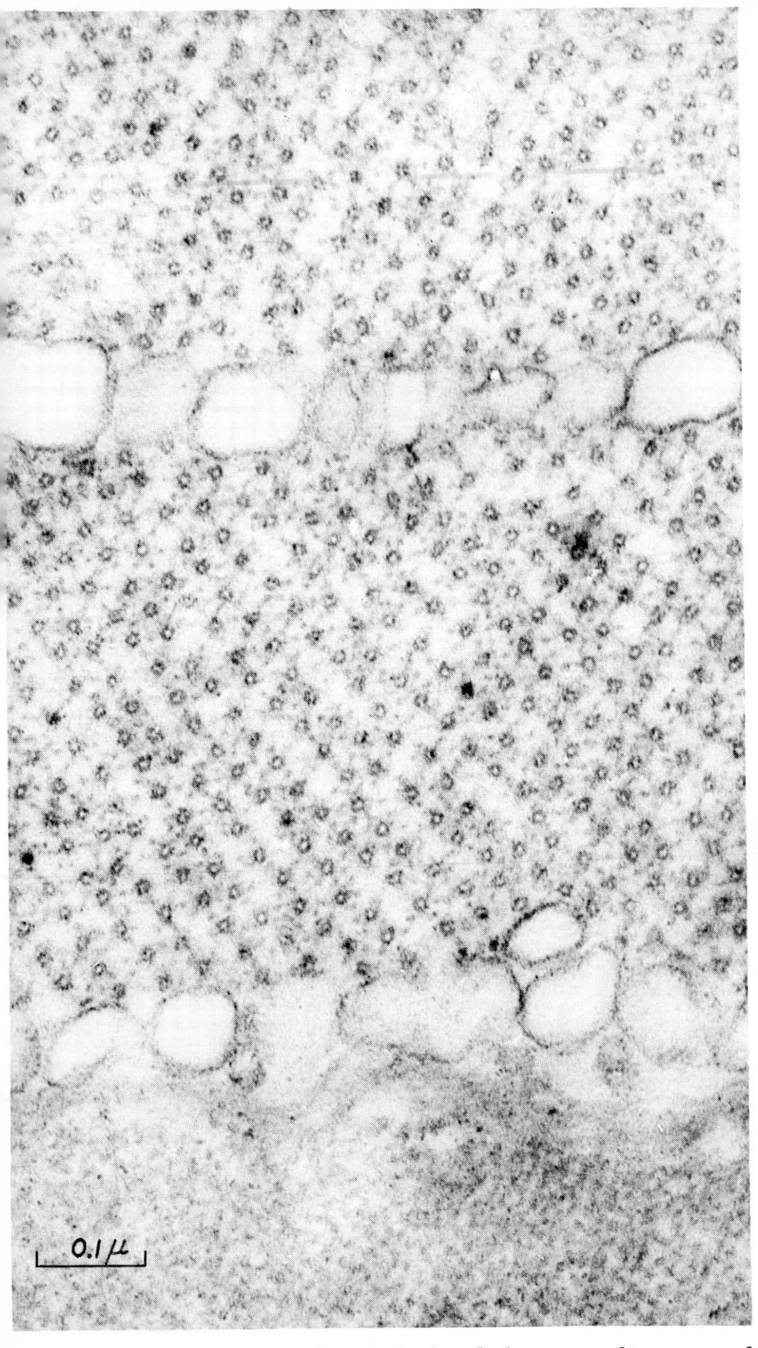

PLATE 29.—In cross-section the muscle threads form a regular pattern of thick and thin fibers.

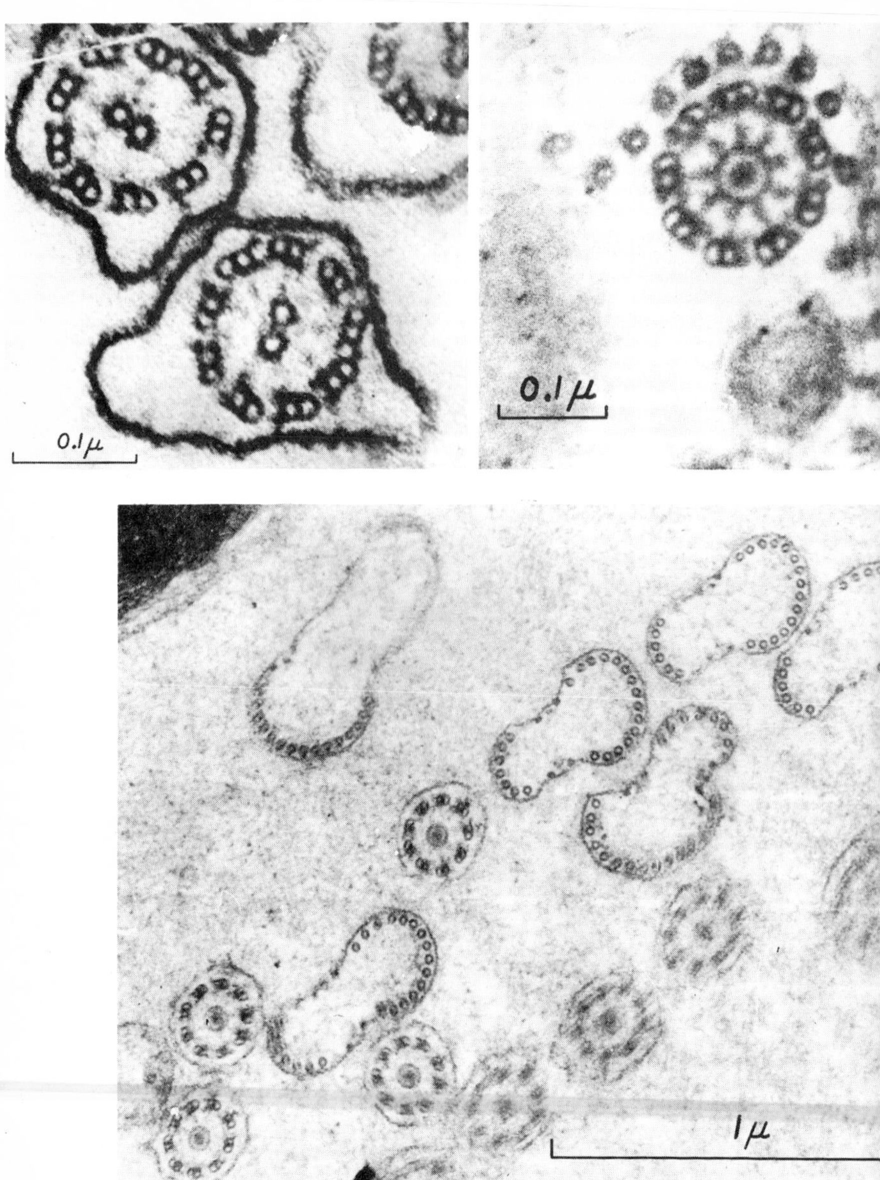

PLATES 30 through 32.—The sperm tail normally has a 9 + 2 pattern (Plate 30), occasionally 9 + 1 (Plates 31, 32). The "footsteps" in Plate 32 are cell extensions containing a framework of microtubules.

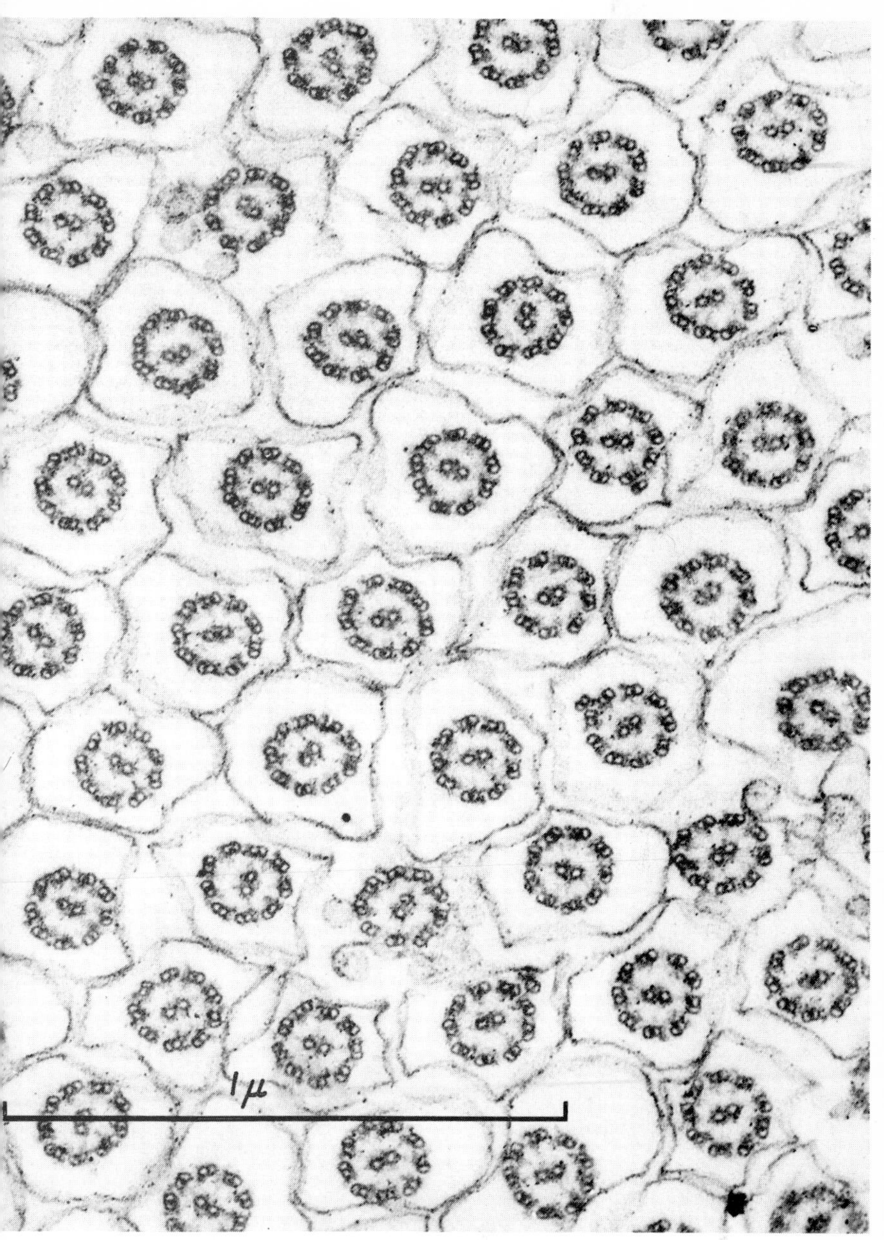

PLATE 33.—Cilia have an easily recognizable structure composed of 9 peripheral and 2 inner components. In this picture three cilia are shown with a deviating pattern.

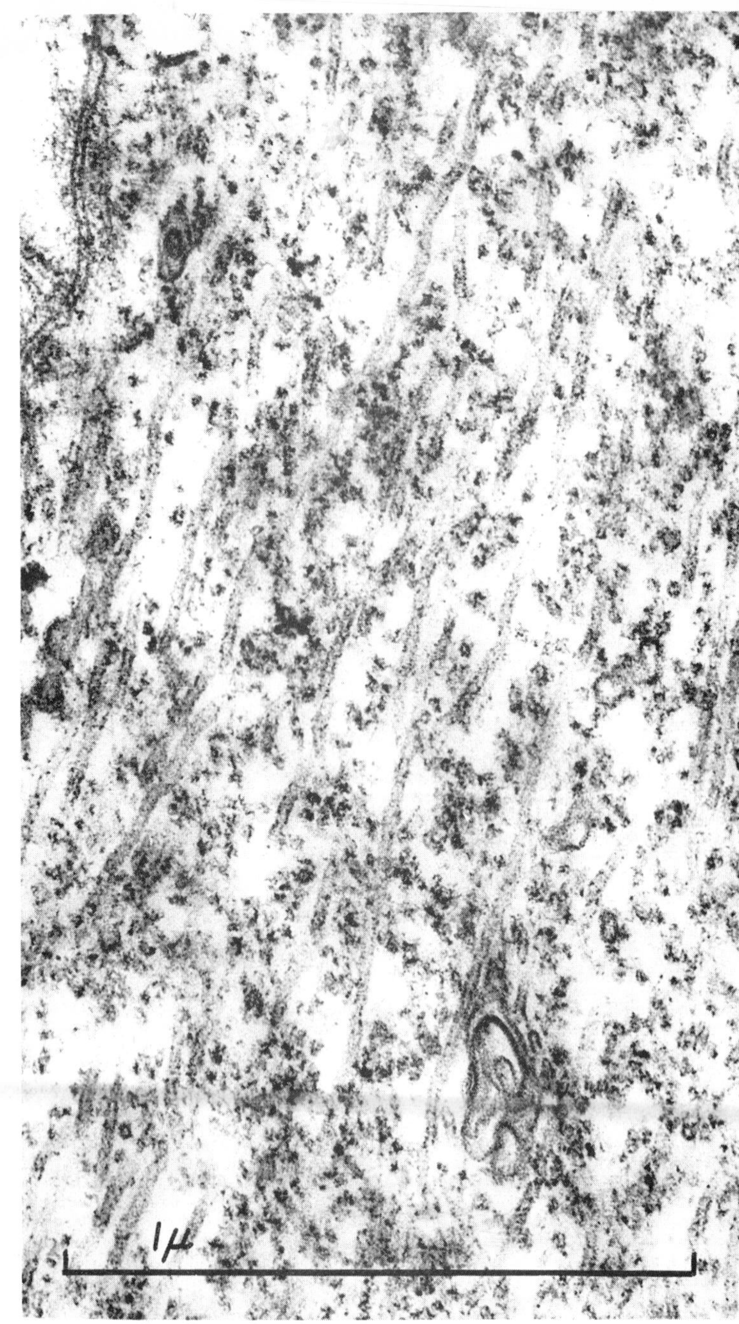

PLATE 34.—Microtubules cut lengthwise

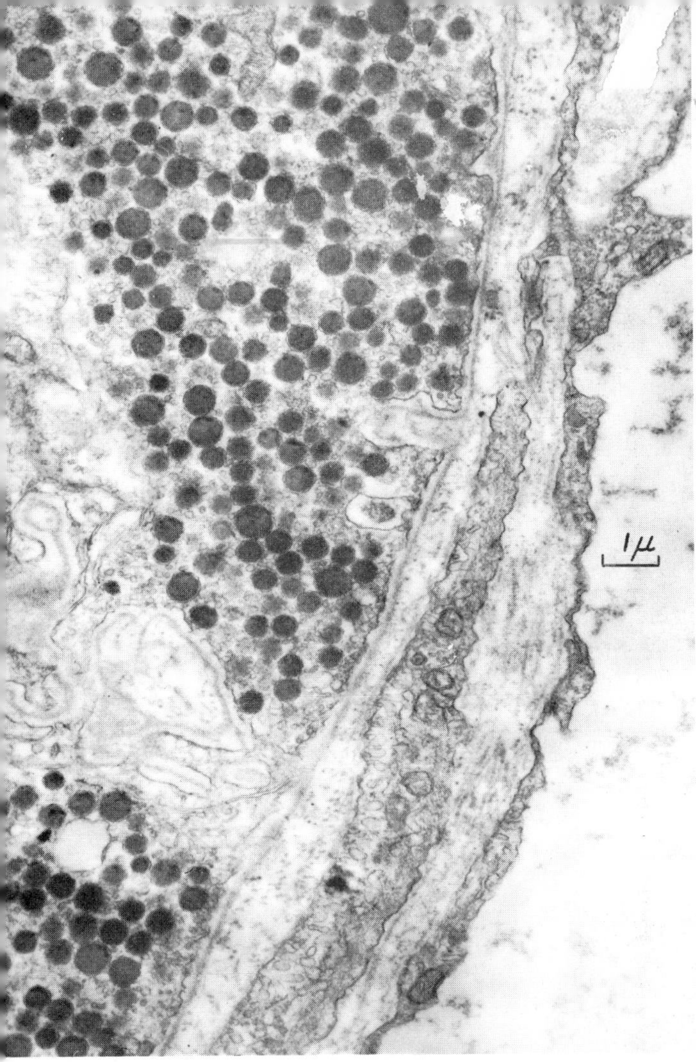

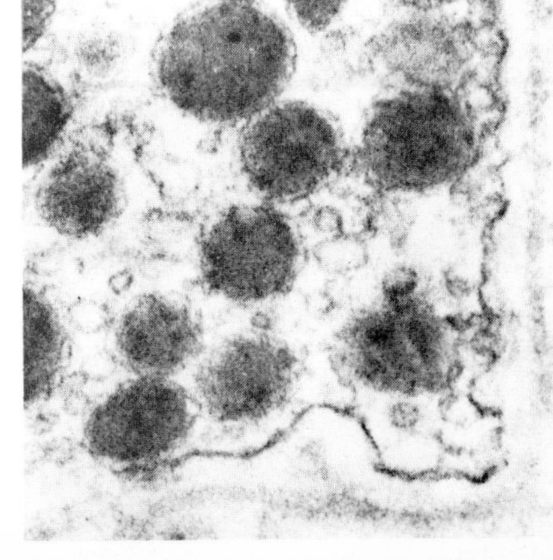

PLATE 35.—A neurosecretory cell ending close by a blood vessel (*to the right*). The insert shows that synaptic vesicles and neurosecretory granules appear together.

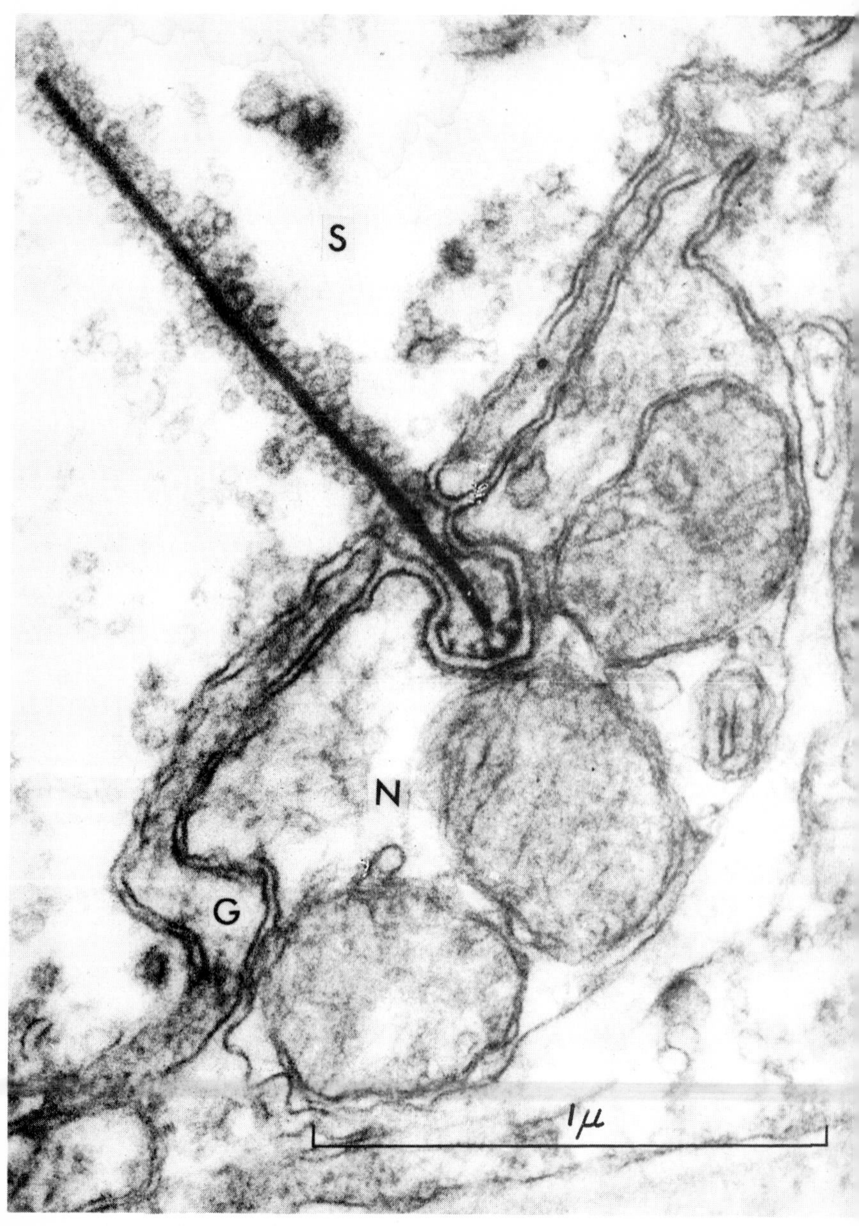

PLATE 36.—A sensory cell with a large number of synaptic vesicles, of which are adjacent to a dense ribbon. The sensory cell forms a projec which plugs into the nerve cell. *S* = sensory cell. *N* = nerve cell. *G* = cell.

mopsis sanguisuga. Fixation after Caulfield. Epon embedding. Uranyl acetate stained.

PLATE 24.—Ribosomes from the lens of a 4-day-old chick. Fixation after Zetterqvist. Methacrylate embedding.

PLATE 25.—Ribosomes from an unfertilized egg of the sea urchin *Paracentrotus lividus.* Fixation with osmium tetroxide in sea water. Uranyl acetate staining. Epon embedding. Electron microscopy by Jane Baxandall.

PLATE 26.—Microbodies and one mitochondrion in a hepatic parenchymal cell from a dog. The clusters of dark particles represent glycogen. Fixation after Millonig. Epon embedding. Lead citrate staining.

PLATE 27.—Some organelles from a dog liver cell. Two mitochondria are at the bottom. Some microbodies are in the upper half of the figure, and one particle in the middle might be a lysosome. Fixation embedding and section staining as in Plate 26.

PLATE 28.—Longitudinally sectioned muscle fiber from a rat gastrocnemius muscle. Arrows mark the junctions between transverse and longitudinal components of the sarcotubular system. *m* means mitochondrion. Fixation after Zetterqvist. Epon embedding. Lead hydroxide staining.

PLATE 29.—Cross-sectioned body muscle cell from the arrow worm, *Sagitta elegans.* The upper part of the picture represents the dark bands (*A* band) of the muscle fibril, the lower fifth is the light band (*I* band) of the muscle fibril. Fixation with osmium tetroxide in sea water. Epon embedding.

PLATE 30.—Cross-sections of sperm tails from the sea urchin *Psammechinus miliaris.* Fixation after Afzelius. Methacrylate embedding.

PLATE 31.—Cross-sections of sperm tails from the flatworm *Mecynostomum auritum* (Turbellaria). Fixation after Zetterqvist. Epon embedding.

PLATE 32.—Sectioned spermatozoa from the liver fluke, *Fasciola hepatica* (Trematoda). Some cross-cut sperm tails (9 + 1 pattern) and some cross-cut cell body extensions with microtubules are visible. Fixation after Zetterqvist. Epon embedding.

PLATE 33.—Cross-sections of cilia of an epithelial cell from the body cavity of the marine polychaete worm *Tomopteris helgolandica.* Fixation with osmium tetroxide in sea water. Epon embedding.

PLATE 34. —Longitudinally sectioned polster cell from a comb of a comb jelly *Beroë ovata* (Ctenophora). Fixation in glutaraldehyde after Sabatini, followed by osmium tetroxide after Millonig. Araldite embedding. Lead citrate staining.

PLATE 35.–Terminal end of a large neurosecretory cell in the caudal part of the spinal cord in the skate (*Raia batis*). Fixation with osmium tetroxide in sea water. Epon embedding.

PLATE 36.–Sensory cell in the so-called ampulla of Lorenzini in the Starry Ray (*Raia radiata*). Fixation with osmium tetroxide in sea water. Epon embedding. Electron microscopy by Bernard Waltman.

I want to extend my sincere thanks to my collaborators at the Wenner-Gren Institute, University of Stockholm, who placed their unpublished micrographs at my disposal (Plates 1, 2, 4, 7, 9, 22, 28, and 36) and to the colleagues with whom I have had the benefit of discussing different sections of this book.

index

PRESENTING
Chris Crutcher

Terry Davis

Twayne Publishers
An Imprint of Simon & Schuster Macmillan
New York

Prentice Hall International
London Mexico City New Delhi Singapore Sydney Toronto

Twayne's United States Authors Series No. 693

Presenting Chris Crutcher
Terry Davis

Twayne Publishers
An Imprint of Simon & Schuster Macmillan
1633 Broadway
New York, NY 10019

Library of Congress Cataloging-in-Publication Data

Davis, Terry
Presenting Chris Crutcher / Terry Davis.
p. cm.—(Twayne's United States authors series ; TUSAS 693. Young adult authors)
Includes bibliographical references and index.
ISBN 0-8057-8223-0 (alk. paper)
1. Crutcher, Chris—Criticism and interpretation. 2. Young adult fiction, American—History and criticism. I. Title. II. Series: Twayne's United States authors series ; TUSAS 693. III. Series: Twayne's United States authors series. Young adult authors.
PS3553.R786Z64 1997
813'.54—dc21 97-14505
CIP

The paper used in this publication meets the minimum requirements of American National Standard for Information Services—Permanence of Paper for Printed Library Materials. ANSI Z39.48-1984. ∞™

10 9 8 7 6 5 4 3 2 1

Printed in the United States of America

Photos: Chris Crutcher on front jacket, in frontispiece and on page 3 are by Susan Stan. Other photos and captions have been provided by Lynn Hall.

For two good women: Jewell Crutcher and Lucille Davis
Your lives would have been so much different
if you'd been born into your children's generation.

I am part of all that I have met. . . .

Tennyson, *Ulysses,* 1833

Contents

Foreword

The advent of Twayne's Young Adult Author Series in 1985 was a response to the growing stature and value of adolescent literature and the lack of serious critical evaluation of the new genre. The first volume in the series was heralded as marking the coming-of-age of young adult fiction.

The aim of the series is twofold. First, it enables young readers to research the work of their favorite authors and to see them as real people. Each volume is written in a lively, readable style and attempts to present in an attractive, accessible format a vivid portrait of the author as a person.

Second, the series provides teachers and librarians with insights and background material for promoting and teaching young adult (YA) novels. Each of the biocritical studies is a serious literary analysis of one author's work (or one subgenre within YA literature), with attention to plot, structure, theme, character, setting, and imagery. In addition, many of the series writers delve deeper into the creative writing process by tracking down early drafts or unpublished manuscripts by their subject authors, consulting with their editors or other mentors, and examining influences from literature, film, or social movements.

Many of the contributing authors of the series are among the leading scholars and critics of adolescent literature. Some are even YA novelists themselves. Each study is based on extensive interviews with the subject author and an exhaustive study of his or her work. Although the general format for the series is the same, the individual volumes are uniquely shaped by their subjects, and each brings a different perspective to the classroom.

The goal of the series is to produce a succinct but comprehensive study of the life and art of every leading YA writer, as well as to trace how that art has been accepted by readers and critics; to evaluate its place in the developing field of adolescent literature; and—perhaps most important—to inspire reading and rereading of this fiction, which speaks so directly to young people about their life experiences.

Patricia J. Campbell, General Editor

Preface

Chris Crutcher and I have been friends for 24 years. This isn't vital information about Chris, of course; I just want you to know it here at the beginning. If the perspective of a long friendship exists, there should be a place for it in a book the purpose of which is to *present* a writer to his readers.

I knew Chris by reputation before I met him. We both lived in Pearce Hall on the campus of Eastern Washington State College in Cheney. He was captain of the swim team and lived on the seventh floor with the swimmers and other athletes. This was the fall of 1965, and now as I sit at this keyboard I can see the real guys—and the girl—we know from *Stotan!* eating dinner together in Tawanka Commons, radiating the vibrance of youth and the audacity of stotans. Along with those qualities, they always had wet hair—the ones who hadn't shaved their heads, that is. I had dinner with some of these people recently; there's gray in their hair now, particularly in the guys' beards, but the stotanic quality remains.

Chris graduated in '68 and went "to look for America," as Simon and Garfunkel sang. I graduated in '69 and found a high school teaching job. He came back to Eastern to get his teaching credential and wound up with a student teaching assignment at my school. He needed a place to stay, and I offered to share the little house I was renting. I was willing to do this with someone I knew mostly by reputation because my impression of Chris had always been so good. Never in all these years—before we became friends and after—have I heard anyone speak of Chris Crutcher without respect. Of course, people might be guarded in what they say to me about him because they know we're friends. What gives value to my having watched him from a distance and known him by reputation is that I had no stake in forming a positive opinion; I just took in information, and all the information I took in about Chris was positive.

Spring of 1970 is when we got to be friends, and I was grateful for a friend. The width of the cultural and generational gaps among Americans in 1969 and 1970 cannot be exaggerated, and I needed a kindred spirit. I remember my principal wrote in my first evaluation that I attempted to court the favor of students by wearing bell-bottomed pants. Sounds like a stunted insight one of the school administrators in *Running Loose* might express. In fact, the funeral scene in *Running Loose* had its germination in the funeral of Charlie Stewert, one of our students that year, a smart, funny kid who'd come back from the edge of trouble to play a fine junior season of basketball before he drowned in the spring.

Chris doesn't get caught up in styles. In the sixties and seventies, for example, he didn't experiment with drugs. He didn't even smoke cigarettes. What's more interesting, though—and probably more admirable—is that he never judged the people who did. I remember thinking about this quality in his character, and I remember concluding that he was not only independent, he was so independent that he didn't need to reinforce himself by ridiculing people who were less so. In the Robert B. Parker novels, Susan Silverman calls Spenser the most autonomous person she's ever known. Chris is the most autonomous person I've ever known.

People who've read about Chris have probably run into some version of the following passage:

> While Chris had been doing his student teaching in Monroe, north of Seattle during 1970, he stayed with a former Eastern classmate, Terry Davis, author of *Vision Quest*. Says Chris, "Terry was in the process of becoming a writer, and I got to watch him do it. When I moved down to the Bay area, Terry was a Stegner Fellow at Stanford, and we would get together once a week, run and talk about writing. I had this *Running Loose* story running around in my head then, and we talked about it. Years later, I came up to Washington on vacation, and Terry and

> I were on a run, and he said, 'You ought to write that story. Do it!' I went back to the Bay and, from the time I quit working in the school until I moved up to Spokane, I had about three-and-a-half months. Because I didn't have to look for a job, I just sat down and wrote it. For whatever reason, it fell together really well in the first draft.
>
> "I sent a copy to Terry who called me up within a week and said, 'I'm calling my agent and sending it to her.' Within another week, she'd accepted it and shortly after that it was bought. So I didn't get the runaround and the jillion rejection slips. I don't have the constitution for that. I'd have stopped long before. There's a path there that I got on somehow that was an easier path than a lot of really good writers get on. Some luck and being in the right place at the right time were involved."[1]

Although Chris says he wouldn't have the constitution for all the rejection most writers get starting out, this is not so. He's being modest. He was smart enough to start out in a different way than most of us and at a different time in his life, and as a result he didn't have to endure that rejection. Chris has the constitution for anything.

We're talking here about a 50-year-old man who runs a 10-kilometer race—that's 6.2 miles—under 40 minutes. A guy who can swim a mile, climb on a bicycle and ride 25 miles, then run 6.2. He can do a hundred straight push-ups, for God's sake. Although not right after he's finished a triathlon. At least I don't think he can.

Here's what he looks like: a fraction under six feet, one inch, 160 pounds. That's what he weighed in college. He went up to 195 in 1970, but he lost those pounds again when he quit eating with me. The man is thin. Remember the old Jimmy Dean song about "Big Bad John" who was "broad at the shoulder and narrow at the hip"? Well, Chris is narrow at the shoulder *and* narrow at the hip. If we search the animal kingdom for a metaphorical correspondent we might picture a high-mileage greyhound or whippet; an aging cheetah; any of the various antelopes in a salt-and-pepper beard. Chris has built his body for endurance as well as speed. As he ages the speed falls off, but the endurance. . . . What does endurance do? It endures.

Here's a passage from an early draft of *Staying Fat for Sarah Byrnes* where Chris gives a sense of how he thinks of himself on the subject of endurance. The narrator is Eric Calhoune:

> At any point in the race there's a chance [the other swimmers] will die, but that's never happened to me. Whoever beats me will have to swim a good race, because I get tougher with added laps. Probably I'll be the oldest fart to get into the Guinness Book of World Records by swimming the Behring Strait some New Year's Eve after I turn ninety.[2]

People who haven't put a lot of time into athletics might think I'm talking about a purely physical endurance here. I'm not. Get 20 miles into a marathon and see if it's not your mind that screams at you to quit over the pleas of your legs and lungs.

Or look at it another way: It's break time for the men's group at the mental health center, and you're the therapist. You're in charge—you're Chris—standing in the hall with a man who's raging at you because you've spent the last 15 minutes trying to help him get to the truth of his life, which he's been trying most of his life to avoid. This man has lost his kids because he abused them physically and sexually; he doesn't care what he does to anybody, and he believes *you* are the reason he can't have his kids back. You are, in fact, the focus of his contempt for himself and his bitterness at the world.

You're tough, but the man is said to be a martial arts killer, and whether he is or not, you know he can hurt you. You see in his eyes that he's on the edge.

Your legs don't want to stand up for the man's kids anymore; they want to run. But they won't run without your mind's permission; and your mind is thinking maybe you should have found work in a health club or selling athletic shoes.

But you don't run.

Here's what you say when you're Chris Crutcher: "You can do it or not, but nothing changes. I'll be hurt and you'll be in jail, but other than that nothing changes. I told myself a long time ago that if I ever back off a kid because I'm scared, I don't belong in this business."[3]

At such times the strength people exercise to stand up for what's right is the strength of character. An old-fashioned term. A term almost vanished from the contemporary vocabulary.

Chris possesses an extraordinary measure of physical, emotional, and intellectual strength. Put aside for a minute consideration of what it takes to stand up to people who want to kill you and think about what qualities a man needs to work daily in the domestic violence business and write eight books in 10 years. I don't think I could get up at 4:30 every morning for any reason except to save my children's lives, but Chris got up that early so he could run and write before he headed for work at Spokane's Community Mental Health Center. No number of rejections would have stopped him from writing, and—like Wilson Corder in *The Deep End*—no threat would stop him from standing up for kids.

I have a little story I'd like to tell that has, for years now, illustrated to me the depth of Chris's character. When he's appreciated beyond the bounds of young adult literature this information will probably appear in a book entitled something like *Papa Crutcher*.

As Chris has told various interviewers, after he quit as director of Lakeside School in Oakland and moved up to Spokane he lived on savings while he wrote *Running Loose*. Before any money came in from the book, though, his savings ran low and he needed work. But he couldn't find any. Not teaching, not social service, not work in a health club, not selling athletic shoes, *not nothing,* as we say in northeastern Washington.

Chris and I were running two or three afternoons a week then, and not only did he slow his pace so I could keep up but he listened to *me* whine about my life and spent energy supporting *me.* And I wasn't suffering anything but the normal anguish of a man who loves his children and doesn't live with them. I wasn't the one looking for work.

But Chris lived through this period in his life with an amazing equanimity. And with grace. He got close for the position of director with the Big Brothers organization. He figured out later, and told me on a run, that after they asked him if he was married and he said no, they must have concluded he was homosexual. Which he isn't. "They should have had the guts to just ask me," was all he said.

Things got desperate. Or at least they looked and felt desperate to me. If I'd been the one out of work I'd have probably lapsed into catatonia and let my mother feed me with a spoon.

But Chris wasn't desperate. Or what I should say is that he didn't show any desperation. All of us feel some measure of desperation. We all feel some measure of fear, envy, sexual desire, jealousy, anger in its many forms—we feel *all* those emotions because we're all human and nothing human is foreign to any of us. This is true even in those of us who pretend the current sociopolitical perfection.

One day Chris answered an ad for "a sales opportunity." At a Frankie Doodle's restaurant he met a farmer who'd lost his farm and was selling AMWAY. The sales opportunity was an AMWAY distributorship.

Chris did not snap. He did not stab the guy with his fork. He looked at the man's hands, and they were the big-knuckled, rough hands of a working man. And the man's presentation was rough too; he stumbled through the spiel. To Chris's way of thinking this displaced farmer was in tougher shape than he was. So as the man was counting his change to see if he could pay for their coffee, Chris told him to put away his money. And Chris picked up the check.

A short time later Chris signed on with the mental health center, and the rest is literary history.

There are probably a couple of people besides me who know this story, but nobody else who might have written this book would know to ask them about it, so I've told it here. And those same people know that Chris asks his friends not to give him Christmas presents, to give him money instead so he can give it to clients at the center who need it more than he does. He gives away clothes he says he doesn't need anymore, but they look new to me. He tried to give away his dad's old Chrysler after he died, but he discovered you can't exactly give a car away. Somebody's got to pay the title transfer, and the people Chris tried to give it to didn't have the money. So he paid it for them.

I said that Chris started writing in a different way than most writers and at a different time of life. He was 35 when he began work on *Running Loose,* and he has never taken—nor would he ever take—a creative writing class. He's taught some, however.

In 1973 when I was at the University of Iowa's Writers Workshop, Chris hitched out to Iowa City to visit. He went to a class with me and met some of the aspiring literati. "I learned my lesson," he says. "It took me about 10 years to want to write again after watching that competitive thing those people did to each other." Nobody is more competitive than Chris, but that wasn't an arena he wanted to compete in.

He wanted to write, but he was smart enough—maybe *mature* enough is more accurate—to know that a writing class wasn't the place for him to learn it. You can read that he attended a writing workshop, but that isn't accurate.

"I never took any writing classes because that kind of stuff doesn't do me any good," he says.

> When I get a new electronic device, a computer or something where you're supposed to read all the instructions before you do anything, it does me no good. It does me no good to read the instructions. [But] if you leave me with this thing and let me learn it from the backside—learn it from the inside out—I can do it.

Here is how Chris says he learned to write. I'm presenting this because it's part of the apprenticeship of an important writer and the information isn't presented fully anywhere else. I'm honored to have played any positive part in Chris's writing life, of course, but the emotion hasn't addled my brain. I realize my role could have been played by anyone who happened to be writing a book. This took place in the Bay Area when Chris was director of Lakeside School and I was at Stanford:

> I don't know what would have allowed me to write if I hadn't been around when you were writing *Vision Quest* and watched the process. You bringing me a chapter and me kind of editing it for believability, and then seeing the chapter again, then seeing it again, then finally seeing it in galley form. I could see the subtle changes and know why. That's how I learned to write. That's how I learned to do the really good carpentry. I've always thought of myself as a good storyteller. I could always tell a good story. But the idea of being able to put a story into a book. . . . It was seeing those changes, watching that fine-tuning. That's how I learned to write.

Chris isn't a literary man. He's a careful and perceptive reader, and there are books he loves, but he's not a dedicated student of the craft of writing.

Chris's consuming passion is Life, not Art—although he is an artist. What consumes Chris is people. People are what his work as a therapist is about, and people are what his work as an artist is about.

Chris is a storyteller because stories open up people's lives for inspection and understanding. Stories often—and this is almost always true of Chris's stories—show us how people got to be the way they are. And when we discover how we got to be the way we are, we create the opportunity to change. And being able to change is certainly among the miracles of life.

We don't need to haul out the megaphone here and lead cheers for Chris's work. Readers and critics of young adult literature have done that, and later we'll examine what they've had to say. He was presented the ALAN award for "significant contribution to Young Adult Literature"; a film of his short story "A Brief Moment in the Life of Angus Bethune" has been made, a film of his adult novel *The Deep End* is nearing production, and both *Ironman* and *Staying Fat for Sarah Byrnes* are also being adapted. That's four films based on his work. Once these films are out—or maybe even before, considering the enormously positive response to *Sarah Byrnes* and *Ironman*—Chris's national reputation will have transcended genre.

What we do want to say is that Chris Crutcher is not only a fine writer but an exemplary man who has the generosity and the old-fashioned sense of obligation to pass his wisdom along to young people. Particularly generous—and courageous—it seems to me, is the openness with which he talks about his life in the following pages.

Acknowledgments

I got sick a few months after I started this book and stayed sick for three years. If it hadn't been for medication and the kindness, encouragement, and indulgence of Patty Campbell, editor of the Twayne Series, and of my wife, Becky Davis, I never would have finished it.

Chronology

1946 Christopher C. Crutcher born July 17 in Dayton, Ohio, while his father is stationed at Wright-Patterson Air Force Base; in six weeks the family moves to Cascade, Idaho, his mother's hometown.

1961 Begins writing a column called "Chris's Crumbs" for his high school newspaper *The Cascadian.*

1964 Graduates from Cascade High and enrolls at Eastern Washington State College in Cheney, Washington; after earning his third-class broadcaster's license in the first term he plans to major in radio-TV journalism.

1968 Graduates from Eastern with a B.A. in sociology-psychology; heads south on Route 66 in his Plymouth Valient and winds up in Texas pouring prestressed concrete bridge beams for $2.17 an hour.

1969 Returns to Eastern and earns a K–12 teaching certificate.

1970 Works as maintenance man at Mt. Hood ski resort, Oregon, takes pay cut to $2.00 an hour, characterizes self as "#2 man on two-man totem pole."

1971 Teaches "drop-out school" in Kenniwick, Washington, for students who quit or were kicked out of public high schools; building is an old YMCA shared by spiders of frightening size and deportment; not one other adult enters the building in two years.

1973 Teaches social studies at Kamiakin High, Kenniwick.

1974 Moves to Berkeley, California; teaches elementary students at Lakeside School in Oakland.

1975 Becomes director of Lakeside School.

1981 Quits Lakeside on his birthday; lives on savings while writing *Running Loose.*

1982 Moves to Spokane and coordinates Child Protection Team.

1983 Takes position as child and family therapist with Spokane Community Mental Health Center while remaining coordinator of Child Protection Team; *Running Loose* is published.

1986 *Stotan!*

1987 *The Crazy Horse Electric Game.*

1989 *Chinese Handcuffs.*

1990 ALA votes *Running Loose* onto its list of "Best of the Decade."

1991 *Athletic Shorts: Six Short Stories.*

1992 *The Deep End.*

1993 *Staying Fat for Sarah Byrnes.*

1994 *Ironman.*

1994 ALAN award from Assembly on Literature for Adolescents of the National Council of Teachers of English for "significant contribution to Young Adult Literature."

1996 Feature film *Angus,* adapted from the story "A Brief Moment in the Life of Angus Bethune."

1. Lifeguard

Wilson Corder, the man Chris Crutcher created to narrate *The Deep End,* originally titled *Lifeguard,* is a child and family therapist like Crutcher himself. Corder isn't Crutcher, but he's like Crutcher in many ways. Early in the book Corder says:

> I was a competitive swimmer in high school and college and spent those summers as a lifeguard at a lake beach, and I was a *hawk*. Even during breaks I positioned myself to see the water. Something in me believed that as long as Wilson Corder stood watch, no one would drown. No one *could* drown. And in fact, the only drowning in the eight years I worked there, happened on my day off.[1]

Crutcher lifeguarded at pools and beaches in his youth, and he remained a lifeguard when he became a child and family therapist, chairperson of Spokane's Child Protection Team, and a member of the community's Fatality Review Board. In this latter role it was his duty to examine a lifeguard's inevitable failures. A swimming lifeguard is positioned to see what's happening in the water, but child-protection lifeguards don't even see who it is they're guarding until the kid has gone down once or twice. And once they know where to look, they have to try to see through locked doors, closed curtains, and lies. A lot more kids are lost at home than at the beach.

Crutcher is also a lifeguard as a storyteller. In all his novels and nearly all his short stories, either the life of the body or the life of the spirit, or both, is at stake. And he infuses each of these narratives with the intent to save the corporal or spiritual lives of young people. "I have just seen so much damage done," he says.

Crutcher also infuses his stories with humor, no matter the depth of pain the stories present.

He is a writer whose stories arise out of an ethical intent, are fueled by conflicts of classic magnitude, and ring with humor. It's no wonder Crutcher is considered "among the most respected writers of young adult literature to have emerged in the 1980s."[2]

How does such a writer—such a lifeguard—come to be? Crutcher believes that the kind of people we become is the result of how we've been treated, particularly how we were treated in the first two years of our lives. In *The Deep End* he presents this idea as The Law. One of the abusive fathers in the men's group Corder directs tells the group that his boy was placed in foster care because the father beat him up. He would have acted differently, the father says, if he knew why he did it in the first place. And then a man who lost his son for the same reason but has spent more time in the group tells him: "You done it 'cause it was done to you. It's the law. It's the law" (*DE*, 35). Later Corder tells the reader: "[Y]ou can take any of these parents and turn back the clock ten or fifteen years and you'll find the very child you're trying to save" (*DE*, 72).

We *learn* to be who we become. Cause-effect. Not magic, not coincidence. Cause-effect.

But if The Law is valid, it has to have a positive corollary: people who value life were raised—or at some point early in their lives were touched—by people who valued them.

Christopher C. Crutcher was born in Dayton, Ohio, on July 17, 1946, and raised in Cascade, Idaho. "My dad was in the Air Force, and my parents were just passing through," Crutcher says. "They were in Cascade before I got dry" (Jenkinson, 67).

Chris was the quintessential postwar baby. His parents—John, whom everybody called Crutch, and Jewell—like millions of Americans at the close of World War II, were in a hurry to get their lives going again. In Cascade their two-year-old son, John Jr., was waiting with his maternal grandparents, May and Glenn Morris. Also waiting in the Northwest was a flying job for John, who had piloted B-17s in Europe. But before John could take that

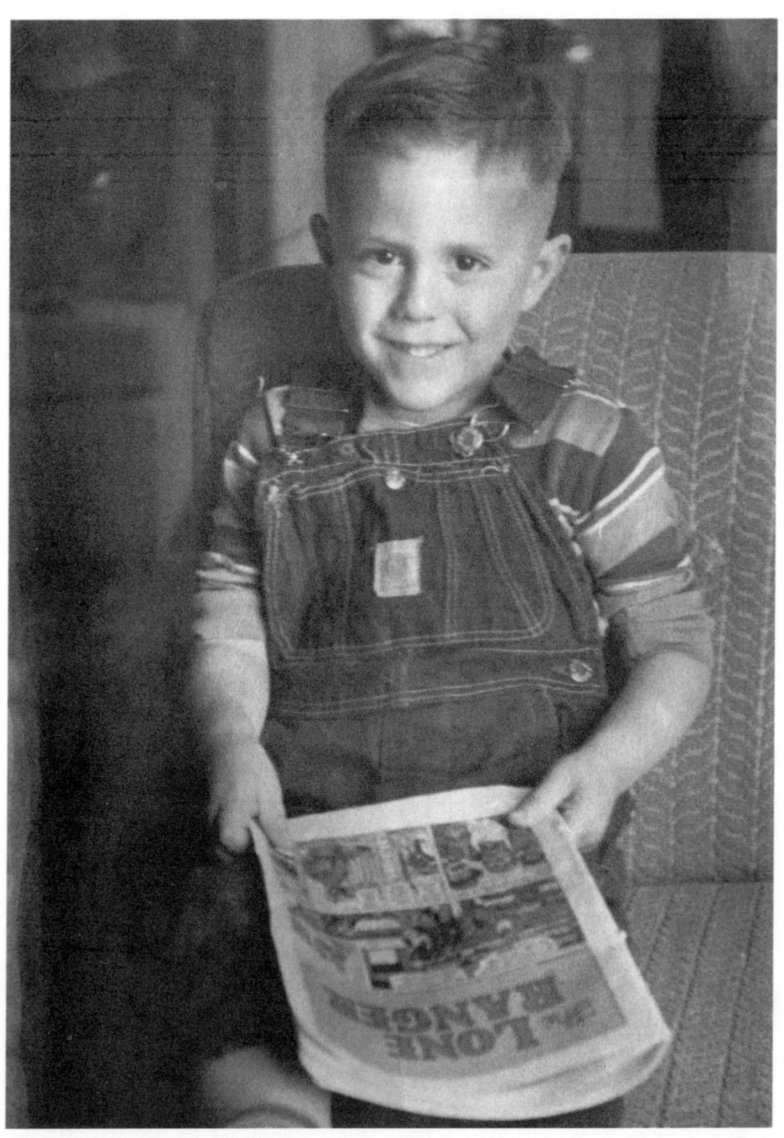

Chris Crutcher as a young reader and adventurer.

job his father died, and while he was with his mother in Kellogg, Idaho, the job went to someone else.

John Crutcher joined Glenn Morris in his Mobile Gas service station, so Chris Crutcher grew up in Cascade, a lumber and logging town of 950 people in the mountains of west-central Idaho. He lived the first years of his life in a little house across a dirt street from his grandparents, and later, like Louie Banks in *Running Loose,* he pumped and delivered gas and diesel. Morris-Crutcher had become a Phillips 66 distributor then, with two gas trucks and a pickup. The Morris-Crutcher sign hangs on the wall of Chris's garage in Spokane today.

Chris remembers his grandfather Morris with respect and affection, and with a certain awe.

> He was an amazing lifeguard. He just wanted to take care of things. "You know," he'd say, "you shouldn't have more kids than just two. You should just replace yourself." He died in 1952, so I'm talking about the late forties, early fifties. He was just careful with things. When I look back on it, you couldn't tell the difference in how he treated animals and people.

Chris remembers the time, before he started school, when a bird built her nest at the top of one of the hollow pillars on his grandparents' porch. Soon after the eggs hatched the nest fell down inside the pillar. The mother bird would come to where the nest had been and look around. She heard the baby birds peeping in the dark but wouldn't fly down to them. Glenn Morris looked the situation over and figured that if the mom was going to get to her babies she'd have to do it in a different way. So he cut a little hole in the pillar just above the porch floor.

Chris would bring his friends over to watch the mother bird and listen to the babies. "There's birds in there! There's birds in there!" he'd say. The kids would get down on their hands and knees and peer through the hole. They'd stand back and watch the mom fly up with a worm, disappear through the hole, then come out with an empty beak.

Glenn checked on the birds every day. They grew feathers and started peeking out of the hole in the pillar. And Glenn would tell the kids all about birds. When they got big enough they flew out the hole and off the porch. When they didn't return, Glenn took the piece he'd cut out of the pillar and glued it back. It's still there.

Glenn liked to explain how things worked, and he gave Chris one of his first lessons in cause-effect as they considered the aphorism "the early bird gets the worm." Many early mornings they had seen the mother bird pulling a worm from the grass. The grass was wet in the mornings, so the worms came to the surface. As the day warmed the grass dried, so the worms went back into the ground where it was cool and damp. It was *because* the bird arrived early, Glenn pointed out, that she got the worm. That's when the worms were there to get. Glenn was proud of himself for helping Chris see one of the ways the world worked. Chris's response was, "Yeah, but how do the worms like that?"

Glenn loved stories. "He would take a story and tell it a thousand times," Chris says. One of Glenn's favorites was the cookie story about Chris. Glenn had a gas delivery to make after lunch one day, and there was going to be room in the truck for Chris and his older brother, John. But John wanted his pal Joe Boyd to go, so he began negotiating with Chris, who was five at the time. Negotiating didn't work because Chris really wanted to go. So John was reduced to begging. He begged and begged. Finally he said, "If you'll let Joe go, I'll give you my cookies."

The cookies were right there on the table. The cookies were now, and the trip was later. Chris grabbed the cookies.

As Chris was finishing up the last cookie he started to cry. He was in tears when his mother returned from the kitchen. "I wanna go," he said. "Well, why'd you do it?" Jewell asked. "Because I like cookies," was Chris's reply.

"Glenn Morris was a man who just couldn't accommodate anybody being in pain if there was any way in the world he could stop it," Chris says. "If you were stuck in the middle of the night out in the snow someplace, and there was nobody to tow you, you called Glenn Morris, because Glenn Morris did not ever say no when somebody was in trouble."

A few years ago Chris found out something about his grandfather he hadn't known. Chris was back in Cascade for a high school reunion, and a distant relative gave him a photograph of Glenn as a young man. For Chris, it was like looking at a photo of himself. People had always wondered why Chris wasn't as heavy as the rest of his family, and here was the young, thin Glenn Morris. "He was never heavy," Chris says. "And facially, we really look a lot alike. It's incredible."

All his memories of his grandfather are enduring to Chris, but one endures with a particular sheen and is of particular relevance when we consider the man he grew up to be. This event took place before Chris was born, so—like many memories we have of our grandparents—it's not a memory of an observed event but a memory of a story. In this case Jewell is the one who kept the past alive by passing it down.

> My mom was twenty years old when my brother was born, and my dad was still in the service. The war was still going on. It was the old leave your birth control on the table so in case my husband gets killed I'll have memories of him. Well, she has this kid, and by her own admission she's scared to death of him and way too young to be raising a kid. And she was living at home. She was in the bathroom, and Glenn heard her whomp him one. And he just went in and took him. He just grabbed him and took him into his bedroom and said, "You just don't be hittin' kids. You don't hit 'em."

And from his own time Chris remembers, "You'd go into Glenn's bedroom and he would be sitting in bed reading the newspaper, and my brother would be sitting right next to him reading a comic book."

"The vision I want people to have of their kids so that they won't hurt them or humiliate them," Chris says, "is the vision that I always thought my granddad had."

Here's how that vision translates into the words of the therapist in *Chinese Handcuffs*: "[K]ids have an inalienable right to unconditional care, and parents who don't give it are breaking a spiritual law."[3] And listen to the grandfather in that book speak to his granddaughter: "Can't spoil a five-year-old. Not with time.

Not with love. . . . Don't ever believe that. Anytime anyone tries to spoil you, just soak it up. You hear?" (*CH*, 35).

"There's a playfulness, a lightness. There's a sense of comedy and tragedy juxtaposed that I have in thinking about my granddad that I don't have anywhere else," Chris says. "And we did not have a particularly special relationship. I wasn't special to him anymore than my brother. But I can remember—I can almost see—this thing we had about play going back and forth between his and my head," Chris says as he gestures to illustrate a psychic stream of playfulness flowing to and from his forehead. "He was a wonderful joker. He liked to mess you up. But it was always fun, and it was always fixed at the end. You'd be sitting there talking to him and he'd be eating your ice cream. But then he'd figure out a way to get you more."

Glenn Morris also had a temper. Chris was at his grandparents' house one day when Glenn and Chris's brother, John, who was seven then, had been working in the basement. Glenn was gone, but Chris heard John hammering, so he walked downstairs to see what he was making. And there was John at the workbench, hitting close to his thumb, going, "Goddammit! Goddammit! Goddammit!" in imitation of his granddad.

Chris remembers more than one day at the station when Crutch would say, "Glenn, if you put all your weight on the wrench, and the concrete is right here, and you don't save anything back, you're gonna skin your knuckles." And it never made a bit of difference. Glenn would ram his fist into the concrete and take the Lord's name in vain.

Glenn never verified one of Chris's favorite stories about him. Chris was just a kid when a Cascade resident from the early days was back in town for a centennial celebration and told Jewell about the time he and Glenn had been deputized to bring a man out of the backcountry. Two prospectors had been out a year when word reached town in the fall that one had killed the other. So Glenn, the old-timer who told the story, and other men were deputized. They hiked in, found the killer, and arrested him without incident. When they brought him back to Cascade they were told they had to hike back in again for the body.

Snow had begun to fall, so they found a toboggan and took turns pulling it. It snowed and snowed. And it was cold. That winter turned out to be one of Idaho's worst. When Glenn and the others reached the campsite they found the body frozen. They tied it to the toboggan and pulled the toboggan up the hills through the deep snow. And, according to the storyteller, they rode the toboggan—and its contents—down the hills.

Chris remembers looking up at his granddad. "You guys really rode him down the hills?" he asked. "You rode a dead guy?" And he remembers Glenn just smiling.

Glenn Morris grew up as an orphan. "He grew up living in people's sheds," Chris says.

> He worked for everything. He worked for his food from the time he was a young kid. He was the antithesis to my dad. God only knows how much schooling he had—it wasn't much. He wasn't a reader. He could cut to the emotional heart of things in a second the way my dad could cut to the intellectual heart.
>
> Those guys really, really loved each other. I never saw my dad have a more powerful reaction to anything than he did the day my grandfather died. He was just devastated.

Chris doesn't know how old Glenn was when he was orphaned or anything about his parents. But there's something Chris concludes about Glenn's upbringing from what he saw in the man the orphaned boy became. Glenn Morris was a man who valued life, and he learned that somewhere.

> "In the context of the time," Chris says, "it wasn't an abusive thing to let a kid live in your shed. It was an act of kindness to let him have a place and work his way. There was a sense in Glenn of gratefulness for the kindnesses he'd received.
>
> "There's a whole different feeling that I have inside of me when I think about my granddad. When I think about it, a lot of what goes on with me makes more sense."

People in the domestic violence business use the term *risk matrix* for a family situation in which people are likely to get hurt by family members. If The Law has a positive corollary, which it does, then there must also be a positive corollary for the *risk matrix*. And there is.

Plenty of kids grow up in families where they learn that living things have value. They learn that people can love one another and be kind to one another—that such behavior is normal, that it is human. Kids can exercise a sense of humor among such people without getting smacked or humiliated. There are family situations where a kid can grow up to be a lifeguard.

2. Cascade and Beyond

"He's very straightforward, quite articulate, and closely in touch with his feelings," observes Jennifer Larson in a biography of Chris Crutcher that she wrote for a high school English class. "He answers any questions without hesitation, and yet the answers seem well planned. I had the definite impression Chris is a man living life just the way he wants to live it."[1]

The reason Crutcher can respond without hesitation to questions about his life in answers that seem well planned is because the answers *are* well planned. He's been asking himself the questions, working with clients on the questions, and creating literary characters who battle through the questions for years. If he is the man Ms. Larson perceived, he didn't become this man by accident. It's because he works at it.

> One of the reasons I stay in mental health—as many times as I've almost gotten loose from it—is that I get called back by that miracle of change. I spend a lot of time looking through people's lives and looking through my own life for something that matches so I can come up with that one little thing.
>
> Sometimes I think the process of going through that with somebody is the same process you go through when you're trying to tell your story, to try to help your character find what it is he needs to find. It's not too much different from piecing through someone's life—or my own life—to find out what change is possible.
>
> You need to remember your youth because you need to find out where the glitches are. You need to be able to go back and find out who told you what and evaluate it when you have the capacity to do that. I think we need to remember our youth because we are the sum of our experiences—actually, the sum of

> our perceptions of our experiences. If you don't remember it, you tend to package it or cliché it or just make it okay.

So let's go back. Let's head for Cascade where Crutcher spent his youth. And let's take his motorcycle.

You know Chris's bike: It's the 700cc Honda Shadow that Big Will and Willie Weaver ride around Coho, Montana, in *The Crazy Horse Electric Game,* and it's also the 1100cc Honda Magna that Wilson Corder and Molly Comstock ride along the back roads through the wheat country west of Three Forks, Washington, in *The Deep End*. How can it be both? Because such transmogrifications take place in the fictional worlds created by storytellers. The bike you'll see Chris riding around Spokane has the word STOTAN! painted in gold across the maroon gas tank.

We'll ride south through the wheat country. We'll take the route Chris took to and from Eastern Washington State College in Cheney. And we'll take our time because there's beautiful country to see.

We ride through a region of bare, rounded hills called the Palouse. *Pelouse* is the French word for lawn. There weren't many trees when the French explorers described the area this way, and trees became fewer as farmers grew in number. We ride through places where nothing but green wheat grows on the hills all around. There is green wheat and blue sky and nothing else but the wind moving in currents that wave the wheat like eel grass in a stream. And because we're on a motorcycle we're *in* the moist, fragrant air—not shielded from the air as we would be in a car—and so it's like we're riding under water, along the bed of a clear, fast-flowing stream that is the whole world.

Not many miles south of Pullman, the home of Washington State University, we cross the border into Idaho. We stop and take off our helmets here—like Big Will and Willie when they're out of sight of Mrs. Weaver—because Idaho has no helmet law. We do this because we don't like wearing a helmet, even in city traffic where we feel more secure with one on. We are aware of the irony of a motorcyclist going down with a helmet strapped to the sissy bar, but we live with the knowledge of this possibility because this is the way we like to live and because we don't like wearing a helmet. Crutcher says it this way:

> Somebody comes up to me and says, *Man, you're crazy if you don't wear a motorcycle helmet.* I don't wear one more often than I do, and there's an element of risk there. There's something to be said for caution, and there's something to be said for risk. And it's real hard to find that line sometimes. 'Cause if you cross it the wrong way you splatter yourself.

The land levels and the elevation drops as we roll south on Idaho 95. Then all of a sudden it looks and feels like we're about to ride off the edge of the earth. All we can see to the south is sky. What we're about to ride off the edge of is the Columbia Plateau, a section of the largest lava plateau on the planet. Hundreds of feet below us, about as close to straight down as one cares to imagine looking from the top, lie the confluence of the Snake and Clearwater Rivers and the towns of Lewiston and Clarkston, named for the explorers who followed the rivers through here in 1805. The view is literally breathtaking. As we wind down the grade we see signs that note the distance to the runaway truck ramp. The only people in whom these signs inspire confidence are drivers of runaway trucks. This is a *steep* grade.

The two-lane blacktop takes us southeast along the tree-covered valley floor into the Nez Perce Reservation. A look at our map shows the many French names surviving here, the name of these Indian people included. *Nez perce* means "pierced nose." Plenty of Indian names, too, of course: We passed the turns for Potlatch, Walla Walla, Lapwai, and Weippe a while back, and Waha, Wallowa, Lolo, Kamiah, and Kooskia are down the road.

Riding straight south now, a few miles below Grangeville, we hit another stretch of grade that takes our breath away. Gaping is hazardous on a motorcycle because of the various things that fly into your mouth, so we ungape fast. We've reached White Bird hill, a 1,500-foot drop to the floor of White Bird Canyon in eight winding miles.

And this is the new road. Back in the sixties when Chris was making this trip regularly, the only road through here lay one mountain to the east. The distance to the canyon floor was 11 miles then, with 15-mile-per-hour switchbacks.

Chris likes the story about the man who ran the service station in White Bird. People driving down the hill for the first time would have smelled so much burning brake lining by the time they reached the bottom they'd think their brakes were gone. So the man at the station would tell these folks to go over to the restaurant and have a bite to eat while he looked at their brakes. What he looked at was their license plates. If they weren't from Idaho he'd tell them he'd had to do a brake job. Their brakes would have cooled by then, so the burning smell was gone. The people would pay the man, and off they'd go.

The new White Bird hill isn't as long as the old one, and it's not as dramatic as the Lewiston grade, but it offers a truly awesome view. We pull into a turnout and stop to look at the vista and at our map again. The mountains to the east are part of the Gospel Hump Wilderness, and further east lies the Salmon River Breaks Primitive Area. The map calls the Salmon the "River of No Return." The peaks to the east go over 9,000 feet, and to the west, in Hell's Canyon National Recreation Area, He Devil Mountain in the Seven Devils range goes over 9,000 as well. Hell's Canyon itself, cut through those mountains by the Snake River, is almost 8,000 feet deep. *Awesome* is no cliché here: This radical topography inspires in us the mixed emotions of reverence, respect, dread, and wonder.

The mountains close in as we ride south into the Salmon River Canyon. In some places the rock walls narrow to the edge of the road. We run into a traffic jam in the tiny town of Riggins. The highway is the town's only street, and this is where the Salmon cuts east into the primitive area and where white-water rafting tours thrive.

Riggins is also the northernmost town in the Long Pin League, the high school athletic conference the Cascade Ramblers play in. During football and basketball seasons 1962, 1963, and 1964, Chris Crutcher made the 75-mile trip to Riggins on the team bus. That's a long haul on mountain roads in winter, but the Ramblers make longer trips than that. Midvale is about 30 miles west of

Cascade over the mountains, but it's a 90-mile drive around the mountains to get there. Chris used to fly to the Midvale games in a friend's plane.

Back when Chris was taking the bus home from college, and later when he was driving the '57 Plymouth he bought from his brother, he'd feel like the trip was about over when Riggins was behind him and the canyon walls finally fell away.

We jog east onto Idaho 55 at New Meadows, and before long we're cruising through McCall on the shore of Payette Lake. The mountains open wider here, and the highway swings back south into a long valley where alfalfa grows and dairy cattle graze. We're in Valley County, of which Crutch was county clerk. The Payette River flows into the Cascade Dam Reservoir a little north of Donnelly, and we parallel the shore the last few miles to Cascade. This is the first year since Chris was in high school that the water has been high enough to flow over the spillway. If we've read *Running Loose* we can look up to the west as we near the bridge and see Louie Banks and Carter Sampson dumping a box of fish guts into the water as it shoots down the spillway into the Payette. When the accelerating mass of entrails hits bottom it fragments into a great gory shower that rises and then descends on the people fishing from the rocks.

As long as people read the book, Louie and Carter will be up there, and Becky Sanders will have a life before she swerves to miss the kids on the motorcycle and runs her car into the bridge at the south end of town. And Louie's parents, Norm and Brenda, will live their middle years forever.

This is the immortality that art offers. It is neither mystical nor a matter of dispute. As long as the art exists, the characters in the art go on living.

Over the bridge, reduce speed as the sign instructs, and we're in Cascade, a lumber town of about 900 on the western edge of the valley. Highway 55 is the main street; the other streets are dirt. The house Chris lived in from the age of seven, the house with the 360 little panes in the windows, is down on the south end of Main next to the Forest Service office and across from the mill. A quick right up the hill, two dusty blocks, and we've reached Valley County Hospital, the residence of Jewell Morris Crutcher.

Crutch died of a heart attack in 1985, and since then Jewell has been the only Crutcher left in Cascade. She owns the house she and Crutch built in 1974 after Candy, their youngest, was grown. It's a few blocks south of here, past the school. Every day when she looked out the picture windows that face the valley she saw at the bottom of the hill the house she was born in, and across the narrow dirt street from it she saw "the little house," as the family calls it, where they lived until they moved to the bigger place on south Main. Jewell lived alone in the new house after Crutch died, and then a year ago when her emphysema began putting her in the hospital and she needed oxygen to recover from even minor exertions, she went in one time and stayed.

Jewell is a handsome woman, as we used to say. There are still plenty of handsome women, but we don't call them that anymore.

Chris with older brother John and younger sister Candy.

This is odd, because the word denotes physical strength as well as strength of character. It's hard to think of Jewell as sick—even as she sits on her hospital bed with the oxygen within arm's reach—because she looks so good. She's in her 70s, but her posture is excellent. She's groomed as though she might be about to take a stroll downtown. Jewell won't be taking any stroll, though, because she can't walk to the door without turning back for the

Chris's mother, Jewell Crutcher.

oxygen. And yet she looks robust. Strength of character creates such a quality in people. The cotton pads taped to her forearms where she leans against the edge of her bed table suggest eccentricity rather than infirmity. This woman defeated alcohol, and then she defeated cigarettes, and now she's facing with grace the battle none of us wins.

"I'd love to have the family around me," Jewell says, "but I don't want to leave here. They're around me more by coming to see me than they ever would be if I lived in their towns. And here it's so small. And I've lived here forever, so people I know come and go all the time. And the kids make an effort to see me, and that pleases me."[2]

Jewell never dreamed of Chris being a storyteller. He wrote a column for the school paper called *Chris's Crumbs,* and she thought he might be a columnist or a TV comedy writer.

John, her eldest, was valedictorian of his class. "Chris and Candy were both mediocre students," Jewell says. "I was a mediocre student. John seemed to have Crutch's mind—the mathematical, logical mind. They never had any flights of fancy.

"John [who also had Crutch's heft] always said the thing about being big was that you never had to fight. Chris wasn't a fighter. He wasn't big. He wasn't going to scare anybody. Chris could make everybody laugh, and he saved his hide that way. He gets his sense of humor both from my father and Crutch's mother."

Jewell is amazed that Chris has become a professional storyteller, and his success in working with young people is a little amazing to her, too, although she sees it as part of his character. "He was essentially doing what he's doing right now in that school in Oakland," she says. This was Lakeside, the K–12 alternative school for inner-city kids where Chris was director, the model for One More Last Chance High School in *The Crazy Horse Electric Game*.

> He has letters from mothers who just fall all over him for saving their kids in that school. They really thought he was wonderful. I think before maybe their kids had teachers who just put up with them every day. But Chris seemed to care. And that's the core of him right there—the caring.

The Crutcher boys—Chris with his father John and older brother John—enjoying a swim.

"My mother was a *word* person who wrote poems for birthdays and anniversaries, played Scrabble with a vengeance, and corrected my grammar like a woman possessed," Chris has written.

> [And] my father was a smart and insightful man—for a Republican—who read voraciously and indiscriminately. He was a World War II B-17 pilot as conversant in the latest private eye novel as he was in the classics, as familiar with ancient biographies as

Chris—the young cowboy.

popular fiction. He loved the act of reading, of gathering information.[3]

My dad didn't disdain the emotional side, he just didn't have anything to do with it. You just didn't see his emotional side. And my mom was highly emotional. I grew up thinking that was the difference between smart and not-so-smart, and I was wrong.

We need to remember our youth because we need to find out where the glitches are.

A *glitch* is a cause the effect of which is to prevent a mechanism from operating as it should. And how should the mechanism of self operate?

Crutcher believes that human beings run their best on the fuel of the truth. He believes that we need to see the truth in our lives and take responsibility for it—"own it," he says. We tell the truth to ourselves, and we tell the truth to others when the truth is necessary. As he's gotten older and seen more of himself and others, Crutcher has come to believe that standing up with the truth is an heroic act. Crutcher believes that by telling the truth we create a *congruence* between the world within ourselves and the world without. But he knows that such a state is always tentative, always a struggle to achieve and maintain.

> I struggle against lies. I struggle against lying. And yet if I'm not feeling strong enough to say the thing I know is going to make somebody feel bad, if I'm not feeling strong enough to allow myself that I'm doing my best, I lie. I either lie [explicitly] or I lie by omission. And I struggle against it all the time.

Chris looks back to the years when Jewell was drinking and Crutch was just being Crutch, and he sees where this struggle began.

> I used to sit in the kitchen and lie to my mom like crazy, tell her how everything was all right. And she was too drunk to remember what we talked about. Lie my ass off. *No, Mom, I don't feel bad about anything. I don't feel neglected. I don't feel like breaking your goddamn head open because I can't get out of this kitchen. No, I don't mind that my dad is asleep in the living room instead of sitting here having this conversation with my mom while I'm outside playing.*
>
> For a long, long time I never saw my dad's part in it—my mother's dissatisfaction about being alive, her depression, her willingness to just medicate herself. He worked hard, came home. . . . [But] he didn't do the relationship. He didn't know how.

So Chris became the *peacemaker*.

> If you're a peacemaker, you're a liar. If it's your job to make sure that people feel okay, if you're a leveler in your family for whatever reason, if you take on that responsibility of making people feel okay, you're a liar.

> And this is deadly to relationships. I can't have a relationship with somebody who doesn't fight. Because if I can't fight with you, I'm not going to be able to tell you the truth, because I'm not going to be able to talk about my anger. I'm not going to be able to show it. I can only deal with it when I explode. I don't want you to feel bad. I want everybody cool. And I can't do that without lying.
>
> I'm not saying the only way to get through life is to always tell exactly the truth, because we're really talking about the emotional truth here. And that's a hard thing to tell, because sometimes words don't cover it. And sometimes the person receiving the information isn't capable of receiving what you have to say. But that can't be your responsibility.
>
> I can probably trace every lie I ever tell. And it never turns out good. It *never* turns out good.
>
> It would be nice if you could come to these conclusions and then just act on them. But you have to pay attention all the time, because it's just too easy to not face up to the part of yourself that you hate.
>
> You get a million chances to tell the truth. A million chances to be heroic and a million chances to be a coward. And they always have to do with standing up for yourself, saying who you are, and saying that's the way it is.

Probably the toughest place to stand up for ourselves, to say who we are and that's the way it is, is in the war zone of romance. Of all the lies men tell, most of them are told to women. A lot of men would rather take a beating than tell the truth to a woman, because, as Crutcher says, to tell the truth is to say who we are. And saying who we are is not only among the most courageous but among the most intimate of acts.

Romance—*the love stuff*—is a part of life where Chris has struggled hard to tell the truth.

> People always say, *Why is the love stuff always so tentative in your stories?* And the answer is: Because it was always tentative in my life. It was always dangerous. You never came through clean. There was always something to feel bad about. There was always something to be ashamed of. There was always a lie. There was always a place where you hadn't told the truth because you didn't want to hurt somebody's feelings, or you

> hadn't told the truth because you didn't want to face the way you looked if you told the truth.

Chris says it would have been helpful to have a practice run on the romance track, so he'd have known what to expect. And in *Stotan!,* in Walker's struggle with his inability to tell the truth to Devnee and his confusion about his feelings for Elaine, Crutcher presents such a practice run for his readers.

Crutcher has lived alone for years, except for a fluctuating number of cats and whatever wild critters slip in through the cat door. He has fathered no children, has never been married, and doubts he ever will. For the past eight years, though, he's been in a relationship, and this past year while the woman was building a house, her 17-year-old son lived with Chris. The relationship that Wilson Corder has with Molly Comstock in *The Deep End* mirrors Chris's relationship. Here's what Corder says about it:

> Molly is the one woman I've been with since my divorce who understands in much the same way I do, the dilemma of men and women getting together. Each of us believes the more that happens *outside* the relationship, the better we are *in* it. We have each tried it the traditional way, and in both our cases the results were dismal. There are parts of Molly's life she would never invite me into, not because she keeps secrets, but because I don't fit there. (*DE,* 40)

Crutcher cites an example of the difficulty of explaining the decision they have made:

> All [her] friends believe that the reason she tells them she likes not being married is because I won't marry her, 'cause she can't get married, that she would in a second if she could. And believe me—believe me: she wouldn't.

They have created the *congruence* Chris talks about. They've created a measure of peace between the world within themselves and the world without.

Crutcher would say he's been fortunate with the women in his life. The women—and the men—who raised Chris showed him examples of intelligence and courage, and maybe more important

than anything they loved him and created in him a sense that he was worthy of love.

Chris remembers his grandmother, Crutch's mom, May, whom they called G.G.

> My dad was a smart guy, but my grandmother was every bit that smart with a soft side. She was a voracious reader and a wonderful storyteller. She could remember things. She was real small. She had these elegant wrinkles. She had the softest skin. She was an amazing woman.

Chris was just out of college, back home in Cascade, taking G.G. for a ride in her car, which was keeping her independent. She was talking about Chris's grandfather, her first husband. "You know," she said, "men don't want you to have money." Chris asked her why. "Because it makes you powerful to them," she replied. "I remember I used to have a little cache of money that I kept because I'd always wanted something for myself," she said, "and he found a way to get it from me."

Her tone was as if that was just in men's nature, Chris says. It wasn't really all that critical a statement. "Men don't want you to be smart," he remembers as the gist of what G.G. had to say, "and they don't want you to have any power and they don't want you to have money. They don't want you to have your own money."

A few years later, not long before G.G. died, Chris remembers being outside with her, walking, when out of the blue she stopped. "You know," she told him, "you're like your dad. Only you'll go a lot farther. 'Cause you have a soft touch that he doesn't have. A thing about people."

"It came out of nowhere," Chris says. "It was like this piece of information that she'd been waiting for the right time to give me."

A thing about people. Crutcher knew that. He didn't need the information. We grow wise enough so we don't need information about ourselves from the people we love anymore. But we never get too wise to need that kind of love.

3. Carpentry on the Keyboard

> I call myself a natural storyteller because I love stories. But I certainly wasn't a natural writer.
>
> There was a part of writing that came natural to me, and that was humor—outrageous humor. I had a real ear for that.
>
> I always describe the writing as the *carpentry*. I don't think about the carpentry being painful. Scanning through the thesaurus for just the right word—really precise stuff after a while. Thank God for the thesaurus, because there are words there I'd never think of. And sometimes there'll be a word that in terms of precision might not be quite the one, but lyrically it's perfect.
>
> I'm surprised how much I like to choose words. I've played this anti-intellectual role in every way that you can possibly play it for so long that I sometimes forget that some of that shit is just fun—doing that carpentry.

Crutcher's writing career can be traced to his high school days when he played the anti-intellectual with aplomb. "Rebellion felt good," he says. "I didn't like people telling me what to think."

Or what to read. He was forced, however, to tolerate people telling him what to write.

> Teachers used to like to give me 500 word [punishment] themes, and I gave them lots of reasons to do it. I would get real creative doing these because there was no school structure to them.

When Chris was in the eighth grade the journalism teacher saw one of his themes and invited him to write for the school paper. From then until his senior year he wrote his *Chris's Crumbs* col-

Chris as a young athlete.

umn. "They didn't like to let me report because I wasn't a good reporter, but I had this column where I took pot shots at everybody" (Jenkinson, 68).

Chris did one kind of report with facility. That was the book report, and his facility was making up the books.

> [T]elevision came in when I was in the fifth grade. As far as I was concerned that was a much better way to get stories than books. I began . . . making up my books and getting my authors out of the phone book. The critique of the book would always be that I thought it was a stupid story and I could never understand why it was written. (Jenkinson, 68)

Sometimes he took a break from invention and plagiarized.

> My brother was not only real bright, he was also somewhat compulsive and kept everything that he ever did in high school in the storage closet up in his room. A lot of times I would take one of his book reports and misspell a few words, take it *down* a few notches, and turn it in. (Jenkinson, 68)

Crutcher's outrageous sense of humor is still with him three decades later, and so is his sense of rebellion. We see both qualities throughout his work: the huge pepperoni that Louie Banks carries in a gun rack in his pickup in *Running Loose,* Johnny Rivers's puns in *Crazy Horse,* and the tabloid satires that Eric and Sarah create for their underground newspaper *Crispy Pork Rinds* in *Staying Fat for Sarah Byrnes.*

To catch some of Crutcher's most outrageous humor, however—and to hear that his potshots continue to fly—you need to call him on the phone. You don't want him to be home, though, because you've called to listen to his answering machine.

A *best of* Crutcher answering machine greetings reads as follows:

> You have reached the secret love nest of Dan Quayle and Murphy Brown.
>
> "Hey, you guys, Murphy Brown isn't even real. I mean she's really Candice Bergen, daughter of Edgar Bergen, the famous ventriloquist. And that's a good thing for me 'cause this chick really knows her way around a dummy.
>
> "Well, I'm bushed. Leave a message."

> You have reached the Hotel and Restaurant Workers of America. We're giddy at the results of the recent election, as it's a little-known historical fact that the wife of the vice president gains and retains an average of 50 pounds yearly. That leaves us with four years of—you guessed it—a heavy tipper.

> (Over the hymn A Mighty Fortress Is Our God) You have reached Oral Roberts's older, wiser brother, Anal Roberts. . . .

> You have reached the home of Chris Crutcher, author of the best-selling self-help book People Who Need Peepholes.

> (The opening notes of Beethoven's Fifth) You have reached . . . Hell. If you want to talk to The Big Guy, wait for the beep. If you're looking for Dan Quayle, you're a bit premature. If you want David Koresh, please hold. He's being processed . . . by Jeffrey Dahmer.
>
> And if you want to speak to the Right-to-Lifers, you're outta luck. They've lost their phone privileges. You have to have some manners even here.
>
> You have reached the home of Chris Crutcher, author of the best-selling self-help book *How to Commit Suicide or Die Trying.*
>
> This is Chris Crutcher, your relationship guru for the nineties and author of the runaway best-seller *Women Who Love Men Who Love Barnyard Animals.* I'm into a sequel, *Men Who Love Women Who Think Men Are Barnyard Animals,* so I can't come to the phone right now. Leave a message.
>
> You have reached . . . beyond your grasp. But leave a message anyway.
>
> (in the voice of a cretin redneck) Thank you for calling 1-800-MILITIA. Your orders for the day: rise up and storm your local Kmart and Shopko stores and come away with as many tank tops as you can possibly lay your hands on. For, like every man, woman, and child in this free country of ours, you have a right to bare arms.

Writing is never torture for Crutcher because he won't let it be. He doesn't put himself on a schedule. If he doesn't have anything to write, he won't sit down and face the blank screen. He makes time to write whenever he can.

> Most weeks on Sunday night, I'll say, "OK, this is what I'm going to do this week." It hasn't happened in ten years that I did what I said. [But] when I'm hot I can write. If I have time and if I have a laptop computer along, I'll pull it out and write. If I'm not hot, just starting something, it's like pulling teeth. I'll watch TV, I'll wash dishes, before I start writing.

> When I'm in the middle of the story, I actually write very fast. But getting going is the toughest. And I haven't come up with a way to do it. It helps that I live alone and it helps that I don't have a family, because that would just add to the craziness.[1]

Chris needs quiet when he composes, but when he's editing he listens to music: some country-western, a Kris Kristofferson retrospective, Paul Simon, but mostly old rock-and-roll.

He has no audience in mind when he writes, because thinking of a specific audience makes him self-conscious. He starts worrying about how the material is going to be heard as opposed to how it's coming out of him, and he loses his spontaneity. "What I do is choose the age of the protagonist," he says. "And then I tell the story; and if we have to edit it later, then we do" (Smith, 67).

Chris's editor at Greenwillow Books, where all his young adult work is published, is Susan Hirschman. The only circumstance under which he will change editors, Chris says, is if Susan dies.

> I let her do the worrying about audience and then I decide if I can afford to edit whatever she thinks about. She's very liberal. I mean, there are very, very few times where we've ever clashed and never seriously. (Smith, 67)

The image of *carpentry* is accurate to describe the craft of writing. The skill of choosing words with precision and then using these words to construct sturdy, balanced sentences and paragraphs is fundamental. But to think of Crutcher as a *carpenter* diminishes what he is and what he does. If we follow his analogy we need to think of him as an *architect* who not only conceives and designs the structure but enjoys building it himself.

It's characteristic of Crutcher to be self-effacing; he refers to himself as a storyteller rather than an artist, and he describes himself this way:

> I am not a well-read writer. I haven't read the classics in any but comic book form and I do a horrible job of keeping up with new

> writers or literature in general. I have very little formal training and usually feel hopelessly inadequate in the company of other writers.[2]

He doesn't have the time or the inclination to be the student of literature some other writers are—particularly those who have chosen writing as their only job or who combine writing and teaching. But, like the architect—who is an artist—his concerns go beyond construction into concept and theory and into a consideration of the work of other artists.

On the question of writing for a particular audience, for example, he's come to this conclusion:

> It's bad to have an idea of young-adult literature when you write a young-adult book because it comes out sounding like one. You don't elevate into limitless exploration, step up into the world of literature, of ideas.
>
> Tim O'Brien is exactly right about storytelling. Story is the thing. If you could read and understand *How to Tell a True War Story* and maybe two or three interviews O'Brien's given, you would absolutely understand how to elevate your storytelling to the world, to the universe.
>
> You don't write a YA book; you write a book to the whole world.
>
> I think it is no coincidence that the one book I did read in high school was *To Kill a Mockingbird,* because fifteen years after I graduated from college, became semi-literate, and decided to become a storyteller, stories like Harper Lee wrote were the only kind I had any desire to tell: stories about real life as I see it, about my sense of justice and injustice. (Gallo, 59)

In addition to Tim O'Brien and Harper Lee, Crutcher admires the work of Pat Conroy. *The Prince of Tides* and *The Great Santini* are his favorite Conroy novels. Although he contends that his readers would never know it, Crutcher knows he's been influenced by Conroy's "lyrical flow of words" and "wonderful storytelling." He admires the work of Larry McMurtry, particularly *Lonesome Dove.* He owns a videocassette of the TV miniseries, but he's afraid to start watching it because the story fascinates him so much he might not get back to writing.

"I loved [Joseph Heller's] *Catch 22,*" Crutcher says.

> There are very few books I've read once, but there are *very* few I've read more than once. I learned a lot reading that book. I learned a lot about humor. I learned a lot about going out to the edge.

And Crutcher does go out to the edge in his work. As an architect and carpenter of stories, he conceives, designs, and builds in words; and his words often upset people. His books are frequently *challenged* in schools and public libraries by people who believe his concepts—and particularly his words—go over the edge of appropriateness for young readers.

Like any builder, Crutcher uses the materials he believes are strongest and with which he's most familiar. Even people who don't object to his work ask him if it's necessary to use "that kind of language in young adult books." But, again, Crutcher doesn't make that distinction.

> If I'm writing it's either literature or it's not literature, but I don't separate young adult from adult.
>
> No, it [the language] isn't necessary. It's not necessary at all.
>
> But I grew up in a lumber town. And I started working in my dad's service station when I was nine years old. The high school kids were all there—they worked for my dad. And the loggers were all there, and all the people who lived in my town at one time or another were in that service station. And that's the language I grew up with.
>
> And then I taught for 10 years in the streets of Oakland. . . .
>
> It's just language that's used. It's current English. And it isn't a bit necessary.
>
> But it is the voice that I'm talking in. It's the voice that my characters speak in. And it's my view of the world. And to leave it out would be to leave out that part of my view of the world.

Crutcher writes in the language "that's out there," as he says. And many of his readers wonder if he also writes about people who are *out there,* if his characters are real people.

"The two guys, Jeff and Lion, in *Stotan!* were drawn from real characters," Crutcher says. "And they pretty much held that way through the book. They're the only two characters I've ever used that were really somebody. Everybody else is made up."

To make up a literary character Crutcher often uses *a germ of somebody real* (Smith, 69). The *germ* might be an element of a real character's personality; it might be a real character's voice or a physical quality—like the injury Willie Weaver suffers in *The Crazy Horse Electric Game*; it might be an incident from a real character's life—like the death of Willie's little sister Missy to sudden infant death syndrome. By the second or third chapter, though, the literary character has grown beyond the link to actuality and become *real* within the separate reality of the book.

Virtually every time Crutcher gives a reading or speaks to a group, he's confronted with the following question: "What happens if somebody thinks they see themselves in one of your stories?" He's begun to respond with a measure of fatigue:

> I don't know what happens. It just kind of depends if they see a good guy or a bad guy. I can only take so much responsibility for that.
>
> I understand I'm in a somewhat dangerous or somewhat blamable position because I'm a therapist; [and] the fact of the matter is that if I take eleven years of stuff, there are a whole bunch of people who could look at any one of those stories and see themselves there.
>
> I have 50 years of experience, and I'm going to write about it the way I want to. And if somebody sues me and they win, they win. If they get all my money, they get all my money. But I just can't think about that when I'm telling stories.

Crutcher understands the motivation behind the question, and he has a certain empathy for it. After all, if a story is any good it *feels* real; it *feels* like it really must have happened to some real person at some historical moment in some real place.

One of the reasons this question can fatigue and irritate storytellers, though, is that it's often based in an insufficient appreciation of their craft. It doesn't acknowledge the power of imagination storytellers exercise. A lot of us assume novelists take an incident from real life, change the names of the participants, and hope nobody catches on. But it's more complex than that, and it requires greater skill—which are two of the reasons we call it art.

4. A Healing Vision

In 1994 Chris Crutcher received an award from the Assembly on Literature for Adolescents of the National Council of Teachers of English (ALAN) for "significant contribution to young adult literature." Crutcher's books are accessible, funny, compelling, and relevant, and these are elements of his significant contribution. The essence of that contribution, however—as it is in any literary genre—is the accuracy and scope of his vision of the world, his description of *how the world works*.

Crutcher is absolutely serious in *Chinese Handcuffs* when he presents information he calls "the secret of life" (*CH* 46, 87). To understand what Crutcher believes, why he believes it, and why he tells his stories, we need to consider the intertwining lives he's lived: therapist and storyteller.

About five years ago, after hearing hundreds of times the question "where do you get your ideas?" Crutcher the storyteller began to feel that he needed to give people a better answer. "And at that time I started stepping out a little more about why I was passionate about certain things," he says. "There's no question: I have just seen so much damage done."

It's Crutcher the therapist who's seen this damage in his clients.

> One of the ugliest scenes I have in my mind is of a kid waiting. When you're in this business everybody is waiting for crumbs. They're waiting for this little hour experience where you're going to walk through their shit with them. Where you're going to walk through their horror.
>
> There's no answer. Things don't get fixed. You get this kid to a place where he's willing to jump off a cliff, and then what?

> Then he jumps. All you can do is jump with him. That's what good therapy is about for me.
>
> I can't fix these people's lives. I have absolutely no right to judge them. I can feel myself reeling out line. I'm just reeling these people more line.
>
> You never have enough time. And this is what gives me such strong opinions about things. And the really strong opinions it gives me are opinions about the damage that gets done.

"There's something about walking through that kind of stuff with those people," he says. "I'm not exaggerating when I say I get more out of it than anybody ever gets out of it with me."

So what does the storyteller do to correct the damage the therapist says he can't fix? He tells his readers the secret of life. He presents a new vision of the world. A healing vision.

Crutcher explains himself in an essay titled "Healing through Literature":

> Louie Banks in *Running Loose* has grown up believing that life is fair; that adults don't lie, that if you work hard you get what you deserve, that good intentions count, that disappointments can be overcome by hard work, that his parents and teachers and coaches have his best interest at heart. Then his coach asks him to play dirty football and, though Louie refuses, he sees that cheaters *do* win—at least in the sense he has always considered winning. Lies *work*. When he loses his girlfriend senselessly in an automobile accident, he learns that not only are *people* not fair, *life* is not fair.[1]

Chris goes on to quote the passage from *Running Loose* where Louie asks Dakota "what kind of a worthless God" would let Becky get killed.

> "Louie," [Dakota replies,] ". . . one thing I'm pretty sure of is that if there is a God, that ain't His job. He ain't up there to load the dice one way or the other. . . .
>
> "There's one thing that separates a man from a boy, the way I see it, and it ain't age, it's seeing how life works, so you don't get surprised all the time and kicked in the butt. It's knowin' the rules. . . . You go on blamin' God, you get no place. You got to pay attention to how things work. Ya got to understand that the

> reason some things happen is just because they happen. That ain't a good reason, but that's it. You put enough cars and trucks and motorcycles on the road, and some of 'em are gonna run into each other. Not certain ones neither. Just the ones that do. This life ain't partial, boy."[2]

Crutcher continues in the essay to discuss another instance where he presents his vision of "how life works":

> In *The Crazy Horse Electric Game* Willie Weaver hears the same lesson. He wants to know why, if life is fair—if there's a God—he was crippled in a water-skiing accident, robbing him of physical gifts that few are ever handed in the first place.
>
> [Lisa] sits in the doorway of her car, pulling off her shoes. "What would be different if you knew why, Willie? You'd still be crippled."
>
> "I know, but . . . if there's a reason; a purpose."
>
> "I'm going to do you a favor. I'm going to tell you why."
>
> Willie waits expectantly.
>
> "You crippled yourself because you stretched the rules 'til they broke. Simple as that." ("Healing," 35)

Since Crutcher wrote "Healing through Literature" he has written the novel *Staying Fat for Sarah Byrnes,* in which he considers further the question of God's hand in our lives. As the book opens Sarah Byrnes has placed herself in Spokane's Child and Adolescent Psychiatric Unit by faking catatonia. She needs time and a safe place to figure out how to escape her father, who held her face against a burning woodstove when she was three-and-a-half years old. The arena for Crutcher's religious argument is a high school class called Contemporary American Thought—CAT—and his persona is Steve Ellerby, son of an Episcopal minister. Steve drives a Pontiac station wagon he calls "The Christian Cruiser" and fellow swimmer and classmate Mark Brittain calls "blasphemous." Painted on the car is *THE WAGES OF SIN IS A BUCK FIFTY* and *A MIGHTY FORTRESS IS OUR DOG* (*SB,* 22).

The class has been discussing whether the world is a good place or a bad place, and the book's narrator, Eric "Moby" Calhoune, Sarah Byrnes's best friend, uses her as an example. "Every day when she gets up, she knows she has to bring her scarred-up face to school, knowing what everyone thinks and won't say. There's no place to hide and it never lets up. I'd call that a bad place to live" (*SB*, 16). Another student responds that this just makes the world a bad place for Sarah Byrnes, not everybody. During the class's next meeting Steve tells everyone that their discussion has gotten him thinking about fairness. He's been forced to conclude that the world is a pretty good place for him most of the time, and he wonders, if God is fair, how we explain him and Sarah Byrnes on the same planet? And why, if God rewards piety and public prayer, as Mark Brittain seems to believe, does He let Steve kick Mark's butt in swimming? And how come He lets Steve drive the Christian Cruiser without blowing out his tires?

Steve is wound up. He goes on to say he had a Sunday school teacher who responded to all tough questions—such as how come Steve's big brother got killed after he had earned straight *A*s through college and was headed to seminary—with the same declaration: that the Lord works in strange and mysterious ways.

Steve leans forward now, a vein pulsing in his temple.

> "But I think there's nothing strange and mysterious about it. I figure if those things were in God's jurisdiction, he'd do something different about them. But they aren't. Those are in our jurisdiction. . . . From a distance, my car looks like every other car on the freeway, and Sarah Byrnes looks just like the rest of us. If she's going to get help, she'll get it from herself or she'll get it from us." (*SB*, 62)

The class functions as Crutcher has described therapy: The students feel safe enough to tell the truth about their lives, and the teacher, Mrs. Lemry, walks through that truth with them.

The "truth" Steve Ellerby tells here is the same thing Dakota tells Louie Banks and Lisa tells Willie Weaver: God does not take a hand in human life. It's important to note the consistency of this element in Crutcher's vision: in *Running Loose,* published in 1983, Louie Banks disrupts Becky's funeral when the minister uses the "*strange and mysterious ways* defense" (*RL*, 136).

> "He doesn't move in strange and mysterious ways," Louie screams. "He doesn't move at all! He sits up there on His fat butt and lets guys like you earn a living making excuses for all the rotten things that happen." (*RL*, 136–37)

And 10 years later in *Staying Fat for Sarah Byrnes,* that same phrase appears in the rhetoric of Steve Ellerby.

In the Crutcher universe, God does not take a hand in human life. The implications here are many, and they are found in everything Crutcher writes. These implications are (1) the way we discover how the world works is to pay attention to the world; (2) if we want justice in this life we're going to have to create it ourselves; and (3) help is available from other human beings.

If we want to give a name to this worldview we might call it *agnostic,* which refers to the belief that there can be no proof of the existence of God but does not deny the possibility that God exists. It's not Crutcher's intention that readers infer an *agnostic* vision in his work—he says he doesn't know what *agnostic* means—and the term isn't completely accurate in any case because the contention isn't that God doesn't exist but that He keeps His distance.

Empiric might be a more accurate description of the Crutcher world, because *empiricism* contends that metaphysical questions—such as "What kind of a worthless God would let Becky get killed?"—are meaningless.

We might call Crutcher's vision *existential* because it emphasizes our human existence—our freedom of choice and our responsibility for ourselves—over the essence, or spiritual force, that other views see as the controlling and responsible agent in life. A concern with human existence over the continued existence of the spirit is illustrated in the following passages from *Stotan!* The main characters are talking about Jeff's illness, and Lion says:

> "We're clinging to this round ball in space by an accident of suction.[3] . . . I don't care how many times Jeff comes back or what he comes back as. If he dies now, he's leaving *us* forever. And that's all I care about. . . . Life doesn't care, guys. It's just

> there. The only way we have of getting a leg up on the world is to stick together, no matter what." (*Stotan!*, 149)

We're probably most accurate, though, to call Crutcher's vision *humanistic* because it centers on human beings and our values, capacities, and worth.

Hold on! we might say. Human worth? Agreed, there are numerous worthy human beings in Crutcher's work—Dakota, Max in *Stotan!*, Coach Kathy Sherman in *Chinese Handcuffs* to name three. But what about the worth of a guy like Virgil Byrnes, Sarah's father, who held a little girl's face to a burning woodstove, then for 15 years refused her reconstructive surgery so she'd learn to "be tough" (*SB*, 213)? And what about the worth of her mother who wouldn't stand up for her? What about the human worth of the child molester–murderers Dr. Jeffrey Banner and Charles Creech in *The Deep End*? What about the racist hypocrite Coach Lednecky in *Running Loose*? What about the pimp Lacey Casteel in *The Crazy Horse Electric Game* who beat his son nine-tenths to death? What about the psychopathic T. B. Martin in *Chinese Handcuffs*? And speaking of *Chinese Handcuffs*, what about the human worth of that book's protagonist Dillon Hemingway and his brother Preston and their savage killing of Charlie the three-legged cat?

This is the question the thoughtful reader asks: If Crutcher's vision doesn't include a loving or even a fair God, what positive force does he see in the world?

The positive force in Crutcher's vision is the human spirit. Yes, his work is full of ghastly examples of humankind, but it is also peopled with glorious examples. Virgil Byrnes exists in all his lethal toxicity, but so does Sarah Byrnes with her strength and so does Eric "Moby" Calhoune with his commitment to her, and so do Carver Middleton and Cynthia Lemry with the courage and the love they exercise on her behalf. By exercising what's glorious in us—and along with some good luck—we can save ourselves and each other.

Crutcher presents this idea of the complexity of human nature in *Chinese Handcuffs*. Dillon is talking to Preston in a letter:

> I know we promised not to tell about Charlie, Pres, but I did. I told Stacy . . . and she said it was a leak . . . where . . . a crack appears in the structure we've built to keep ourselves decent, and our own personal evil seeps out. . . . It's one of the hard ways, she says, that we learn human beings are connected by the ghastly as well as the glorious. (*CH,* 14)

He presents it again, in his own voice, in a Greenwillow Books publicity brochure:

> What I believe I have gained, and what I hope my writing reflects from working these past twenty years with people in difficult situations, is a sense of the connection between all human beings—the ghastly as well as the glorious.[4]

In the world Crutcher creates in his stories the fact of human ghastliness doesn't negate the fact of human glory. Both qualities are indeed "facts" of life. Humanity is flawed, to be sure, but there is no fatal flaw in the human character, like the idea of original sin, that creates the necessity for divine intervention. There is no divine intervention. The people in Crutcher's world rise and fall, are saved and lost, by the degree to which they are connected to the humanity in themselves and others.

Dakota's advice to Louie in *Running Loose* is the foundation of Crutcher's vision. It is so vital that he presents it twice more verbatim. He quotes it in his essay on healing, and he quotes it again in the story "In the Time I Get" from *Athletic Shorts*.

In the summer after the year chronicled in *Running Loose,* Louie meets a young man named Darren. Darren is Dakota's nephew; he has AIDS, and he's come to Trout to die. In his preface to the story Crutcher writes of Louie: "another challenge, in the form of his own bigotry, stands before him to be confronted. And the stakes are friendship and basic human dignity."[5] These are always the challenges in Crutcher stories, of course; these and mortality itself.

Louie is working in the Buckhorn, Dakota's tavern, and Dakota asks him what he thinks of Darren. "I looked away," Louie tells us, "stacking dirty glasses from a tray beneath the bar, while my face burned and my heart hammered. I can't lie to Dakota. When Becky died, he saw me naked." ("Time," 136) Louie remembers what Dakota told him about how the world works, and Crutcher quotes the passage. Then, after the passage has run its page and a half, Louie says this: "Dakota lives in my soul" ("Time," 137).

Dakota earned this sacred place in Louie's life because of what he told him about the world. He didn't try to comfort Louie—or to comfort himself—with a comfortable lie. Dakota's description of how the world works rang true to Louie. This truth helped set Louie free from the grief, rage, and confusion of the moment, and it set a foundation on which he could create an equilibrium in this world that hurts most of us more than we deserve. Louie does not "reconcile with God," as an *English Journal* article contends.[6] Dakota lives in Louie's soul because, in a sense, he saved Louie's life.

Crutcher remembers meeting Robert Cormier on a panel at an NCTE session, and Cormier seeming surprised at the help Crutcher made available to his characters.

> [H]e'd just written *Fade* and I'd just written *Chinese Handcuffs*. We were talking about the books on the panel and he said: "You use adult wisdom sometimes," as though he was almost surprised. That was something he has usually chosen not to do. I like adult characters to be able to make sense of things and that's what I use them for." (Smith, 67–68)

A close look at Crutcher's work reveals that he uses adult wisdom—and makes help available to his characters—*all* the time.

In a Crutcher world, for example, help would have existed for a character like Jerry Renault in Cormier's *The Chocolate War,* or Jerry would have possessed the strength to help himself. This is not to suggest that Crutcher is a more compassionate man than Cormier. Robert Cormier is a compassionate and gracious man, admired and loved. What it suggests is a difference in vision.

Storytellers are the gods of the universes they create in their stories. If they believe in a glorious aspect to human nature as well as a ghastly aspect, if they "like nice, tight justice," as Walker

Dupree says in *Stotan!* (*Stotan!,* 158), they have the power to create a world where these qualities exist. In *Stotan!,* for example, Crutcher allows the Stotans to rescue Nortie from his abusive father, and Max, their coach, to intercede on their behalf with the Nazi Marty O'Brien.

Crutcher offers a different form of help in *Chinese Handcuffs* when Dillon resolves to seek the wisdom of his father.

> [Dillon] remembered the number of times he'd seen the cheap mahogany plaque on the desk in his dad's study: THE UNEXAMINED LIFE IS NOT WORTH LIVING. *So when it's examined,* he thought, *what then?* He knew how to examine, but he didn't know how to evaluate. He would ask his dad, soon, what the plaque meant to him." (*CH,* 126)

And when Dillon goes to his dad, his dad will be available.

In *Staying Fat for Sarah Byrnes* Eric Calhoune is lying in bed after midnight, staring at the ceiling, examining his life. He has just learned how Sarah's face was burned, and Jodi Mueller, his first and only girlfriend, has just told him that she aborted Mark Brittain's baby. Eric's evaluation is that since life has become more serious around him he needs to get more serious with it. He knows he needs to take greater responsibility, and he knows he needs help. He has a place to go for that help because Crutcher gives it to him:

> [Y]ou know what scares me? It's easy to sit back, like in Lemry's class, and take shots at guys like Brittain, but if Jodi and I end up together, I'll have to perform. . . . When the class is discussing abortion, I can't sit back with no real opinion if I have a girlfriend who's had one.
>
> I need to have a serious talk with my mother before it's too late. (*SB,* 110–11)

Eric has his mother, Sandy Calhoune, to rely on. He knows she'll give him the help he needs in evaluating his life. His teacher Cynthia Lemry, whom he calls "one of the most exquisite human beings alive" and "the women's rights poster girl. I mean poster person" (*SB,* 15), is another example of help available from someone who, because she has lived longer, has had the opportunity to pay attention to life over a longer span of time and to acquire wisdom.

Nowhere in his work does Crutcher present this idea that we can help each other—and the idea of our *connectedness*—more powerfully than in a letter Sarah Byrnes writes to Eric from the psych ward about an experience that not only changes but saves her life.

Sarah explains that she'd always wanted to be as mean as she could to all the people who'd been mean to her. She needed her dad then because being around him kept her that way. But this changed when she got to the hospital and saw some kids who had a lot more wrong with them than she did, except that what was wrong with them wasn't visible. She tells Eric about a girl on the ward who watched from a place under the stairs where she couldn't be seen while her dad kicked her little brother to death. This girl still hated herself for not stopping it, even though she was only six when it happened. Sarah was sitting in the group, pretending she'd been beamed up, when the girl told the story. And then all of a sudden the girl was shrieking and crying. She ran across the circle and hugged Sarah and told her not to give up and that she felt on the inside like Sarah looked on the outside. The girl said she couldn't stand it if Sarah gave up because the kids who were scarred had to stick together. "I wanted to talk and tell her I would stay and fight," Sarah tells Eric,

> but I couldn't because if I talk they'll think I'm better and send me home. It hurts so much inside me I can hardly stand it, and I've thought more about killing myself, but I know I won't. . . . ever since that girl hugged me, I know I'm not the only one in the world who hurts, or even the person who hurts the worst. If the ones who hurt the worst stay, then I can, too. (*SB,* 128–29)

Ghastly lives and yet a glorious transformation. The kids in the therapy group have walked through the horror of their lives together, and it is the connection with them that Sarah discovers along the way that saves her from suicide.

After Sarah has decided she wants to live, her life is still in danger from her father. Eric risks his own life to help save Sarah now, and Carver Middleton, Sandy Calhoune's boyfriend, also does in a sense. Cynthia Lemry and her husband Tom adopt Sarah, who becomes Sarah Lemry. Now that Sarah has a connection to people who love her, and now that she's able to accept love, she no longer needs the bitterness that fueled her life, and this transforms her state of soul.

When Sarah's ordeal becomes public knowledge she's asked by a journalist if she'll finally seek the reconstructive surgery denied her so long, and Sarah smiles and says, "I don't know. It'd be a shame to change just when I'm getting used to it" (*SB,* 213).

The implication here might be that her transformation has been so complete that she no longer wishes she could hide her scars. In any case, it's a powerful example of a soul saved—for a longer stay in this world, at least—by human intervention and human love.

5. The Adventures of Louie Banks

Louie's adventures take him beyond the football field and the running track and even beyond the miasmic territory of romance. We can break our bones on the football field and on the track, and we can be defeated and diminished. In the great swamp of romance we can lose our hearts. But Louie Banks ventures into the realm of ethics, a wilderness that swallows more people than the most remote parts of Idaho or any other bit of earthy geography, a region where it really is possible to lose our souls.

And what might be the quest of this small-town teenage hero? It's not a grail quest. No nice car, no trophy, no fire giver to unchain from a rock, no maiden to wake with a kiss. Nothing tangible. Louie quests for the right way to live.

And how goes Louie into battle, how accompanied and how armed? Like Ulysses has he a gang of kick-ass pals "that have toiled and wrought and thought with [him], that ever with a frolic welcome took the thunder and the sunshine?" No, it's just Louie on this journey. The path to this place is only wide enough for the self. His weapons? Louie's weapons are his intelligence and his will. When he's older he'll have knowledge as a tool. But right now all he has are these qualities of character. And, like the classic hero, he has a guide. Also like the classic hero, Louie undergoes a lapse of self-control and falls into disgrace. Louie's lapse isn't exactly the madness of Hercules; it is, however, inappropriate enough to scandalize the citizens of Trout.

But let's go back to Trout, Idaho, and the tangible: Yes, Louie is hungry to crack the starting lineup on the football team; and, yes, he runs his lungs out to beat Washington in the two-mile; and, yes, in the story "In the Time I Get" he struggles mightily to keep Carter's friendship and still practice compassion for Darren who is dying of AIDS; but more important to Louie than achieving these things is achieving them ethically. If it takes playing dirty football to play for Trout, Louie Banks won't play. If Washington doesn't tell Louie he's giving his all to beat him, then Louie is going to have a real tough time giving *his* all, because his sense of what's right in competition won't let him. And if Carter can't be friends with him because Louie's trying to be decent to a new guy in town who has AIDS, then Louie will forgo Carter's friendship.

It's true that the majority of Crutcher's readers appreciate him primarily for plot and character and for his narrative style, which includes the humor so many readers enjoy. But as fine a storyteller as Crutcher is, the great achievement of the first third of his writing life is the facility with which he integrates ideas into story.

A subtle rhetorical quality runs through Crutcher's work, as it does in all stories of lasting value. Crutcher is relentless in his presentation of plot and character and equally relentless in his presentation of theme. But because he weaves ideas so tightly with events—and because the events are vividly rendered and profound in their effect on character—this rhetorical quality is submerged. As *Running Loose* proceeds, Crutcher presents characters and dramatizes them, and the reader is forced to make ethical judgments along with Louie. The subtlety works this way: Most of us don't realize we're making ethical judgments when we read; our stomachs get tight, or our eyes fill with tears, or we want to stand and cheer—which is to say we react to literary characters and events as we react to real life. It's only later, when those feelings have worked their way into the intellect where they transform into language and become ideas, that we determine what we call *meaning*.

We live in a time when the word *rhetoric* is most often used to describe insincere speech—like the *rhetoric* that issues from our nation's capitol. But the word also refers to *the art of persuasion,* and that's how we're using it here. It's odd in an era when so many of us are concerned with *values* that a writer as ethically grounded as Crutcher hasn't been snatched from the YA genre and brought to the center of our discussion about the right ways to live.

Louie says he got "a pretty good draw" (*RL,* 23) with his parents, whom he calls by their first names. But Louie wouldn't have Boomer's dad if he were the only one left in the world. "It's not hard to see," he says, "where Boomer comes by his sweet attitude" (*RL,* 25).

Here Crutcher presents one of his dominant themes. The theme isn't simply *the dysfunctional family,* it's *why* families become dysfunctional. It's a statement of cause and effect: Children inherit their inability to love themselves and others from their parents because their parents treat them as unworthy of love; kids learn to be mean because they're treated mean.

Louie has already illustrated this cause-effect relationship in one of the anecdotes he used to characterize Boomer. Back when they were in grade school the boys were telling tales about the various things and people that got sucked down into the mud that accompanies Trout's spring thaw. Young Boomer wants to one-up Carter, so he tells the kids his dad's logging truck got swallowed two years before. Louie goes in the house and asks Boomer's dad if it's true. Boomer's dad storms out, grabs Boomer, jerks him inside, and whips "the crap out of him" (*RL*, 13). Boomer returns, his face streaked with tears and his new birthday shirt torn, and tells the kids they have to leave. Then his dad throws his presents away. Boomer blames Louie.

To contrast this image of a parent, Crutcher has Louie describe Brenda this way:

> [S]he's full of love. I mean she loves this family like love's the mail. She delivers through rain and sleet and dark of night and conditions that are a whole lot worse than any of those. (*RL,* 26)

Running Loose is a plot-driven action story. And it is also an inquiry into values. Crutcher sets up the inquiry with his narrative stance. Louie is looking back on a year full of seminal events. He's battled unprincipled men and been hurt by the forces of circumstance. Life demanded Louie's attention in a big way, Louie paid attention, he learned some things, and now he's primed to tell us. It's the perfect stance from which to examine human behavior, to consider whether there might be a guiding hand behind circumstance, and to articulate conclusions.

Crutcher also sets up Louie as a trustworthy narrator and one most readers find sympathetic. In the first few lines Louie admits that he made himself look like a jerk during the past year; a few pages later he admits to being a *wussy* in a number of ways—principally because he spends half his life worrying about hurting other people's feelings and wondering if they like him. We tend to trust people capable of self-deprecation, and we warm easily to those willing to reveal their secrets. We warm to such people, that is, if we sense that their revelations issue from strength of character rather than weakness and self-serving motives. Can we imagine Coach Lednecky and Principal Jasper admitting they made themselves look foolish? No, we can't. Such characters aren't motivated by a desire to get at the truth of their lives. Such men follow the Bart Simpson rule of revelation: "I didn't do it, nobody saw me do it, you can't prove anything."

Lednecky is Crutcher's early focus. Lednecky has a winning record as Trout's football coach, but he makes a sorry human being. At first we might only find him blustery and pretentious, but it's not long before we see he's a hypocrite, a liar, and a stone racist. Here's what he says about Kevin Washington, an opposing quarterback who moved into the league from Oakland: "Now I don't want to sound prejudiced; but I played with blacks up at the U, and there's only one way you can stop them. That's to hurt 'em. . . . I want that Washington kid out of the game! Early!" (*RL,* 49).

The racism and stupidity (isn't that redundant?) are loathsome enough, but what's worse—what eats away at our civilization—is that the man is teaching it to young people. We want our schools to turn on the lights for young Americans so they can find the best in themselves. But Lednecky is perpetuating barbarism. He is, in fact, institutionalizing it.

> "Kill that jungle bunny!" Boomer screamed.
> "Yeah! Yeah!" Guys were going nuts. (*RL,* 49)

The discerning reader will have written Lednecky off before the preceding passage appears. In the first team meeting he tells the boys they can win their third state championship this year, and "we can't allow *anything* to stand in our way" (*RL,* 29). Crutcher uses Lednecky's reference to not allow *anything* to stand in their way to set up Boomer's illegal hit on Washington, which sets up Louie to make a choice that changes the course of his life.

A starting position on the football team is not the sole focus of Louie's desire as that literally fateful senior year begins. Along with every guy in school, Louie has it bad for Becky Sanders. One reviewer wrote that Becky was "perhaps the weakest element in the novel . . . , a young man's dream of love and sweet reason."[1] Becky is a "young man's dream," certainly, and maybe she too clearly speaks for Crutcher; but as an intelligent and sophisticated big-city girl come to the mountains she rings true for many readers.

When Crutcher gets Louie and Becky up in the hills on their first date, he answers a question that both Louie and the reader have been puzzling over: What is this girl who could have any guy in school—Carter the quarterback, for example—doing with Louie Banks who is only marginally cool? The answer comes in a lovely *moment,* as the screenwriters say. Louie and Becky have been talking about the animals that live in the mountains, about how the animals know whether people are there to shoot them or just to look. Becky believes animals can tell what people are like. A few beats later Louie asks Becky why she chose him, and this is her reply: "Because if I were an animal in these woods and I saw you here, I'd come up to you" (44). Just a sweet, simple moment where qualities of Becky's character are illustrated and much about Louie is implied.

So Louie and Becky get together, and she's a support to him and a shelter when he quits the team and the storm blows up at school. Louie believes that as long as Becky is with him he can maintain some dignity. We know, however—because he told us when the story opened—that Becky doesn't stay with him. Crutcher's work with dramatic irony here creates a heightened tension and pulls us deeper into the story.

This use of irony is called "dramatic" or "situational" because it depends on the structure of the work rather than wordplay. When Louie tells us he's okay as long as he's got Becky, he doesn't know that at a point a little further on in the plot he won't have her. But we *do* know, and this knowledge engages our emotions. "Don't count on it, Louie!" we want to yell. "You're gonna get hurt!"

Crutcher uses another kind of irony when Louie returns with Norm and Brenda after Jasper has booted him out of school. Louie describes Jasper as just an older version of Lednecky. He finds Jasper scarier, however, because he's smarter. Jasper might be smarter, and he's certainly more polished, but he's no more ethical.

Norm and Jasper go 'round and 'round. Jasper wants Louie to apologize for his behavior, and Norm says Louie won't apologize because he's not sorry. Finally Jasper says he'll allow Louie back into school under the condition that he doesn't participate in sports. He believes Louie's behavior calls for a public show of punishment because Louie's attitude "could be damaging to the whole school" (96).

Let's consider the irony: What is Louie's attitude? He took a stand against dirty football and in a larger sense racism; he accurately described Lednecky as a liar; he didn't apologize for something he wasn't sorry for. So Louie's attitude is to act ethically, to take "a righteous stand," in Dakota's words (*RL,* 90). And how might taking a righteous stand damage high school students? It wouldn't, of course. To consider values and discover principles to live by is one of the purposes of an education. It might even be *the* purpose of an education. But it also might create inconvenience for the person in charge of those students, and it might also inconvenience the students themselves as it did Louie; they might pay a price for their stand like the students who were hurt or killed during the civil rights movement.

The irony here arises out of the words themselves. Crutcher creates the meaning he wants—which is to say he tries to express the truth—by using words that contradict the truth. The literal meaning is opposite of the meaning made clear by the experience of the story.

Crutcher allows Louie and Becky one more sweet interlude before their time together is up, and rhetoric abounds here. The part Norm plays in their trek to Becky's cabin is noteworthy because to some readers it will contradict his image as a man of principle. Does a man of principle allow his 17-year-old son out on an overnighter with his girlfriend—and assist the boy by lying to his wife about it? This man of principle does, and Crutcher shows us the basis for his action.

We know that Norm and Brenda trust Louie because we heard Norm tell Jasper so. When Louie tells Norm the plan, all Norm says is "You know what you're doing?" (*RL,* 110), and Louie replies that he thinks so.

Here's a father who trusts his son to do what's right. If Louie believes it's right to make love, that's Louie's decision. Everything Norm can do to shape Louie's character he did long ago. That Louie trusts him enough to ask for his help in the first place is evidence of this.

But making love is not the consummation of the trip. When Becky takes off her blouse and crawls under the covers, Louie says, "I don't think I can do this." Becky, who has some sexual experience, responds with words Louie hopes he'll always remember:

> "It's a funny thing about things like sex, that we're supposedly not supposed to do. Once it's okay to do it, it's okay not to." (*RL,* 117)

This may as well be Crutcher's voice, and his voice continues in the conversation Becky and Louie have about sex and love. Becky says the best thing about making love is before and after, lying together, taking care of each other, and getting close. It's Becky's contention that people need not have sex to make love, and when Louie looks back on that night he realizes he wouldn't have it any other way.

Speaking of contemporary sexual values, the view Crutcher expresses here could be construed as a realistic (as opposed to the prevailing unrealistic) argument for abstinence. The subject of mortality enters the story with Becky's death, and from mortality it's no distance at all to religion.

Louie leaves the scene of Becky's death and drives to the lake, then to the meadow where they went on their first date. He walks the woods for hours and ends up back at the meadow. There's a good moon, and he sits down in the dim shadow cast by the big pine that Crutcher introduced in the earlier scene. In moments the symbolic suggestion of this magnificent natural creation will reveal itself. It will strike some readers in the intellect and take the form of language. It will hit other readers in their emotions. They will *feel* the effect, and that feeling may or may not ever translate itself into language.

Louie tells us that he's never been religious but that he prays sometimes. This is such a time, so he looks up through the moonlight at heaven. He tells God he doesn't get this and that it isn't acceptable. If there's a good reason, Louie wants to hear it. And he's not going to listen to the cliché about God working in strange and wondrous ways that people can't understand. "God didn't say diddly," Louie tells us. "The branches moved a little in the breeze, and the moon just kept shinin' on" (*RL,* 127).

Louie waits a little longer, and when he gets no response he grabs an ax from the pickup and chops down the tree, all the time screaming, "Is this yours? How do you like it?" (*RL,* 127).

Now the tree has served its symbolic function. Crutcher set it up as one of God's majestic creations. Louie feels that God took Becky from him, so he takes a beautiful thing from God.

With Becky's death a new antagonistic force and a new theme enter the story. Fate—or whatever we call it: chance, God's plan—is the toughest antagonist we ever face, and none of us defeats it. And this question of why—why do things happen as they do? Why do the good suffer? Where is the justice we yearn for?—is probably the central question of our lives. We probably have to come down somewhere on this question if we're to find peace in a life that hurts us so profoundly.

Crutcher comes down with both feet on the side of chance. In *Running Loose* and each of his other novels he presents a world where things happen "just because they happen" (139), as Dakota says. We took up the subject of Crutcher's vision in chapter 4, so we won't go deeply into it here. One brief reference to chance as the causal force in life appears when Louie finally comes home on the night of Becky's death, and Norm's first words to him are "Bad break" (*RL,* 129).

Where Crutcher elaborates most broadly on the theme is in Louie's talk with Dakota, his guide on this ethical quest, after Louie has disrupted Becky's funeral. Their conversation is discussed at length in chapter 4, but the transitional element Crutcher uses to get into that scene is worthy of a look.

Louie sits down in the dark tavern. The only light comes from across the room, dim and eerie. Louie goes closer and sees it's a beer sign. He stares at the illusion of rushing water. And at a horseshoe with a little banner over it that says "Good Luck" (*RL,* 138).

The careful reader is struck with admiration at such elegant use of unifying detail.

No good story lets its hero off without an excess of pain and trouble, and Crutcher is not through with Louie Banks yet.

Louie is leaving the funeral early, and he's almost to the door when the minister brings up the question of why. "Why, oh Lord? Why, in the prime of her young life was she stricken down?" And he continues. "We cannot answer these questions alone. But we know that you sometimes move in strange and mysterious ways that we, lost in our earthly ignorance, cannot understand" (*RL,* 136).

Louie could have held it together if the man hadn't said this. Instead he flips. "Why are you saying that?" he yells.

> He doesn't move in strange and mysterious ways. He doesn't move at all! He sits up there on His fat butt and lets guys like you earn a living making excuses for all the rotten things that happen. Or maybe He does something low-down every once in a while so He can get a bunch of us together, scared and on our knees. (*RL,* 136–37)

Carter and Boomer, who for the moment is moved to sympathy, rush Louie out through the crowd. Again Louie takes off in the pickup. When he returns that night he has the conversation with Dakota that begins "What kind of worthless God would let this happen?" (*RL,* 139). Dakota's response, as we've noted previously, is "This life ain't partial, boy" (*RL,* 140).

Probably the most negative commentary one can find about *Running Loose* asserts that

> Louie never understands that he is not the center of the universe. Ironically, centering on its young hero as it does, this is also the novel's tragic flaw, for like a short story protagonist its hero never develops. Sadly, he never experiences the epiphany that would open his eyes to his immaturity, either.[2]

The novel's enduring success suggests it has no "tragic flaw," but still this question of Louie's growth and maturity is intriguing. His behavior at the funeral is impolitic, to be sure. It is rash, tactless. But how many of us have wanted to let loose a similar tirade under similar circumstances? Was it maturity that kept us from blowing our corks? Probably not. It was probably socialization. It was probably fear.

We know why Louie blows at the funeral, but let's examine his motivation for destroying Becky's plaque, which isn't Becky's plaque at all but Jasper's plaque.

Louie likes the idea of a tree to memorialize Becky, and a new tree in the world replaces the one lost to his act of revenge; but he's not about to listen to anything Jasper has to say about her. He tells Carter he wishes people would stop trying to remember Becky the way they do. He knew her better than anyone, and he hates it that people remember her as valedictorian, cheerleader, and honor society member. He knows those things weren't important to her. Carter replies that it's not up to Louie to say what Becky stood for, and Louie admits he's right. But Carter's only half right, and Louie gives in too easily. If we want the reality of Becky, rather than the appearance, we have to go to Louie because he's the only one who really knows what she stood for. He's the only one who got past the appearance.

"But Jasper just uses that kind of stuff," Louie goes on. "He'll make it sound like she stood for all the things he stands for, and I *know* that's not right" (*RL,* 173).

Maybe it is immaturity that allows Louie to go after the plaque with a sledgehammer, but it is not immaturity that allows him to recognize and to exercise contempt for Jasper's hypocrisy.

Louie leaves us, in *Running Loose,* with a statement of what he's learned. He mentions a number of things, the most quoted of which is "that there's no use being honorable with dishonorable men" (*RL,* 189). But is having learned some things—even some vital things—enough of a change to fulfill the demands of the novel form? Probably it is, considering the number of readers who conclude their journey with Louie feeling the satisfaction that comes with closure. Closure isn't simply the feeling we have when we come to the end of something; that feeling might just be relief. Closure is the feeling we get at the end of a period of evolution. And evolution, of course, is growth.

"In the Time I Get": The Adventures of Louie Banks Commence Once More

Eight years have passed in Crutcher's life, but only a week has gone by since some crazed vandal bashed Jasper's plaque out of its concrete for the second time. Crutcher wrote the story in 1990, but he set it back in that early summer of 1982. If we're looking for an *epiphany* in Louie's life, a moment of realization, a monumental change, here's where we find it.

Louie is the narrator of his own story again, and again he's looking back. This time the focus of the experience is losing two friends, one his lifelong best friend Carter and the other a visitor to Trout who becomes a friend. They are lost, of course, in different ways.

Crutcher writes a preface to the story in which he says that "all of us prejudge people on *some* basis, be it race, sex, sexual preference" ("Time," 127), and he goes on to say that the challenge Louie faces this time is his own bigotry. So when Louie takes note of Darren's *elegant* quality, we infer *effeminate* and feel that sexual preference might be part of the story's focus. Our conclusion seems more likely—and we see Crutcher working against stereotypes in a subtle way—when Louie tells us Darren's handshake was firm. Crutcher wouldn't have Louie mention the quality of the handshake if he didn't want to counter a stereotypical reaction to *elegance* in a man.

In the opening segment Darren, Dakota's nephew, introduces the subject of death. He's heard that Louie lost Becky, and he wants to know what death is like for the people left behind. At the conclusion of this segment, Darren tells Louie he has AIDS.

Louie panics. Now he knows why he felt uneasy at Darren's appearance and manner: "his *elegance* was something I normally associated with someone who's a homo" ("Time," 133).

Louie lies awake after midnight. He's repulsed by his thoughts of Darren, but a voice in him keeps saying, "Hey, this guy is *dying,* and no matter what else is going on, still, he's dying" ("Time," 134). Louie knows a lot about death. At the conclusion of *Running Loose* he tells us he learned "what a vicious, miserable, ugly thing" (*RL,* 190) it is. Louie feels ashamed at his inclination toward sympathy for Darren, and right here begins his struggle against the bigotry that Crutcher believes infests us all.

Darren has AIDS, but Louie isn't sure he's homosexual. He hates knowing Darren's secret and resents him for revealing it. When Louie can't avoid Darren he takes Carter along so Darren won't have a chance to talk.

Before long Dakota asks Louie what he thinks of his nephew. Louie can't lie because he owes Dakota too much for his kindness after Becky's death. Louie admits that he's keeping clear of Darren. He also admits he doesn't know what to do. Dakota replies that he doesn't have any ideas either, " 'cept to tell the truth" ("Time," 138).

A morning comes when Louie and Darren both show up for work at eight. Louie says he's sorry for having run away after Darren told him. He should have at least stayed and talked about it. Darren says it was a normal reaction. Not many people want to have anything to do with someone dying in such an ugly way.

It takes all Louie's nerve, but he admits that it would help to know how Darren got it.

Darren is truthful in his response. There's no equivocation in the language. "I'm gay," Darren says. "I got it having anal intercourse with another gay man who was infected" ("Time," 139).

The importance of telling the truth is one of the strongest themes in all of Crutcher's work. "Anal intercourse" is what Crutcher has Darren say, and it gives Louie the precise information he needs. Darren takes the chance that Louie will be repulsed at the truth, but if he wants Louie for a friend this is a chance he has to take. Darren doesn't have much time left in his life, and the truth frees him to use that time to the fullest. And Crutcher takes a chance too. He knows that the Cascade High School Library copy of *Running Loose* was locked in the principal's desk because of language and ideas less "offensive" than this.

Darren goes on to tell Louie what it's like having AIDS. He says no one touches him anymore, and this strikes Louie as the worst part of it. Here we see Crutcher setting up the potential for a climactic gesture: Will the voice of decency be louder than the bigot in Louie? Will he give his new friend this small gift before he dies? But Darren says he won't ask Louie to touch him. He knows why people don't do that. He knows about fear. This theme of touching as a manifestation of nonerotic love, or simple human charity, becomes pivotal to the story as the conflicts grow.

There's always a great deal at stake in Crutcher stories. Darren's life is already lost as this story begins; what's at stake for him is a chance to find peace with himself and a portion of charity in the world in the time he's got. For Louie the stakes are, as Crutcher says in his preface, "friendship and basic human dignity" ("Time," 127).

The growth of Louie's friendship with Darren begins to threaten his lifelong friendship with Carter. Carter tells Louie he'd better be careful, and Louie asks of what. Carter doesn't know if Louie's figured it out yet, "but Dakota's nephew is a faggot."

"What?" ("Time," 146) is Louie's response.

The more Louie gets to know Darren, the more his empathy for him grows and the more Darren becomes an individual rather than a representative of a group. Louie knows that if he keeps spending time with Darren he could lose Carter. Darren will be dead, and Carter will be gone. "Boy," Louie says, "nothin' comes cheap" ("Time," 147).

Nothing of value does come cheap, especially knowledge of the world. Crutcher's characters always learn things, and this generosity with knowledge is one of the most valuable qualities in his work.

Darren is in the county hospital, and Louie goes to visit. His room is all the way at the back of the building. He's dropped 15 pounds. His face has gone skeletal. Louie remembers one of the things Darren first told him: *The worst part is nobody touches you.*

Darren asks Louie what it's like to be left behind, and Louie remembers Dakota's words about telling the truth. So he tells Darren how bad it is, how angry you get at the person for dying.

Darren is quiet for a minute, then he asks Louie to hold his hand.

"To this day," Louie tells us, "I hate myself for what I almost said. I almost said no. But I love myself for what I did say. I said yes, and I reached over and put his hand between both of mine" ("Time," 150).

Crutcher shows us what we can earn if we pay the price of doing the decent thing: We can earn our own love. We can be healthy people. We can be at peace. Here's that theme again: There is a way to be happy in a life that's impartial to our happiness, and this way is to tell the truth and to listen to the voice of decency inside us.

But there's always a price.

Louie is holding Darren's hand when he looks up and sees Carter in the doorway.

Darren is later transferred to the hospital in Boise. Louie drives down to see him, but Dakota's in the room, so Louie stays in the doorway. That theme of touch culminates in the scene Louie describes. There's probably not a more moving scene anywhere in Crutcher's work, and it's all the more moving because of the restraint of emotion in the prose. None of our attention is pulled into the writing. The writing is simple and clear; we look through it to the human experience it portrays:

> Dakota was up on the bed with him, his grizzled old arms around Darren's shoulders, and he was kind of petting Darren's head. ("Time," 151)

On a late summer day after Darren's death Louie meets Carter on the football field. Carter has avoided Louie since the hospital. "I told you that guy was a fag" (*Shorts*, 153), he says.

Louie starts to explain about AIDS. He wants to tell him what it's like to look a dying man in the eye. He'd like his oldest friend to know how much bigger his heart has grown. But he doesn't answer Carter at all because he realizes he's getting ready to lose him. What he says is, "Look, Cart, I don't have AIDS, okay? Let's just throw some balls" ("Time," 154).

Carter bullets four or five passes so hard they almost go through Louie, but Louie holds onto them all. The boys don't talk, and this is the last time they see each other before they leave for their different colleges.

"I think I passed Carter up that day," Louie tells us in conclusion.

> All my life I've wanted to be like him, be able to throw a football fifty yards through a tire or pop a twenty-five-foot jumper or drive through the streets of Trout leaning back in my bucket seat with an elbow out the window, people on the sidewalk truly believing I owned the town. But that day *I* was bigger. That was the day, knowing all I had to lose, I quietly turned and stood my ground. ("Time," 154)

Criticism and Conflict

Most of the criticism and commentary on *Running Loose* has been positive, as we would expect considering all the Best Books lists it's been on. Two writers expressed surprise that it transcended the arena of sport. One found it "far more than a sports book: it is a book about decisions and their consequences; it is a tragedy in the classical sense."[3] Another said "it's more than just a sports story. It's a tightly plotted, compelling tale about a boy who happens to be an athlete."[4]

Character is the element most people find to be Crutcher's narrative strength in the book. Representative of the positive comments is this: "Crutcher's characterization is powerful (especially the depiction of the tyrannical and bullying football coach) and his protagonist's tender relationships are equally convincing."[5] Another writer notes the "memorable minor characters as well as major ones."[6]

It's probably more a comment on young adult literature than on *Running Loose* itself that so many reviewers mentioned the "supportive" characterization of Louie's parents and other adults. Such supportive adult characters are relatively few in YA literature.

Nearly every review of *Running Loose,* regardless of whether it finds the book completely successful, sees it as a fine first novel.

It can be a fascinating experience to read a number of reviews of a work; we see a surprising range of opinion, and often not just disagreement but diametric opposition. Most reviewers find Crutcher's characterization successful and Louie an engaging, funny narrator. But one—who also finds the book "not well written"—considers Louie's first-person narration "quite flat" (Ancona, 109).

Readers of "In the Time I Get" are equally divergent in their reactions. In a letter to Crutcher, a library media specialist from a middle school in Vermont says

> I was not prepared for the impact of your last story, "In the Time I Get." That story is one of the finest I have ever read. My seventeen-year-old had tears in her eyes, and the next day gave it [to] her psychology teacher to read. She, too, was moved by the powerful message of Darren's struggle with AIDS and with his family's rejection. Although I felt "sorry" for those dying of AIDS, my heart didn't see Darren, who has become a "real" person that I will remember when I read the AIDS statistics in the newspaper.[7]

In contrast, *Athletic Shorts,* the collection that contains the story, is among seven books discussed in an *English Journal* piece titled "Honor Listing Update, 1991," but the authors of the article, who consulted others to compile the list, say they "didn't much like" "In the Time I Get" and wouldn't have included the collection if they'd made the decision solely on their own. They find the story "reek[ing] of political correctness,"[8] and that the hard-sell didactic message is too big to be stuffed into a short story.

Is It a Tempest in a Teapot?

No area of disagreement about young adult literature arouses as much real conflict as the question of whether a book is *appropriate* for young readers, and a certain passage in *Running Loose* has over the years been the focus of numerous formal challenges.

Are we speaking here of a tempest in a teapot? No, it's a penis in a popcorn box.

Louie is describing Boomer as a person who takes pleasure in the pain of others and lies about his sexual conquests. He recounts one of Boomer's stories about a date at a drive-in movie. Boomer said he cut a hole in their popcorn box and "stuck Ol Norton up through" (*RL,* 12). When his date reached for some popcorn she was, of course, seized by sexual frenzy. Louie makes clear how lame the story is, that Boomer is "so dumb he doesn't know every jerk in the world has told that story" (*RL,* 12).

Among the cities where *Running Loose* has been challenged is Berlin, Pennsylvania. Crutcher wrote a letter "to all concerned" there in which he addresses the question. Here are some of his comments:

> No young person who has read *Running Loose* will ever believe that is a true story. For those of you who haven't read the book, know that the story was told by a bully, and the narrator calls game on it in the next paragraph. Is it a pornographic story? Of course it is—it denigrates women. Is it called pornographic? Yes, it is; Louie Banks plays it up as exactly that.
>
> My guess is that any teacher or parent could clear up any problem a young person might have with that passage in about ten

minutes by talking with them about people who have to put others down to make themselves feel better, or more importantly talking with them about their own fears for children and why passages like that sometimes make adults feel nervous and protective. . . . I have a feeling that considerations about popcorn and penises would fade away, or at least return to their proper perspective.

Besides being a writer, I am also a child and family therapist. I can imagine many of you saying "I'd never let him counsel *my* family" and that would be your choice, but I have observed a lot of family dynamics over the past twelve years and I am certain that a tremendous amount of conflict comes from adults trying to control children's experiences rather than helping them make sense of those experiences. Whether you like it or not, that scene . . . is tame compared to what your children are exposed to every day. If you register fear or rail against something this lukewarm, many of your kids will simply consider you out of touch. When parents put themselves into that position, they take themselves off the short list of people to turn to. When a school puts itself in that position it seems out of touch and loses credibility in many children's eyes. We cannot control what children think—and hooray for that—we can only help them make sense.[9]

6. *Stotan,* Stotan, All the Way!

What exactly does it mean for a narrative writer to get better? For some it means that their powers of presentation improve, which is to say they learn to write a more efficient—maybe a more *elegant*—prose. Others learn to manipulate the elements of narrative with greater facility, and they can use this facility to create a more complex picture of life. Such complexity usually means a greater number of characters and a more intricate maze of plots, and it offers a deeper look into the mysteries of what it is to be human.

The American Library Association named *Stotan!* one of the best one hundred young adult books written in the last quarter century. Why *Stotan!* over *Running Loose* or the other books? The question won't matter to a lot of people who love Crutcher's work. Each book satisfies in its own way. But those of us as interested in the craft of writing as we are in love with the experience of reading will certainly want to root around in the question. If *Stotan!* is a better book than *Running Loose* it might just be because there's more story there to create a fuller satisfaction. Crutcher is also, however, a better writer in his second novel.

One of the qualities we sense right away is the heightened level of language. Walker Dupree is more confident and sophisticated with language than Louie Banks. Absent from this narration are Louie's "I mean"s and "kind of"s. One reason for this might be that the original conception of the book had the characters in college rather than high school, and Walker's maturity might be a remnant of that. Regardless of whether these qualities in Walker's voice are intentional, they still mirror Crutcher's increased confidence as a writer.

Early in the book Walker says he'd like to be a writer, "Maybe a journalist, maybe a storyteller. . . . I love to write things down, be they fact or fiction" (*Stotan!,* 16). And in the conclusion he says he thinks his job in life is to be an observer. "I think I'll learn to see pretty well. I think I'll know how things work—understand simple cause and effect—and, with any luck, I'll be able to pass that on" (*Stotan!,* 182). And here's something else he says:

> Funny: you walk down the street or through a shopping mall or a grocery store and look at people's faces and wonder what their lives are like . . . and you can't imagine some of the horror that goes on. (*Stotan!,* 104)

Walker does become a storyteller, of course, and he also becomes a child and family therapist. He becomes Chris Crutcher, who sees real well—particularly the horror that is hidden to most of us—and knows how things work, understands cause and effect, and passes on a load of knowledge and understanding in this book and all the others.

In fact—although lovers of *Running Loose* might not see it or acknowledge it right away—the style we've come to think of as quintessential Crutcher begins here in *Stotan!* And what is this quintessence? It's his *unequivocal intensity*. The narrative energy never lapses, and neither does the flow of events on which the narrative focuses. Not one sentence goes by that doesn't engage the reader.

The basic engaging element is voice, of course. But along with the engaging quality of the narrative voice there might be humor, a perceptive observation, a rich description, a strikingly honest revelation, an unpretentious contention about how life works, the introduction of another new event, or that old theme they made us memorize in junior high: *man's inhumanity to man*. Some element always exists to glue us to the page with an adhesive quality that resonates the message *this is important*. It always *seems* like there's something going on even when there isn't because the narrative maintains this intensity.

Crutcher's narrative strategy in *Stotan!* is to hook us on page one with the Stotan Week notice and get us to ask, as Nortie Wheeler does: "What's a Stotan Week?" (*Stotan!,* 1). He doesn't define the term *Stotan* until page 27, the boys don't begin to express their sense of what the week will entail until page 52, and the Stotan Week segment doesn't conclude until page 89. But Crutcher establishes so many plots and themes and creates so many effective characters—which is to say he involves us in such a rich story world—that this event is only one among many that we're sticking around to experience.

All the Crutcher themes are here. He established them in *Running Loose* and now sets them in different contexts and explores them more fully. Crutcher has worked the same themes and most of the same character types in everything he's written, and one of his greatest strengths is his ability to create such distinct stories in which to present them. Of course, there's always a sport.

The sport in *Stotan!* is swimming, and the Dakota figure is Max, the swimming coach. Nortie is abused and knows "the bad stuff is real" (*Stotan!,* 147); Jeff dies, but not before he illustrates the necessity of endurance in a life that skewers the innocent on the same brochette with the guilty; Elaine, the smart, independent young woman, is a model for those qualities, a locus for romance, and also splits the mysticism duties with Max; Lion, like Nortie, is acquainted with desolation; Marty O'Brien is the Boomer Cowens figure, which is to say he's among the "fools and crackpots" (*Stotan!,* 39) of which the world is full; and Walker, the storyteller, is the one who comes out the other side of the experience armed with greater knowledge to fight the battle of life.

One of the themes Crutcher established in *Running Loose* was the absence of justice: it is an unjust universe; stuff happens by chance; "the world is full of caprice and missed connections," as William Kennedy says in *Ironweed.* In *Stotan!* Crutcher extends this idea with illustrations and commentary about how we might establish a measure of justice on our own. "I like a nice, tight justice" (*Stotan!,* 158), Walker says late in the book. Earlier, he tells us about a pivotal incident in his life that took place the summer before his sophomore year. He'd gone to drag his drunken and doped older brother home from a tavern and in the process was slapped, threatened, and generally menaced by some guys with a lot of experience menacing people. He went home to bed and trembled in terror at what would happen the next time he ran into that crowd.

Now, what does a Crutcher character do—what does a Stotan do—when he's made to live in terror and knows he's done nothing to deserve it? He refuses to put up with it, that's what he does. He takes action against the forces of injustice by preparing himself for his next encounter with the group. He at least makes an attempt to protect himself and the people he loves. Specifically, what Walker did was go to Max and ask to be put in a karate course. And it worked—at least in the world of this book: "I'm not a mean guy," Walker says, "and I never go out looking, but even though I haven't passed any tests and I don't have any 'belts,' I've developed some pretty classy moves and, if it comes down to it, I can hurt you" (*Stotan!,* 14).

If it comes down to it? Of course it's going to come down to it in one way or another. It always comes down to it in a Crutcher story.

It comes down to it for Nortie in a number of ways, the first of which is the extension of another theme established in *Running Loose* that now intersects with Crutcher's inquiry into the question of justice in our lives. "You have to hurt for Nortie. He's a classic case of what can happen to a guy who's been beat up all his life. Eighteen years old and his old man still punches him around" (*Stotan!,* 20). It's the theme of abuse that Crutcher planted with Boomer Cowens and his dad.

Nortie is driving his dad's car when he's hit lightly by another car in a parking lot. Walker is with him, and they drive to Nortie's house. Nortie's dad sees the damage out the living-room window, comes barreling down the sidewalk, and jerks his son out of the car onto his hands and knees. He lifts him up and slaps the sides of his head as he screams at him. Nortie puts his hands up to protect his head, and his dad gives him a shot in the stomach that drops him.

Walker's reaction is interesting: "To this day I'm embarrassed that I didn't jump out of the car and take my best shot at Mr. Wheeler, but I sat frozen, my eyes glued to his face" (*Stotan!,* 21). One of the things that's interesting about this passage is its proximity to Walker's I-can-hurt-you speech. This is an illustration of Crutcher's commitment to creating strong characters who aren't always able to act out of strength. Walker is a good fighter, okay; but he's not an incarnation of Bruce Lee. Crutcher undercuts his characters' strengths time after time, which is one reason we find the characters credible.

But wait a minute. Who says it would have been *justice* for Walker to dish out to Mr. Wheeler the same portion of physical pain and humiliation he gave his son? That's a kind of justice, but it's also a kind of revenge. There's a quality in us that yearns to balance things, and such an act seems to us to create a balance, if only for the moments we throw the punches or plunge the knife or pull the trigger or throw the switch or drop the gas pellets or press the plunger of the syringe.

Nortie is incapable of standing up to his father in any way, so there's no chance to restore the balance that should exist and no chance to create one in its place. To create justice for Nortie we'd have to turn back time to his great-grandfather or whichever patriarch began the beating cycle. Nortie needs some source of pride to counter his humiliation, and it's his good fortune that Crutcher made him a swimmer: "he pays the pool back for every time his old man ever laid a finger on him" (*Stotan!,* 22). Walker can't create justice for Nortie, but he can jerk him out of a cycle that will destroy his soul if it doesn't kill his body first. So, a little later in the story after Nortie's dad beats him again—and a lot worse—Walker takes action: "I decided Nortie didn't live with his mom and dad anymore and Jeff and Lion and I headed over to his place to get his stuff" (*Stotan!,* 100).

This idea of standing up—particularly for oneself—becomes more and more important in Crutcher's work. He believes that standing up for ourselves is an heroic act and that it's particularly heroic for people who've been beaten down and for whom standing up takes enormous strength. There are great quantities of *mercy* in Crutcher's work and in his life, but he has not a nanosecond for the idea of victimhood as a holy state that has descended like a moronic rapture upon our country on the eve of the twenty-first century.

Walker tells us that Nortie's mom watched the initial beating out the window and didn't make a move to intervene. For a second he hates her guts, but then he thinks of the times he's seen her wearing sunglasses on dark days and long sleeves on hot days to cover up bruises of her own, and he figures she's only doing what she has to do to get along. "Still, [he says] it's hard to respect her" (*Stotan!*, 22). And we know absolutely that she can't respect herself.

Shortly after the introduction of the abuse theme and subplot, Crutcher brings on racial bigotry. The Stotans—this includes Elaine, although she doesn't swim with the guys—are sitting in the school cafeteria, when Jeff, "the serious-minded student of current affairs" (*Stotan!*, 22) shows them a copy of the *Aryan Press,* the front page of which features drawings of an ape alongside a black man, labels and arrows noting their similarities. He says these rags are all over school. Lion stands up on the table and intones across the room:

> I catch anyone passing this crap out and he'll answer to me for it! I'll kick his butt! I've been going to this school for four years and I'm proud of it! This crap stinks and I won't have it! (*Stotan!*, 25)

Good heavens! It's beginning to sound like there's a real martial spirit in this book. You bet there is. The book isn't titled *Stotan!* just to pique our curiosity. But let's hold on; a consideration of the word and its resonant qualities comes later.

There is a martial spirit in the book, but that spirit isn't defined by Lion's response. Lion's is only one of the responses to bigotry that Crutcher presents. When Max hears about the *Aryan Press* he shakes his head and says, "I wouldn't give it my time" (*Stotan!*, 26). The idea implied here—what to let go by and what to take a stand against—is another theme in the book.

And right on the tail of racial bigotry, Walker catches sight of Elaine's "fairly tight britches" (*Stotan!,* 27) as she walks to the counter. The theme of sexual desire and romance is now in the *Stotan!* stew. Walker tells us Elaine's always been one of the guys, and so it feels a little like incest watching her butt through the bug eyes of desire. She's been wedging herself into his dreams lately. But this confusion between friendship and sexual desire isn't the sole complexity: Walker already has a girlfriend. In Walker's inability to break up with Devnee, Crutcher hits hard at what he believes is essential in a relationship—honesty. "I have only one piece of advice about relationships," he says in Walker's voice, "and I learned it from bitter experience. Be straight. Anything that's unsaid is a lie" (*Stotan!,* 167). Walker doesn't come to this realization until the end of the story, however, so for most of the book he lies his head off. He feels lousy lying to this girl he loved such a short time ago, but lie he does.

We're only up to page 27 in present action, and already this seems like an astonishingly complex book. Is this *Stotan!* or *A Portrait of the Artist as a Young Man*? It's *Stotan!,* all right, and upon examination it *is* an astonishingly complex book. But complexity isn't its beauty. It's the access Crutcher gives to the complexity that's beautiful.

On this page a definition of *Stotan* appears:

> "A Stotan is a cross between a Stoic and a Spartan," Elaine says. "The term was coined by Percy Cerruti, coach of the great Australian miler Herb Elliot in the late fifties and early sixties. . . . Ceruti used that term to describe Elliot in his single-minded determination to be the greatest miler of all time. Elliot would do his regular workouts, which were considerable, then throw off his clothes to run dune after dune on the Australian beaches, driving himself to the brink of exhausted ecstasy. Herb Elliot thought American athletes were wussies. Percy Cerruti thought Herb Elliot was a Stotan." (*Stotan!,* 27)

Consider the richness and subtle sophistication of the prose that follows:

> "I would imagine that Stotan Week will be a week in which Max asks you to put forth Stotanic efforts to make yourself less like wussies and more like Herb Elliot." Lion's eyes lit up; you could see his mind whipping along ahead of Elaine, visions of himself and Herb charging over an infinity of Australian sand dunes, then diving into the surf and swimming to New Zealand. Jeff was pissed at having been scooped. (*Stotan!,* 28)

This is another passage where the tone is more confident—and more clearly committed to humor—than the tone that rings in our memories from *Running Loose*. This is Crutcher on stage. We can't call him a stand-up comedian because his material is too filled with pathos. But if we take a moment to close our eyes to the words, we can see him up there under the spotlight telling stories and *entertaining* in the purest sense, which is to engage us fully in the imagined life he presents.

The prose here is also more confident and playful: "Stotanic efforts" is a sweet stroke with diction, and Lion's vision of himself and Herb Elliot charging over that infinity of dunes and swimming to New Zealand is lyrical. Examine the verbs in the excerpt and you'll not only find each of them strong, you'll hear the heightened commitment to a sharper prose. And consider the juxtaposition of different levels of diction: "less like wussies and more like Herb Elliot," the lyricism of the infinite sand dunes, and then the informality of Jeff's being "pissed at having been scooped." No matter how fine a book *Running Loose* is, we're unlikely to find a passage this stylistically fluent there.

The central conflict of the book—the story's *spine*—is probably the Stotans' battle with Marty O'Brien and his Nazi pals. Walker would like "to kick O'Brien's head off his body" (*Stotan!,* 38). Max, however, counsels reflection. "Learn where to make a stand," he says. The world is full of fools and crackpots like O'Brien. They were never given any tools to create meaningful lives, and the only way they can feel good about themselves is to find someone they're better than. No such people exist, of course, so these ignorant souls make them up. "We're the ones who give power to bigots," Max says. "We make their ideas real by opposing them" (*Stotan!,* 39).

In addition to dealing with these fools, there are a number of battles in the book: rescuing Nortie from his abusive home, Nortie himself fighting against the legacy of abuse that causes him to hit the boy in day care, and his sweet but scary fight with himself about whether to go to bed with Milika; Jeff facing his illness and his friends living with his loss; Elaine being locked out of Stotan Week because she's female and having to fight with Mrs. Stevens, the vice principal, to keep her romance with the student teacher Peter Wilson; Lion living with the loss of his parents and little brother and facing life alone at such a young age; Max living with the pain of a daughter so distant from him that she's all but lost; Mrs. Wheeler's fight for physical survival and self-respect; Walker's—wait a minute! It sounds like this book is nothing but battles. That's right. Remember this is a Crutcher world, and in a Crutcher world we are preyed upon by circumstance, and when circumstance is busy tormenting someone else, other human beings get in line to torment us.

And then there's the battle of Stotan Week, which is the battle to get strong enough and aware enough to fight all those other battles. *Stotan!,* more explicitly than *Running Loose,* addresses the theme of life as a battle best fought with a particular strategy.

A Stotan—as an amalgam of Stoic and Spartan—is an existential warrior, and Stotan Week is the boot camp where the boys relinquish their bodies to Max, who provides "a kaleidoscope of land and water drills, performed so intensely [that they] transcend [their] presently accepted limits of emotional stress and physical pain" (*Stotan!,* 54). Stotan Week does, in fact, become a transcendent experience for the boys. Walker tells us that Max drove them "into the soft-bordered world where [the] body is capable of doing whatever it will" (*Stotan!,* 75).

When the week is over, Max tells the boys there are lessons in the experience that can serve them for the rest of their lives. He asks them to remember the times they quit fighting and just gave in to the superior force of Stotan Week and how it felt to allow that current to sweep them away. Your measure, he says, isn't always in how hard you fight, but in your ability to recognize that stronger current and to let it carry you. His concluding Stotanic admonition is this: "Just remember, when it's time to meet the Dragon, that you can't fight him head on; he breathes fire. But you can go *with* him and beat him" (*Stotan!,* 89).

Max's eyes go soft and he says it isn't very often in a guy's life that he gets to pass along the things he's learned that are really sacred to him, and that this is one of those times.

Crutcher passes along the same information in *Chinese Handcuffs,* but there he calls it "the secret of life." In the same way that we can't fight the Dragon head-on but can go *with* him and beat him, we must relax to extricate ourselves from the Chinese handcuffs. Coach Kathy Sherman, in *Chinese Handcuffs,* says this:

> "[A]ll you have in this world, really, are your responses to it. Responses to your feelings and responses to what comes in from outside. . . . You have no control over the world. You have no control over anyone but you. . . . There's nothing in the world outside yourself you can control. . . . Your responses are all you have." (*CH,* 110–11)

Again, we're advised that we can't control forces outside ourselves—we cannot fight the Dragon—so we must concentrate on what we can control, and that is us.

What is the Dragon? Shakespeare's Hamlet describes him as the "outrageous fortune" that blasts away at us with slings and arrows. Louie Banks's friend Dakota might say the Dragon is "how life works." And what are the Dragon's fiery exhalations? They are the motorcycle that swerves out in front of our car, the cell that goes malignant, the water ski that cracks our skull, the "father" who holds our face against the burning woodstove.

The Dragon can't be defeated, but he can be dealt with. And in the two earlier passages and the one that follows Crutcher gives us some information—which is to say some *tools,* some *weapons*—we might use to survive our encounters and maybe create the measure of happiness we deserve.

The Dragon "seems to have come in the form of Death," Max tells Walker, Lion, Nortie, and Elaine when the doctors aren't able to halt Jeff's deterioration. He reminds them of the central lesson of Stotan Week: that the secret to enduring the unendurable is not endurance but in "letting go, accepting reality" (*Stotan!,* 169). He believes that's the only way they'll find the strength to deal with this monumental loss.

Crutcher doesn't allow his characters a great measure of happiness in this book. Walker is able to exact some of the "nice, tight justice" (*Stotan!,* 158) he likes, but he can't change the nature of life on earth. The boys extricate Nortie and his mother from their abusive home; Elaine pays back John Dolan, who told the sexual lies about her, by showing him how embarrassing and demeaning such behavior can be; Max practices some mild violence on O'Brien so he gets a taste of how his bullying affects others, and the boys push his five-week-old Mustang into the Little Spokane River. But they know Nortie's mom will go right back to her husband, and if she doesn't he'll beat the next woman and child unfortunate enough to wind up with him; O'Brien will keep on delivering the *Aryan Press*; and people like Jeff will continue to die while people like O'Brien get baseball scholarships to universities and sign multimillion-dollar pro contracts.

We can't change what is so, but Crutcher—and life—allows us moments of affirmation and soul-shaking beauty. We get the ghastly but we also get the glorious, as he's told us explicitly and as he illustrates here in one of the most compelling scenes in all his work. The boys have completed three legs of the 400 freestyle relay at the state meet, and they stand at the edge of the pool looking down at the empty lane where Jeff should be swimming:

> [W]hile the fury of the fourth leg boiled in the middle six lanes, our lane nine stood smooth as glass, the reflection of the overhead lights shining back at us and the ghost of Jeffrey Hawkins shooting through the still water. (*Stotan!,* 180)

Crutcher concludes *Stotan!* with a summation similar to that of *Running Loose*. Louie told us what he'd learned, and Walker does, too, although he prefaces it with a statement of his intentions as an adult:

> I'm going to spend most of my time dispelling myths, clearing up unreal expectations. For instance, we're brought up to think that the good guys are rewarded and the bad guys are punished; but upon close scrutiny, that assumption vanishes into thin air. Nortie certainly never did anything to warrant the horror of his life, and Jeff sure isn't one of the bad guys. Look what he gets to give up. (*Stotan!,* 181)

What Walker has learned, of course, is a reiteration of the theme Crutcher has pounded so hard: "I've learned that asking 'why' is more often than not a waste of time; that it's much more important just to know what is so" (*Stotan!,* 182).

If we know what is so and if we waste none of our energy asking why it is so, then we can concentrate on the only thing in the world we can control, which is our response to the world. This is what the admonition to "accept responsibility" really means. Our "close scrutiny" of the world tells us that life is powered by the engine of chance rather than the engine of justice, so we can't rely on rewards for our good works. We can rely on something, though: The close scrutiny we give to the world reveals that it operates on the principle of cause and effect. There are rules, and if we break them we pay. This is the theme of the central story in Crutcher's next book, *The Crazy Horse Electric Game.*

We might find it strange that a book judged to be among the best of the past quarter century received any but positive reviews. *Stotan!* was praised as "[a] fine coming-of-age novel [that] teaches young people about responsibility, about courage and heroism, and ultimately about life itself,"[1] as "[m]arvelously realistic in its approaches to contemporary issues and especially strong in depiction of characters' interactions,"[2] and as "depicting beautifully the joy, pain, and emotional strength of a male adolescent friendship."[3]

Research does, however, turn up a couple minor and one major detractor. Among the relative quibbles are "[Crutcher] fails to avoid clichéd situations or to create subtle interpersonal relationships,"[4] and "[t]he pace lags through the story's introductions."[5]

But the major detractor is truly major. This critic has nothing positive to say about the book and makes his observations in a sarcastic tone. He says that "Crutcher and fate loaded the maladies of adolescence and life on Walker Dupree and his . . . cronies," implying that the plot is packed beyond credibility. This is an intriguing point, and one that a number of reviewers make without contempt about *Chinese Handcuffs*. He calls Max a *guru,* implying that he's a cliché and that the boys are dopes for admiring him.

Finally, after he quotes a portion of Walker's concluding statement that "asking 'why' is more often than not a waste of time; that it's much more important just to know what is so," he states that "*Stotan* [*sic*] fails because it advocates stepping aside."

> Crutcher's philosophical hermit-crabism doesn't sell when millions of high school students annually try to end their lives and about 5,000 succeed. The progression of time and events has never explained itself but just because the surf of life gets rough doesn't mean all the swimmers should become beachcombers.[6]

The man sees the book's major theme as "philosophical hermit-crabism" and implies that indulgence in such a view of life might make suicide a more attractive option. Suicide is a vital subject, of course, and one Crutcher himself brings up in Nortie's Stotan story about his brother who hanged himself, again in *Chinese Handcuffs,* and again in *Staying Fat for Sarah Byrnes*. It's doubtful that anyone need remind Crutcher of the potential for suicide among young people.

Negative criticism about books we admire can be intriguing and a powerful motivator to assure ourselves that we've read with care. This negative criticism turns us back to an even more thoughtful consideration of Crutcher's presentations of theme. Do we, for example, find that Walker, Lion, and Jeff are acting like hermit crabs when they extricate Nortie and his mother from an abusive home? Do we find Lion's challenge to the *Aryan Press* paperboys a turning away from trouble? Do we find Walker's rescue of his brother Long John from the tavern and then his renunciation of Long John after he's given Nortie drugs the act of a guy who's afraid of some heavy surf?

7. Yes, There Is This Much Sadness in the World

There's a point near the end of *The Crazy Horse Electric Game* when Willie has gone home to face the people and things he ran out on. He finds his parents divorced and his mom remarried, his dad has become a brutal drunk and tells him "I'm not your dad,"[1] and his old girlfriend Jenny calls him a son of a bitch. He rides up into the hills on the motorcycle he and his dad used to ride together, and the narrator tells us: "Willie can't believe there's this much sadness in the world" (*Crazy,* 207).

When we consider Crutcher's status in young adult literature it might be hard to believe that any of his books were ever met with disapproval or disdain. But *Crazy Horse* was, and so was *Chinese Handcuffs*. *Crazy Horse* is, in fact, the only one of Crutcher's books that wasn't a unanimous ALA Best. He enjoys telling the story of how the novel was effectively banned in Hawaii. In that state, he says, a book has a chance to be reviewed twice. If two librarians veto it, the state buys only one copy. The first librarian who reviewed *Crazy Horse* said it was trash, and poorly edited trash to boot, and such an awful book that it had no right to be published. Crutcher uses the word *vicious* to describe her commentary. The second found it well written but so depressing that she couldn't recommend it for young adults. Proponents of the book worked two years to overturn this initial decision.

Crazy Horse is full of sadness, and so is life—most of us recognize this and admit it. But to call it "depressing" isn't a measure of the book; it's a measure of the reader. Other readers argue that *Crazy Horse* presents a positive view of life and is uplifting because, while it imitates accurately the painful nature of our existence, it also allows for "one more last chance" to learn the rules that can save us.

Art is different from life. Art—at least the storytelling art—is an imitation of life made by human beings in an attempt to bring life's complexity into focus. A story is controlled. Nothing in it happens by chance. Yes, as the story is composed, inspiration and intuition do strike, unconscious forces rise to the light and bestow their surprises. But by the time the story is ready to go out into the world and meet its readers, it's been revised until not just every story element but every single word has become the result of the writer's conscious choice.

We can be there as Willie Weaver puts on the life jacket that's too big for him. When he pushes the limits of his waterskiing ability, falls and gets hit in the head with the ski, "and the life jacket slips up, trapping his arms and head, and Willie slips into darkness" (*Crazy,* 43) and into the brain damage that destroys what might have been a one-in-a-million athlete, we know the cause—not just the only cause we can observe but the only cause Willie could have controlled: He shouldn't have worn a life jacket that was too big. He broke the rules, and he paid.

Here's the point: God's will doesn't matter—not in a Crutcher world. Willie has no control over God's will. Willie can, however, refuse to wear a life jacket that doesn't fit; he can choose not to push his ability when he's too tired to exercise it. He can *do* something to alter possibilities; he can be a causal agent in his own life. There are things he can *control*.

Religious faith, which is to say the belief in realities beyond what we can see or understand, does not bring us control. Religious faith brings peace to some of us, but it doesn't bring control. Religious faith, in fact, is relinquishing control. And control, in a Crutcher world, is a method of salvation.

Listen once more to Crutcher speaking through another of his personas. This is Lisa, the PE teacher at One More Last Chance School, responding to Willie's question about why he got hurt:

> "You mean . . . why you crippled yourself?"

> Willie grimaces and nods. Lisa always words things like that; *why you crippled yourself* instead of *why you got crippled*. . . .
>
> "You crippled yourself because you stretched the rules till they broke. Simple as that.
>
> "God didn't cripple you, Willie. *You* did. You stretched the rules till they broke." (*Crazy,* 141)

This question about why things happen, why the innocent suffer along with the guilty, this stuff about the nature of life is the core element in all of Crutcher's work. This core begins to glow in *Running Loose*; Crutcher puts it under greater pressure in *Stotan!*; it erupts in *The Crazy Horse Electric Game*; and the magma's heat and speed intensify as it flows through *Chinese Handcuffs* and *Staying Fat for Sarah Byrnes*. We have no obligation to believe and adopt this view of the world Crutcher presents, but if we don't see it, then we're missing what he spends so much effort trying to show and tell us.

What is this molten material flowing through the books? It's pain, the most common currency in life, a great deal more common than love. Pain is the element that allows so many readers to see their own lives mirrored in Crutcher's work. We are all experts in pain. Even those of us who can't articulate our pain—*especially* those—recognize it and know absolutely when a storyteller presents it accurately.

In *The Crazy Horse Electric Game* the pain starts before the action of the story. The Dragon, incarnate in sudden infant death syndrome, took Willie's sister Missy. The pain of her death haunts Willie, Big Will, and Sandy Weaver, and the fact of her death—the fact that it just happened, that it was nobody's *fault*—hovers over the story until the final moments.

What we said about *Stotan!* in relation to *Running Loose* we can say about *Crazy Horse* in relation to *Stotan!*: The same elements are here; the differences are intensity and focus. Remember what Crutcher gives as the reason his books become more and more painful: "it is the increased damage I've seen, [and] my increased awareness of what that damage is." He's speaking about the damage we do to one another, and this damage—as opposed to the damage done to us by circumstance—is what he focuses on more closely here and hereafter. In *Sarah Byrnes,* for example, the damage Virgil Byrnes did to his daughter is what fuels the central action of the story; in *Ironman* Beau Brewster's central battle is to let go of the anger that's the result of the damage his father did him.

There are the same thematic elements and similar character types, but there's also something different about *Crazy Horse*. We *feel* it in the opening sentence: "Sometimes he remembers it as if it were unfolding in front of him this very minute" (*Crazy,* 1). What's different about this narration?

What's different is a shift in point of view. The position from which the author allows us to view the action of the story has changed. Crutcher has chosen third-person limited narration over first-person here. "Limited" refers to the degree of omniscience the narrator exercises. In this case the narrator limits to one the number of characters whose minds we're allowed to enter. He can shift focus into Willie's mind, allowing the reader to see as Willie sees and be present in his thoughts.

This change from first-person narration is another example of Crutcher's increased confidence in the craft of writing and maybe also in the magnitude of his subject matter. It takes courage and skill to abandon the first-person narrators with whom he's had so much success. These characters' voices alone are engaging enough to hook readers. But Crutcher steps outside his main character here and allows a more distanced, objective persona to tell his story. Then again we can look at this in another way: one might say that now, in third-person, Crutcher can tell the story himself—in his own voice, out of his own experience, directed by his own passions—rather than under the limitations inherent in a youthful pose.

The biggest difference this change in point of view creates is seen—is *heard,* really—in the story's tone. *Tone* refers to the storyteller's attitude toward subject matter; in *Crazy Horse,* since the narrator is no longer invested in events, the presentation of events has a more distant, objective ring. If the narration is successful, as Crutcher's is, there's no loss of emotional intensity. The source of the intensity just shifts from narrator to focal character.

An intriguing and illuminating way to consider *Crazy Horse* is as the fulfillment of Walker Dupree's musings at the conclusion of *Stotan!* We remember that Walker says if he ever makes it to adulthood and decides to turn back and help someone grow up, as a parent, teacher, or coach (or writer), he will concentrate on "dispelling myths, clearing up unreal expectations" (*Stotan!,* 181). And this is just what Crutcher does in *Crazy Horse.* Before Willie's injury changed everything, "his father was mythic to him" (*Crazy,* 6), and part of the positive transformation that results from the way Willie's injury changes his perspective on the world is that this mythic quality gets busted.

The other word Walker uses is *expectations,* and in the book's final pages, when Willie learns about the hell his parents' lives became, we hear his mother tell him something that warrants quotation:

> "[Y]ou don't always get what you expect. I wish someone, sometime when I was growing up, would have told me what expectations would get me. . . . Our parents, schools, everyone tells us things will be a certain way when we're adults and if they're not that way, we should make them be; or at least pretend. But after a certain point that just doesn't work." (*Crazy,* 208)

What Willie's mother says here about parents, schools, and everyone telling us things will be a certain way—and that we should *pretend* they are even if they aren't—leads us into another theme that evolves from *Stotan!,* which is the theme that to speak and act honestly is the healthiest way to live for us and for the world around us. If this isn't the major theme of *The Crazy Horse Electric Game,* it is certainly the novel's driving force.

Consider, for example, how directly it evolves from the concluding lines of *Stotan!*: "But first things first," Walker says. "Right now I've got to get dressed and go pick up Devnee. Gotta set her straight" (*Stotan!,* 183). What Walker has learned about lying—along with coming to believe that everything unsaid is a lie—is that lying unbalances the liar and the world. Walker lies to Devnee, and neither of them is able to make decisions based on "what is," because what is can no longer be perceived accurately.

The theme of honesty permeates *Crazy Horse*. As chapter 2 opens, Big Will and Willie take one of their evening rides on Big Will's 700 Honda. They wear their helmets for Willie's mom's benefit as they pull out of the driveway but take them off at the edge of town. It's dishonest, and it's also messing with "the rules." This story element wouldn't be particularly significant if Crutcher hadn't made it a part of the unity of his story by returning to it in the conclusion. Now that Willie has learned from pain and from the wisdom of others, he "thinks of strapping the helmet to the sissy bar . . . , but that's just like the old days and he keeps it on" (*Crazy,* 208). Willie won't lie now, not explicitly or by omission; and if he's going to break the rules—like Crutcher himself does by not wearing a helmet—he's not going to be surprised when the rules break him.

Willie's mom knew all along that the guys dumped their helmets. She reveals this to Willie just moments before he hurts himself waterskiing. "Don't get too taken by fast things," she says. "They can hurt you. One of these days you and your dad may have to pay for all your recklessness" (*Crazy,* 39). Consider this and then remember what Max told Walker in *Stotan!*: "This is a world where you pay for everything you do" (*Stotan!,* 130).

Crutcher shines his honesty spotlight on Big Will again as chapter 2 closes. Willie is thinking of Missy's death and how it caused the Weaver universe to shift. "Big Will held the family together with his powerful, stoic presence," and finally time began to dull the pain. This was "something Big Will couldn't take head on, something he had to turn his back on" (*Crazy,* 18). Here's Crutcher's point: if we turn our backs on it—on pain, on loss, on the truth—it will come back and kick the hell out of us, which is exactly what Missy's death finally does to the Weaver family. Powerful stoicism doesn't do it. Allowing ourselves to feel and to express the pain is what keeps us from being devoured by it. Crutcher tells us again and again: we can't fight the Dragon head-on, but we can go *with* him and beat him.

Cyril Wheat, the therapist Willie sees after his injury—and after the frightening reaction to the LSD he took at the party—is a Crutcher persona more Crutcher-like than most, particularly in his sense of humor and his commitment to honesty. When Willie first meets him Wheat is wearing his GAY VEGETARIAN NAZIS FOR JESUS T-shirt, and when Willie gives him a look he shrugs and says, "I'm a joiner" (*Crazy,* 61). This is vintage Crutcher humor in real life (he wears a NUKE THE CHILDREN shirt), as well as in writing. Wheat's response to the events and feelings Willie recounts is this:

> "A lot of what happens now depends on truth. When you're afraid your girlfriend is going away or your friends are keeping you around just because they feel sorry for you, you have to *say* that to them." (*Crazy,* 65)

Some of the book's most incisive and painful honesty is present in Willie's feelings about Jenny. He's accepted the manager position on her basketball team, and "he's aware that something nagging down deep in him wants Jenny to blow it" (*Crazy,* 69). This honest portrayal of human reactions is one of the reasons people trust Crutcher as a storyteller. We all know—even those of us who can't articulate it—that this is an accurate portrait of pain.

Willie tells Cyril about his jealousy, and the therapist's response is grounded in the healing nature of the truth, in spite of how much the truth hurts: "That golden boy isn't you anymore, and as long as you keep measuring yourself up against him, you're gonna be mad as hell at *everybody*. . . . And you'll lose your girl" (*Crazy,* 71).

The pain becomes too much for Willie to handle when his loss of Jenny is confirmed. She couldn't muster the courage to tell Willie she liked another boy. "I didn't know what to do," she says. And Willie replies, "You . . . coulda . . . just . . . told me . . . the . . . truth" (*Crazy,* 86). Jenny then goes on to tell him the truth that if he'd made any attempt to be decent she'd have stayed with him. "But no! Not Willie Weaver! If he can't be a hero, then to hell with everyone else." Willie "just wants to hurt her back" (*Crazy,* 87). When he calls Jenny a bitch his life in Coho, Montana, has unraveled to the last thread. That night he steals money from his folks and catches a Greyhound west.

We need to remember that Willie is "a cripple" (*Crazy,* 93) now. This is his physical state when he arrives in Oakland. Crutcher doesn't use the term *physically challenged,* because his commitment is to accuracy. He uses *crippled* because Willie is, indeed, "a damaged or defective object." This diction is another element in the matrix of honesty Crutcher creates. It's also important to consider in terms of story structure that if Willie isn't profoundly damaged, his recovery can't be profound or heroic enough to touch us as a great story does; if he's not brought low, he can't raise himself high.

The worst of Willie's pain isn't physical, although the beating he gets from the Jo Boys is no fun. The worst of Willie's pain is the fear and humiliation he feels now that he's been brought so low and found himself so alone. *"If I were okay, I'd beat this kid to death"*(*Crazy,* 103), Willie says about the gang's leader. Before he loses consciousness he realizes "he'd give anything in the world to be back in Coho" (*Crazy,* 104). Willie never realized there was this much poverty and savagery and desolation . . . and pain in the world. Willie continues to suffer in Oakland, but this is probably his low point.

Crutcher shifts his focus slightly after Willie moves in with Lacey and enrolls at One More Last Chance School. This is a new Willie in a new world. There's so much for Willie to learn now that he's been forced into a new perspective and rendered capable of learning from it. Among the vital things he learns is the reason he's able to learn them. Crutcher makes this clear in Willie's speech to the commencement audience. He says he's aware that if they had known him back in Montana they would have hated his guts because he had everything, including people around him to protect him and make sure he didn't lose it. "And there are lots of people like that," he says, "people whose lives are protected from the day they're born until the day they die."

> But no matter how wonderful those lives seem, if they're not contested, never put up against the wall, then they exist inside very narrow walls, and because of that I believe they lose value, in the most basic sense of the word. I guess what I'm saying is

> that my life is more valuable because I got knocked out of my favored spot. I can't believe I'm saying that, but I am and I know it's true. I learned it from the people who picked me up here. (*Crazy,* 194)

We hear Crutcher's voice in the passage, of course. In a body of work packed with vital exposition, there's probably no expository passage more important than this one. Remember, again, that Crutcher has seen so much damage done. So, how do the damaged make something positive out of all their pain? We accept our new condition and the new view of the world it gives us, and we act on our new perception.

Willie's first positive contact with humanity in Oakland is Lacey Casteel, bus driver and pimp. Lacey is not a role model, but there is much to learn from him. He's capable of kindness in spite of the overriding brutality in his character. He takes Willie in after the beating, and he is sincere at the end of the story when, in his note to Big Will, he says: *"Here you boy back. He fix. Be careful how you treet him, he special. If you don't want him, send him back"* (*Crazy,* 212).

Lacey tells Willie he's taking him in for a reason Willie doesn't know. We discover Lacey's motivation after he's helped Willie enroll at One More Last Chance. Lacey comes home drunk late one night and finds the note Willie has left him about a phone call from his former wife. Lacey says he needs to "purge his soul" (*Crazy,* 147) and takes Willie out for a drive. "I beat my boy," he tells Willie as they drive. "Start on beatin' him. Couldn't stop. Beat my boy numb" (*Crazy,* 148). They park and walk to a huge, dark institution, climb over the fence, and stop beneath a window too high to see into. And then in one of the most powerful scenes in Crutcher's work—reminiscent of Jeff's empty lane scene in *Stotan!* because of the power and sharpness of focus but more complex and illustrative of greater skill with prose—Lacey grabs a drainpipe and pulls himself up even with the window. Willie hears a moan and looks up to see Lacey's face go soft. Willie watches the man stare into the window through a "bottomless despair." Lacey drops to the ground and tells Willie to look. "Don' worry," Lacey says, "he don' see you" (*Crazy,* 149). So Willie climbs on Lacey's back, stands on his shoulders, and looks in. He sees

> a tall, extremely thin black boy; he could be anywhere from fifteen to forty. His long arms hang out of his plain white state-issue shirt like useless ebony twigs, their outstanding features the gnarled, twisted elbows and knuckles. . . . A narrow string of spittle hangs from one side of his mouth, and as it lengthens, finally dropping to the floor, the boy makes no attempt to stop it. He's vacant; gone. (*Crazy,* 150)

Listen to the passage Crutcher presents as transition from Willie's visual recognition of what Lacey has done to Lacey's explanation of its consequences. This is Willie's intellectual recognition:

> [T]his is *family* gone crazy. It comes in a flash the boy before him is wrecked; the man beneath his feet, desperately holding on with everything he's got to stay just above the quicksand. This is what happens when we astonish ourselves with our capacity to be vicious; when we realize so late how our expectations have betrayed us. (*Crazy,* 150)

We hear, of course, the theme of the destructive power of expectations.

Willie feels through his feet the vibration of Lacey's sobs. Lacey falls and Willie tumbles to the ground. Lacey lies there crying. "He jus' there hauntin' me," the man says. "He there an' I can't see him; they won't let me go close" (*Crazy,* 151). Now Willie knows that Lacey took him in to take this boy's place.

This passage is illustrative of a number of things, only a few of which we've discussed here. But too important to go unmentioned is how the passage illustrates Crutcher's growth as a writer. The writer of *Running Loose* could not have written this. It's too understated—which is to say too *restrained*—in its description; it's too complex, and it's also too wise. Crutcher has seen so much more damage now and knows so much more surely the source of it.

Willie's physical healing begins at One More Last Chance. The school enhances his emotional healing also, to be sure, but Willie has hit bottom now and he's ready to start stroking back up. Crutcher makes this clear in Willie's response to the school's required resume. He was "absolutely straight" about the reasons he left home, "crystal clear in his final statement that he wasn't going back to Montana" (*Crazy,* 113). Willie has changed: no more lies, not explicitly and not by omission. The truth does set us free, and one of the things it sets us free to do is heal ourselves.

Andre, the school's director, is another Crutcher character. His physicality, his forthright speech, his humor, and his honesty are mirrors of these qualities in Crutcher himself. Look at him and listen to him, and you'll see and hear Crutcher. Except that Andre is black and Crutcher is white. Listen, for example, to Andre describing the Last Chance students: "Some of these kids seem pretty damaged before you get to know them. Some of them seem pretty damaged *after* you get to know them, but I'm sure there are friends for you here" (*Crazy,* 116).

And Willie does make friends at school, two of whom are women: Lisa, the PE teacher, and Angel, a fellow student and prostitute who works for Lacey. Few readers would dispute that these are "strong" women characters, but few would think of them—particularly Angel—as role models. Lisa, whom we can see as an older Elaine Ferrel from *Stotan!,* might be more overtly sexual with Sammy, the Tai Chi teacher (and a Max Il Song character) than some readers find appropriate in a school setting. And Angel isn't simply a teenage prostitute, she's a teenage prostitute resolved not to give up the trade. Willie asks Lacey to let Angel go, but Angel doesn't want out. "You think I'm a whore because of Lacey?" Angel asks. "If Lacey wasn't my pimp, I'd get someone else. I'm a whore because that's how I survive" (*Crazy,* 165).

When we talk about "strong" characters in literature we don't mean "admirable," although strong characters are often admirable in at least some ways. Lisa is a fine athlete, for example, and it's through her coaching that Willie learns to compensate for most of the physical damage he has suffered. She's also honest, which Crutcher accents particularly in the ease and openness with which she's able to be sexual with Sammy while Willie's around.

Literary characters are referred to as "strong" when they are sharply delineated and consistent and when they know and accept themselves. Angel, for example, does not lie to herself, and she knows the source of one of the strongest currents in her personality. "You know how girls get to be whores?" she asks Willie. "Girls get to be whores when they grow up thinking sex is the only way to get anything" (*Crazy,* 165). She then goes on to say she had sex first with her uncle when she was 7 and that it went on until she was 17. It was ugly and she hated it, but he was nice to her and gave her things she never would have gotten in another way.

Lisa and Angel are deeply tied to the unity of the story. They're important to the plot because of Lisa's role as mentor figure and Angel as the focus of Willie's romantic interest and the source of some painful information about the complexity of life. And they are integral to the theme of honesty.

It's not hard to see that *The Crazy Horse Electric Game* ventures deeper than the previous books into wild country, and we are not, of course, speaking about California here. We're speaking about the wild country of human life. In spite of language and subject matter that make it more difficult to teach in public school, it is still a novel full of victories for the damaged souls who populate it. Hawk, the basketball player who becomes Willie's friend, attends their graduation ceremony with a cast on the arm he broke protecting his mother from his drugged-out brother. Hawk stands when he receives his diploma, looks out at his father and says, "I tol' you I ain't no worthless shit" (*Crazy,* 190). And Telephone Man, one of Crutcher's strangest and most touching characters, "who wears a full set of telephone repair tools on his hip, giving him the appearance of an AT&T gunslinger from outer space" (*Crazy,* 118), concludes his commencement speech by looking over at Hawk and saying, "Hawktor Doctor must really like me . . . and that's the first time anybody really liked me and I'm glad I went here" (*Crazy,* 191).

But here's the kind of victory that makes the book most difficult for teachers and librarians in schools besieged by book *challenges*:

> [Angel] takes the diploma, looks out at the audience, then over to the graduates and simply says, "Thanks." Willie looks out to see Lacey nodding his head and clapping. (*Crazy,* 190)

It's difficult to justify this complexity and lack of resolution to some people. Such people want Lacey and Angel, pimp and prostitute, nailed up tight in a box with the word BAD written on it. But Crutcher is wiser than that. He knows that human beings are both ghastly and glorious, and that even in their ghastliness and pain they are capable of heroic endurance, such as he implies here as Willie's bus heads out of Oakland, taking him back to Montana and more heavy jolts of sadness:

> Willie watches Lacey standing, arms folded, looking powerful and confident, without a trace of the horror in his life, and Willie marvels at the astonishing ability of human beings to go on. (*Crazy,* 198)

8. Allegory of the Chinese Handcuffs

Crutcher was chin deep in damaged lives as he wrote *Chinese Handcuffs*. When we're that deep in anything—particularly pain of the intensity suffered by Crutcher's clients and by his literary characters—and then we bend down to take the closer look we need to examine those lives, we're going to get good and blue before we come back up for air.

Although no one mentioned this word, some reviewers suggested the novel might be *suffocating* under an excessive burden of affliction. "[T]he overloaded plot strains the novel's structure and diminishes the vital message Crutcher is trying to convey,"[1] said *Booklist* in a column devoted entirely to *Chinese Handcuffs*. "This reader was turned off by such a surplus of serious issues,"[2] said *Children's Book Review Service*; *Bulletin of the Center for Children's Books* proclaimed the novel a "plethora of woe" and that "all the problems don't really add up to a plot"[3]; *Kirkus Reviews* concluded that "Crutcher probes so many tender areas here that readers may end by feeling exhausted and emotionally bruised"[4]; and *VOYA* was moved to sarcasm in its observation that

> nearly every problem that has ever been explored in a YA novel visits itself upon Dillon, his family, and/or his friends. A partial inventory of plagues includes divorce, rape, incest, alcoholism, drug abuse, and suicide. Some of these afflictions are recurrent.[5]

Publishers Weekly, too, commented in the negative on plot density:

> Because of the book's complex structure, and because the issues are so gritty and realistic, parts of the resolution become melodramatic in contrast.

But it went on to say, "Nevertheless, the book is riveting despite those clumsy moments."[6]

Booklist has a "recommended only" policy, so the decision of the editorial staff to devote its *YA Connection* column to make clear the reasons for not recommending *Chinese Handcuffs* was an affirmation of Crutcher's stature in the world of young adult literature after only three books.

A host of publications disagreed with *Booklist*'s judgment that the novel was "unsuccessful" and "a disappointment," however. *Quill and Quire* found Crutcher deft in his creation of plot: "He hurtles his reader through the story, interspersing letters with narrative, and tension-filled basketball scenes with gripping dialogue, until *Chinese Handcuffs* reaches a most satisfying conclusion."[7] And *Horn Book* was laudatory about both plot and character:

> Crutcher constructs his tangled web with intelligent insight, creating a painful, powerful story. Dillon is a wonderfully drawn, complex character; he is tough, vulnerable, and something of a loner, who delights in devising ingenious schemes to outrage the high school principal.[8]

Among the most intriguing and valuable of the many thoughtful comments on the novel were some that appeared in *The Five Owls*. The writer chronicles the afflictions Crutcher puts his characters through and obliges his readers to believe and then says this:

> To Crutcher's credit he more or less pulls this off.
>
> This is the kind of book that could open up rather than close off serious discussions about subjects as diverse as sexual abuse, suicide, chemical addiction, sports ethics, and feminism. It could also generate interest in the limits of fiction as a means of discovering or creating truth.[9]

That concluding line demands repetition: *could generate interest in the limits of fiction as a means of discovering or creating truth.* Certainly a worthy function for a book to perform, particularly a book written for young people.

Whether the novel suffocates under its burden of affliction is a matter of aesthetic judgment. Some thoughtful reviewers found it so and others found it full of the breath of life. One thing for sure: Crutcher himself was near to suffocating at the time he wrote it.

Up to this point in his life as a therapist and writer, he had always been able to balance the two commitments. His clients' pain stayed at the mental health center, and his literary characters' pain stayed in his imagination. But when he was writing *Chinese Handcuffs* that balance shifted, and the pain and craziness of the real and imaginary people's lives merged. He could no longer tell one set of lives from the other.

This was not Crutcher's most pleasant writing experience.

When he finished the writing and came up for air he felt the literal need to wipe off the residue of pain and suffering and guilt and violence and depravity, the whole cyclical infinitude of abuse we human beings inflict upon one another.

He shakes his head when he thinks of reviewers' contentions that the density and coincidence of his characters' suffering strains credibility. "There's nothing coincidental about it," he says. "People are magnets. We look around for other people who'll understand us. And that is not coincidence; it's cause-effect."

He acknowledges that there "really is a lot going on in the book, and [that] from an artistic point of view there may be some legitimate complaints." But he's confident about the accuracy of the imagined life he presents. "I can sit down, and without thinking very hard give you at least 15 people who have had a streak in their lives that was way worse than anybody's in *Chinese Handcuffs.*"

Crutcher sees this question of accuracy about life—the reader's sense that his story is *true*—as a greater measure of success than the aesthetic quality of the story's presentation.

Hold on a minute! we say. Doesn't the story's presentation *determine* the degree to which it strikes us as true?

Yes. The answer is a flat yes. But the point is this: *to whom* is the story presented? Is it written for readers who have the developed aesthetic sense that makes them aware of and concerned with presentation over the subject presented? The answer in this case, of course, is no. *Chinese Handcuffs* was written for young people—particularly for young people in pain—and the focus of these readers is almost exclusively life over art. Such readers don't know or care much about art, but they sure as hell know about life, and particularly about pain. About pain such readers are tough to fool.

The truth of the book was affirmed for Crutcher twice, both times by young women whose comments imply that they had experiences parallel to that of Jennifer Lawless, one of the book's focal characters. The first, a client, walked into his office, slammed the book down on his desk and said, "That's exactly how it is. And no one will believe me." The second instance took place in Houston when a woman came up after Crutcher gave a presentation to her high school. "I just want you to know that I read *Chinese Handcuffs,* and I thought you knew me."

"That," Crutcher says, "put most of my concerns about the book to sleep."

In *Chinese Handcuffs* Crutcher does what he's done before, but here—as virtually all reviewers agreed—he does a lot more of it, and he creates a higher degree of viciousness than we've seen up to now. We do, however, see this vicious quality continue in subsequent novels.

What might strike the analytical reader first about *Chinese Handcuffs,* though, is that Crutcher takes another audacious stride with point of view. He chose first-person narrators for *Running Loose* and *Stotan!*; he broadened the point of view to limited omniscience in *Crazy Horse,* and now, rather than going with either one, he exercises an omniscience broad enough to include both.

Crutcher opens the story with a prologue in omniscient narration focusing on the protagonist Dillon Hemingway; he begins chapter 1 as the first of the series of letters Dillon writes to his dead brother Preston; then he breaks back into omniscience to present an event Dillon alludes to in the letter; and he concludes the chapter with Dillon's long *P.S.* Crutcher returns to omniscient narration in chapter 2, now with his focus on Jennifer. And so goes the flow of information as Dillon gives his perspective on events through the letters, and Crutcher's omniscient narrator—unencumbered by constraints of time or the limits of any single character's perspective—gives us everything else.

But what does the unanalytical reader, the reader who couldn't care less about technique, get out of this? That reader gets a novel packed, stocked, chock-full, replete, loaded to the gills, stuffed to the brim with story.

Not all readers were captured by this breadth in point of view, of course. One reviewer noted that the letters and the shifting focus give the story "a patchwork quality" (*Kirkus,* 290). Crutcher receives more correspondence about *Chinese Handcuffs* than any of his other novels, though, so it's probably fair to infer that a combination of his manner of presentation and the compelling subject matter he presents is responsible for this unusual degree of narrative power.

The source of this power was Crutcher's need to suggest a way out from under the pain he saw burying people alive and that had begun, in a vicarious way, to bury him as well. But is there really a path to freedom from the things that work to destroy us? Crutcher says there's "a secret of life" (*CH,* 45), and he shows throughout the story that the path to this secret, and to whatever other life-saving secrets there might be, is the path of telling the truth. Honesty with ourselves about those things that terrorize us is hard enough to come by, but then to summon up the courage to tell the story of what we've done—or what's been done to us—can be almost impossible. For some of us, telling this story is the most heroic thing we'll ever do. But that's the way to freedom.

Preston, in the opening lines of the *confession* he makes to Dillon before he shoots himself, says this: "I got to go out honest. If nothing else, I got to go out honest" (*CH,* 54). And then he lets loose the load of envy, guilt, and humiliation—the pain—that has shaped his life right down to the curve of his finger around the trigger.

So telling his story could have saved Preston? Confession can counteract the shaping forces of the world? Maybe. But maybe not in Preston's case. Crutcher makes clear how different physically and emotionally the brothers are. Maybe the source of Preston's pain was in his genes. But about Preston's recognition of the *need* to tell there can be no question.

This theme has its matrix in the story of Charlie the Cat, which *Booklist* said—with no hint of understatement—"has meaning beyond mere violence" (Zvirin, 1966).

Dillon is 8 and Preston 10 when they decide to teach Charlie, Mrs. Crummet's three-legged cat, once and for all not to mess with their dog. It's a painful passage to read, it's painful to write about, and—considering how much Crutcher loves cats—we can be sure it was painful to write. The boys lure Charlie into a gunnysack, and Preston whirls the sack, smashing it against all the hard objects he can find in their garage. Charlie is crawling across the floor, almost dead, when Dillon takes his part. "He brings the tire iron down again, then again, until Charlie is still" (*CH,* 12). This is a degree of viciousness we haven't seen in Crutcher's work before.

Instantaneously the boys feel a bone-deep guilt. It's a pervasive, elemental, primal guilt. It is also a guilt out of which Dillon learns something about his core and the core of humanity. They bury Charlie's mutilated body "so deep no one will ever find him" (*CH,* 12). That night, when they can't sleep, Dillon asks Preston if he thinks there's something wrong with them. He says he doesn't know, maybe there is. His voice is choked. Dillon cries and cries.

> "We have to tell," he says when he can finally talk, but Preston's head shakes rapidly—more a vibration really.
>
> "No," he says. "We can't ever tell anyone. Ever." (*CH,* 13)

Years later, writing to his dead brother, Dillon says he's thankful to Charlie the Cat because "he's the one who taught me not to judge. Since the day he died, I can't look at the horror in anyone without looking at the horror in myself" (*CH,* 14).

This is the transition into one of the most important passages in Crutcher's work. When Dillon told Stacy—the girl both boys loved, but who chose Preston and who is the mother of his child—the Charlie story, she said it was

> "a leak, a wrinkle where . . . a crack appears in the structure we've built to keep ourselves decent, and our own personal evil seeps out."
>
> "It's one of the hard ways," Stacy told him, "that we learn human beings are connected by the ghastly as well as the glorious, and we need always to walk around inside ourselves looking for those leaks. And plugging them up." (CH, 14)

Stacy, too, has a *confession* to make, but she makes hers publicly. The story she's been telling about her baby has been that his parents, relatives from far away, weren't able to care for him, so her parents adopted him. But one day at school she gets on the intercom and comes clean. The student aide Stacy lied to so she could use the intercom tells her that what she did took guts, and Stacy replies, "The truth will set me free, right?" (*CH,* 149).

Stacy's tone here is light, but she's not being cynical, and Crutcher means it literally. *The truth will set me free.* We hear the phrase so often that we feel a little self-conscious using it; maybe it rings as cliché. But this doesn't make it any less accurate a description of how the human psyche works.

One of Crutcher's favorite scenes in *Chinese Handcuffs* is Dillon's *confession* about killing Charlie. We've come to the end of the story, but there's just this one more thing Dillon needs to do, and so he knocks on the door of the house where Mrs. Crummet and Charlie lived. The old woman's daughter answers. Yes, Mrs. Crummet is still living, she's right here, and she would love to see Dillon. She doesn't get many visitors. Mrs. Crummet doesn't have the foggiest notion who Dillon is. She's 83. She gets confused. She thinks Charlie's out back.

> "He's not out there, Mrs. Crummet. My brother and I—we killed him."
>
> "Well, you boys should be ashamed," she said. "The very idea. . . ."

Dillon explains that it was 10 years ago, that Charlie hurt their dog. Mrs. Crummet asks after the dog and says she'll have a word with Charlie.

> "Our dog's fine," Dillon said. "I mean, he's old now. He's gone. . . . I came to say I'm sorry."
>
> "We'll that's nice," she said. "More people should say that. More people should say they're sorry."
>
> Tears well in Dillon's eyes and he runs his fingers softly over Mrs. Crummet's wrist. She places her other hand over them as he stares into her face.

Then her daughter puts a hand on Dillon's shoulder.

> "She doesn't understand," she said. "I do, though. Let yourself off the hook, Dillon. You were a little boy." (*CH,* 202)

Crutcher concludes the scene with this line from Dillon: "I guess some things just can't be fixed" (*CH,* 202).

Yes, Preston and Dillon should have been ashamed for killing Charlie, and they were ashamed. And, yes, some things just can't be fixed. So what do we do? We tell the truth, and we try to let ourselves off the hook. The thing is, it's impossible to let ourselves off the hook without telling the truth, without telling our story. "This is what people go to confession for," Crutcher says. "This is the use of telling your story."

And this is what the allegory of the Chinese handcuffs tells us: "you have to let go" (*CH,* 87).

Of the many hard stories in this book, the story of Jennifer Lawless is the hardest, and Jennifer is the object of the most vicious treatment. As a very young child Jennifer was secretly abused by her natural father; her grandfather, the only adult who offered her a refuge, died when she was five; and then, after her mother remarried, her life got worse:

> Managed without explicit sexual details, the depiction of Jen's further victimization by T.B., her stepfather, is one of the most

> chilling portrayals of sexual exploitation in teenage fiction. (Zvirin 1966)

With the introduction of T.B., a vicious and smart antagonist, Crutcher moves deeper into the action genre. He used action elements in *Stotan!* with the neo-Nazis and in *Crazy Horse* with the Jo Boys; and he moves on from T.B. to a more developed action plot centering on Sarah's father in *Sarah Byrnes*. His adult novel, *The Deep End,* is fully action centered, of course, and in it the T.B. character transforms from a family lawyer to a child therapist in whom we see more of that mixture of viciousness and intelligence put to perverse use.

Crutcher takes care to make clear that Jen's story—and all the stories like hers—is not only enormously difficult for her to tell, but that it will take more than the telling to set her free.

Her first admonition to secrecy comes from her father: "It's something we can never tell or Mommy will get very sick and people will come and take Jennifer away" (*CH,* 37). After her grandfather's death, her father's nighttime visits to her room became unbearable, so she told her mother. But her mother got mad and said it couldn't be true and that she should "never, *never* say anything like that again" (*CH,* 67). So Jen told her teacher, and then she got some help. She and her mother went to a therapist, and her mother said she was sorry she hadn't protected her. But her mother wasn't really sorry, because she started bringing home mean men.

T.B. seemed different to Jen at first, but when she was nine he raped her. T.B. didn't just tell her to keep the story secret; he took a photo of her puppy's head under the wheel of the family car and said, "I saved him just in time. If you tell anyone—*anyone*—what happened in here tonight, I won't be able to get to Rolex in time next time" (*CH,* 74).

Two years later Jen found the courage to tell Child Protective Services, and the next day T.B. ran over Rolex's head and left her on the porch. T.B. had no trouble convincing Jen's mom that Jen was lying. CPS put her in foster care for a while, but they left Dawn, her younger sister, in the home.

"[T.B.] handled those people like school kids," Jen tells Dillon. "They never even saw his temper. He was 'just as concerned' as they were and just as worried about my traumatic past with my real dad" (*CH,* 120).

Jen told her story, but that wasn't enough. She didn't know it, but she hadn't told the right people. But Jen tells someone else later, when she's in high school—she tells Dillon. And Dillon, although she has sworn him to secrecy, tells people who can help.

First, Dillon tells Dr. Newcomb, an authority on child abuse and sexual victims and offenders. But Newcomb says there's probably nothing they can do, and that Dillon is probably smart not to have taken it to CPS. Hear Crutcher's voice as Newcomb tells Dillon that there are a few things he should know if this is his girlfriend:

> "You need to know that she sees relationships very differently from other people, particularly if there's anything remotely sexual about them. She's spent her life being invaded—unable to protect her body, that one part of her most of us have control over. . . . You can't repair that kind of damage without a lot of therapy." (*CH,* 154)

Telling her story isn't enough to free Jen from it. This is a story in which she's too deeply enmeshed to just let go. She has to have help, and even with help it's going to take time. This is a set of handcuffs so specialized that it doesn't allow any single gesture to relieve the pressure.

Dillon asks what makes a guy like T.B. do the things he does. Again, hear Crutcher's voice in the reply:

> "I'm sure his childhood was filled with monstrous acts against him, but don't even think about it. When a dog turns rabid it doesn't do you a bit of good to think about when he was a puppy." (*CH,* 155)

It would seem that the stakes couldn't get much higher, that life couldn't get any more painful, but then Jen finds out her mother is pregnant. She can't live with the thought of another girl subjected to a life like hers, so she tries to kill herself. It's only with the last of his endurance that Dillon is able to stop her.

Jen and Dillon have their backs jammed tight against the wall now. They must have help. And since this is a Crutcher novel help is available. Dillon tells Jen's basketball coach, Kathy Sherman, and he tells his father. Coach Sherman helps by trusting him and by not reporting the information, which she is obliged by law to do, and Dillon's father helps by convincing him not to kill T.B.

T.B. is smart, but Dillon Hemingway is no dummy either. He gets hold of sophisticated video equipment, hides it in Jen's room, sets the timer, and—by virtue of a power that we find difficult calling *luck* but nevertheless works out to be truly *lucky*—tapes T.B. in the act of sexual assault. He takes a copy of the tape to T.B. "I could beat this in court, [T.B. says]. You may not know who you're dealing with."

Dillon shrugs. "Be my guest. I've got good people behind me if I need them. Not public defenders with caseloads backed up into the alley. Good people. Smart ones. Some maybe as smart as you" (*CH,* 193).

Knowing she was taped is awful for Jen. She beats Dillon around, tells him she hates his guts and hopes he rots in hell, then she grabs his face in her hands. "*Do you know the one thing in the world worse than having that bastard on me all the time? Inside me? It's having someone watch it. It's having someone see it. And know it*" (*CH,* 195).

Dillon isn't taking the tapes to the police unless T.B. shows up again. But Jen knows that somewhere it won't be long before T.B. puts another girl in the same situation he put her in, and Jen can't let this happen, so she takes the tapes to the law.

Even though Jen isn't free of what he's done to her, she is at least free of T.B.'s proximity. It will be some time before she is truly free. But then again, the experts also tell us, it might be never.

Dillon, though, is able to break free. Preston's life and death have haunted him; the guilt he felt for being part of Preston's pain is what has held him. But this book is the story that sets Dillon free. *"My struggle with you is finished,"* he writes to Preston.

"I'm going to let you go, push my finger in and release us from these crazy Chinese Handcuffs" (*CH,* 198).

Pimples on the Butt of *Chinese Handcuffs*

If we like a book it seems magic to us. We don't think of it being conceived and constructed by another human being; it seems to us as though it's always existed, like a part of nature that we've only just discovered.

But books aren't like that, of course. They are conceived and constructed by people who try lots of different conceptions and constructions to get their story right, so it seems like one of nature's perfect creations.

When Crutcher submitted *Chinese Handcuffs* he included a segment that he meant to suggest a *cause* for the monster T.B. grew to be. It wasn't an excuse but a cause. He gave T.B. a childhood in which his father left when he was four and his mother brought in a 20-year-old 270-pound stepfather filled with rage. The mother gave the stepfather charge of T.B. He beat the boy, shut him in a closet for two days at a time, and when he was six and wet his pants practiced a perverse method of toilet training on him. He was going pheasant hunting, and he told T.B. he'd better not go to the bathroom until he got back, which would be almost two days. T.B. holds it until the man drives up to the house and gets out of the car, then he lets go and pees all over the porch. T.B.'s stepfather threw him in the trunk of the car with the birds he'd killed. The boy screamed and screamed, but the trunk slammed shut and everything went black. But that wasn't the worst thing. The worst thing was that T.B. thought he heard his mother laughing.

"I let her [Susan Hirschman, his editor] talk me out of it," he says. "Basically what [she] said is nobody wants to have sympathy for this guy. And I missed a huge point by editing that out. I made reference to his bad life, but I really didn't let anybody in."

If the story of T.B.'s childhood rings familiar, it's because Crutcher used it later for a character in *The Deep End* (*DE,* 76). And he made sure in *Ironman* to give a picture of Bo Brewster's father's childhood so the reader would know how the man came to be who he is. He had resolved not to edit it out, but Susan didn't ask him to.

Also in that first draft, Crutcher had gotten rid of T.B. by having Dillon's dad kill him.

> What I did was had Dillon's father kind of make this commitment, basically saying I'm going to try to do something that's worthwhile in this world—I haven't so far and this is one of those times when you put yourself on the line. What he did in the first writing was to wait and kind of stage an accident when he knew that [T.B.] was going to come along the road. He hit him and knocked him over the edge, and, of course, he doesn't get caught.

Usually Susan gets right back to him when he sends something. But the first week went by, and then the second week went by, and Crutcher thought, "Oh, God, here it comes. This is it." The third week Susan called and said, "Oh what am I going to do? How can I justify this? I mean basically a murder with no punishment? That's a place where young adult teachers would crucify this."

Crutcher said he expected her reaction, and Susan was relieved to hear that he'd consider changing it.

> But I don't like to put in something that just sticks in my craw as unbelievable [he says], and when Dillon puts the camera in her room and records this guy molesting her, I don't believe that.
>
> What I finally decided to focus on was her reaction. He was kind of expecting her to be happy that it had happened, that somebody had finally caught this guy. Her reaction was, "You think I want anybody to see what my life is like? Get the hell out of it."
>
> I thought that reaction was worth going ahead and leaving that other bit in there. Of course, by the time the book gets edited I think of a million ways I could have done it. But it's too late.
>
> So that's the pimple on the butt of that book, as far as I'm concerned. I just have to live with it. (Smith, 70–71)

He lives with it a lot more easily now. He wrote *Chinese Handcuffs* in 1989, and technology has advanced so far now that the video taping in the dark doesn't seem so unbelievable to him. Essentially, the passage of time has popped that pimple, and the butt of *Chinese Handcuffs* is almost as flawless as a baby's.

9. Succeeding in Saving Sarah Byrnes

When John Irving's new book, *Trying to Save Piggy Sneed,* came out, Crutcher bought one and in no time was on the phone long distance, reading the title essay to a friend.

Piggy Sneed was a retarded garbage collector Irving and his friends made fun of when they were young. The man raised pigs and lived with his pigs in a barn. The bad luck that nature dealt him extended to his powers of speech: the only language he was ever heard to utter consisted of the grunts and squeals and oinks of his pigs.

Years passed and one night Piggy Sneed's barn burned. Irving was a teenager then and a member of the volunteer fire department. He started his first story as he stood watching the blaze. He told his friends that Piggy Sneed wasn't in those flames and neither were his pigs. Piggy had retired to Florida. But a speechless pig man might not do so well in Florida, Irving reasoned, so he *revised*. Piggy could speak; he had chosen not to. He was really European and had returned to his homeland. "It was essential," Irving says, "to rescue Piggy Sneed."[1] And creating the separate reality of a story where Piggy could live a new life was the only way to do it.

In actuality Piggy Sneed was not in Europe. In actuality he was a lump of charcoal that Irving dragged from the ashes on a tarp.

But the writer's business is not actuality. "The writer's business," Irving says, "is *both* to imagine the possible rescue of Piggy Sneed *and* to set the fire that will trap him" (*Piggy,* 20).

The tone of Crutcher's voice as he read these words was a mixture of surprise and pleasure. Surprise to hear someone articulate this element of the storyteller's art that is so fundamental and yet so often unacknowledged, and pleasure that the someone who knows this same thing he knows and does this same thing he does is John Irving, the man who wrote *The World According to Garp,* one of the literally *wonderful* novels of our time.

Hold on a minute, we say: if Crutcher is to save Sarah Byrnes, he must first create her father, Virgil Byrnes, to hold her face against a burning woodstove and to be a malevolent presence in her life ever after?

Yes, there has to be *something* to save Sarah from. Sarah has to be hurt profoundly, her life must be in the direst peril, if easing her pain and bringing her to safety are to touch us.

And he has to motivate Jody Mueller into bed with Mark Brittain, get her pregnant, allow her to let Brittain talk her into having an abortion, then commit the first-degree hypocrisy of marching with him in an antiabortion protest, all of which leads her to say, "I felt so bad about myself, so really desperately bad" (*SB,* 110), before he can allow her to find the friendship and the strength she needs to step out of the shadow of Brittain's twisted Christianity so she can see the world with her own eyes?

Yes, that's right. Crutcher must cast her into darkness and pain before she can find her way to succor and light.

One of the fundamental reasons for the popularity of Crutcher's novels, *Sarah Byrnes* particularly, is that Crutcher provides so much pain to save his characters from. Most readers wouldn't list this as a reason for their devotion to his work, but we feel it; it's not only the reason we turn the pages but also the reason we feel relieved and revitalized when the story is over. If Crutcher didn't do this, all the other wonderful things he does in his work wouldn't come to as much. Even in *Sarah Byrnes,* probably the jewel among seven shining novels, with its humor and finely crafted *thriller* quality, the story could not move us as it does without the corresponding measure of pain. For the humor to be most effective there needs to be a darkness that our laughter turns us from, and for the quest of saving Sarah to be thrilling, there must be an antagonistic force so powerful that we are made to doubt the protagonists' ability to save her.

School Library Journal calls *Staying Fat for Sarah Byrnes* "a masterpiece,"[2] and *Publishers Weekly* says

> Such superlatives as *riveting* and *powerful* can only hint at the craftsmanship on display in this transcendent story of love, loyalty and courage. Superb plotting, extraordinary characters and crackling narrative make this novel one to be devoured in a single unforgettable sitting.[3]

We've spoken at length about *Sarah Byrnes* in chapter 5, *A Healing Vision,* so we probably don't need to go on longer here. This may be the point in our examination of Crutcher's work, however, to consider a story that Crutcher himself finds exemplary of both the importance of pain in storytelling and the role of the storyteller. It's a story most of us have heard all our lives.

God decides He wants to give His wayward children a second chance for communion with Him, so He sends His son to live among us. Jesus is, in fact, God's son, but He's also human. He performs miracles, but He also feels pain. He's human. Jesus knows the ultimate end of this mission He's on, He knows the price He'll pay, but He sticks it out. He offers us a home in our father's kingdom for eternity.

What do we pay for such a rapprochement with our heavenly father? Not much. We're obliged to believe in Jesus. It's one of the all-time great deals.

What does Jesus pay? Jesus pays a lot. He pays with suffering and death. Jesus knows He'll be resurrected, but He's human, and He knows that before He's resurrected He's going to suffer. His awareness of this is so acute that He asks God if there might be another way to make it work. But no, this is the only way.

People think of Jesus in different ways, of course, but one of the things Jesus is, indisputably, is a literary hero. If He hadn't gone through that pain, salvation wouldn't be a possibility. And if God hadn't provided the pain, then Jesus wouldn't have been able to make so profound a sacrifice.

What touches us about this story is Jesus' courage, His suffering, and His death. We like the idea of salvation, of course. Eternal life has an appealing ring to it, but the truth is that it can't touch us like the courage, suffering, and death of another human being, even if the other human being did know He'd come out the other side. We can't imagine eternity because it's abstract. But the visual and tactile *concrete* sensations of having nails driven through our wrists and hanging from a cross until we suffocate find a home in our imaginations. Even those of us who prefer to evict these sensations find it tough to do.

The storyteller is god in the universe of the story. That's how it is. "This isn't an analogy," Crutcher says, "it's true."

This reference to the story of Christ brings up one of the few negative comments made about *Sarah Byrnes*. *Kirkus Reviews* found that "Crutcher doesn't always play fair in developing his themes—all the conservative Christians here are humorless dupes or hypocrites."[4]

Crutcher says the following about Christianity in the foreword to a book he's writing on what he's learned about teenagers:

> I am not a Christian. I have tremendous respect for my interpretation of Christian teachings, and that same respect for my perception of what an amazing person Jesus must have been. But the "Spare the rod and spoil the child" philosophy carries absolutely no weight with me (it's Old Testament anyway) mostly because of the acts I have seen committed in its name. I also do not respect the rigidity with which a great number of so-called far right Christians raise their children because it usually requires a child to learn from the parent's experience rather than his own; and the idea of breaking a child's will before she knows she has it, brings out a quite un-Christian response in me.[5]

The key term here isn't so much *Christian* as it is *rigidity*. Mark Brittain, in *Sarah Byrnes,* is a fundamental Christian. But it's not so much his Christianity Crutcher goes after as his rigid thinking. Steve Ellerby is a Christian, too, and so is his father, Reverend Ellerby. They're Christians, but they aren't rigid thinkers. A list of rigid thinkers in Crutcher's work is lengthy: Coach Lednecky and Principal Jasper in *Running Loose,* Marty O'Brien in *Stotan!,* Willie's dad in *Crazy Horse,* Bo's dad and his former football coach/English teacher Keith Redmond in *Ironman,* and Brittain, his dad, and Principal Mautz in *Sarah Byrnes.*

Brittain is in trouble as a human being not because he's a Christian but because he accepts easy answers in place of real ones. He and his father look outside the world for information about it. They only see what they want to see, as the omniscient narrator in *Chinese Handcuffs* says of Principal John Caldwell, "it was a well-known John Caldwell policy to figure out how he wanted things to be, then the facts be damned" (*CH,* 93). Crutcher himself says of another rigid thinker, Principal Mautz in *Sarah Byrnes,* "Mautz is a guy who believes that the world's a certain way and you've got to learn to live in it no matter who you are. [Such thinking doesn't] consider the circumstances of people's lives."

The circumstances of our lives and how to stand up for ourselves against those circumstances are what *all* of Crutcher's work is about. Rigid thinking—whether it be Christian rigid thinking or dogmatic thinking of any kind—does not allow for circumstances. The theme runs throughout Crutcher's work, and the rigid thinkers are always ridiculed. In the case of one such character, Bo Brewster's father in *Ironman,* however, Crutcher allows us a look at the source of this character trait. We are all shaped by the circumstances of our lives, and Crutcher lets us see one of the events that shaped Bo's father into a man unable to be friends with his son. Because we're allowed this view, it's difficult for us to write the man off entirely. We see his pain, and we pull for him to find his healing.

10. Bo Brewster, Ironman

"What I like about you," Bo tells Larry King, the famous interviewer to whom he narrates his story, "is you listen."[1] Bo's father doesn't listen, which is one of the reasons Bo is talking to Larry King. There are worse fathers than Lucas Brewster, however: "The one thing he wouldn't do [is] hit me" (*Ironman,* 24), Bo tells us. But the man will not listen.

Let's say Lucas would listen, though. What would he hear? He'd hear circumstances. And rigid thinkers like Lucas Brewster, Crutcher has told us, don't allow for circumstances. They have one policy to cover all situations. One way to see the world. One right, and everything else wrong. And this can make it tough on their kids.

Bo and Lucas are talking about Bo's trouble at school. Bo is attending the school's anger-management class, so he's been allowed back. Lucas—who has talked to Keith Redmond, Bo's former football coach and current English teacher—believes that Bo's trouble started when he quit the football team. Lucas's feeling is that—on the field and in English class—Redmond "holds a position of respect and I would demand that you respect it, and that's that" (*Ironman,* 49). Bo says he respected Redmond when he taught him how to catch a football, evade tacklers, and throw a block, but that his "respect went down the toilet when he had to scream at me and question my manhood in front of the rest of the guys" (*Ironman,* 49). Bo respects Redmond for some of the things he teaches in English, too, "but the second you don't do everything his way, he has to embarrass you" (*Ironman,* 49).

The word Lucas Brewster is using here to make his point is *respect,* but even though he is possessed of good intentions and genuinely believes what he's saying, he's not talking about respect at all; he has *misnamed* this emotion. Listen to Dillon Hemingway address the question in *Chinese Handcuffs*:

> Today Mr. Caldwell told me I didn't have any respect. What he meant was, I'm not afraid of him. Mr. Caldwell calls fear respect. That's really not a bad trick if you can get the right people to buy it. See, respect is a good thing, at least the way most people see it. Fear is a bad thing, but it's a lot easier to create. So if you're lazy, or dumb, or don't want to go through what you have to for respect, your next best option is to call something else by its name, like fear. It's like fool's gold. Fear is fool's respect. (*CH,* 75)

Consider this interchange between Redmond and Lionel Serbousek, our old friend from *Stotan!,* who is Bo's swimming coach and has spoken on his behalf:

> "The kid has no respect."
>
> Lion is quiet. He's heard that terminology all his life, usually directed at himself, and he knows it's misnamed. He respects many things, as certainly Bo must. . . . "Maybe that's not the point."
>
> "I don't know why you always take up with the riff-raff," Redmond continues. "It does those kids no good to have an adult entertaining their ideas. . . . you'll learn that coddling kids doesn't make them strong."
>
> *Right,* Lion thinks. *Humiliation makes them strong.* (*Ironman,* 16)

We hear Crutcher's voice in Lion's sarcasm. The way we misname behavior and then teach the lie to our children is a vital theme in Crutcher's work as a writer and as a therapist.

That early conversation between Bo and his dad goes on from the subject of respect to another example of misnaming and rigid thinking. Bo starts to explain why he quit football, and Lucas interrupts him. "You quit because you lack character, son. You were—are—a quitter" (*Ironman,* 49).

No consideration of circumstances. Bo competes in triathlons and has worked two jobs for the past three years while earning *B*s in high school. Still his dad tells him he lacks character. Bo quit the football team because Redmond humiliated him. He quit the football team because he has self-respect, because he *has* character. He stood up for himself, which in the Crutcher universe is the fundamental heroic act. But Bo is young, and he's incomplete. Just because he's got a mountain of endurance doesn't mean he can carry the weight of his father's contempt.

Bo's father is acting out of good intentions, no question; and so is Redmond; and so are Lednecky and Jasper from *Running Loose,* Caldwell from *Chinese Handcuffs,* and Mautz from *Sarah Byrnes*. But that doesn't let them off the hook for the damage they do, and Crutcher is committed to making this point.

> Some of the people who could most benefit from what I write wouldn't be caught dead carrying one of my books. It's very seldom that I consciously try to point something out to a kid. For one thing, I don't believe it can be done. [But] I want so-called responsible adults to know the damage that can be done through good intentions and bad information.

And what is the *bad information* out of which these so-called responsible adults are acting? Crutcher's years of experience with children damaged by the good intentions of adults have taught him—and all of his storytelling makes clear—that they don't understand how young human beings develop. They think they do, of course, but they don't.

There's a *seminal* event in *Ironman,* and it's not the confrontation between Bo and his dad over slamming the door. It's not even an event in Bo's life, although it has certainly affected him. Bo's anger *does* come from his life, as Lion tells him. And the confrontation over the door is what fueled Bo's anger as a child and what fuels our story. But the origin of that confrontation lies in Bo's father's life. If we look for cause and effect, as Crutcher suggests we do, then we have to go back through the process. We have to follow The Law, as he tells us in *The Deep End:* "You done it 'cause it was done to you" (*DE,* 72). And what was done to Bo's father by Bo's grandfather is revealed to us in the book's conclusion when Bo and his dad are in counseling and his dad tells the story, which Bo relays to Larry King.

Lucas Brewster grew up on a ranch. Once, when he was a boy, he left a corral gate open. Some cattle got out, made it to the interstate, and a bull got hit by a semi. It cost his father several thousand dollars. To punish him, his father made him

> brace his back against the kitchen wall in a sitting position—with no chair under him—for more than a half hour. Sweat poured off Dad's forehead as he recounted his story, and his voice choked nearly into silence. He screamed at Grampa that he hated him and would never close another gate on the whole goddamn ranch, and Grampa whipped his trembling legs with a willow switch. Dad didn't give in, though; he never sat down. (*Ironman,* 178)

At least two elements in this passage are intriguing. One is Lucas Brewster's character. Bo realizes he and his father are a lot alike, and this scares him because he knows he could end up like his dad, leading "a desperate life" (*Ironman,* 177). That Bo is like his father is no surprise to us, because we're familiar with The Law. But Bo *knows* he's like his dad, and he's working to change, so maybe he can subvert the law. The second element relates to the first: Bo's grandpa hit Bo's dad with the willow switch, but Bo's dad will not hit Bo. Maybe this is an illustration of progress, and maybe it suggests a little elasticity in the law. Lucas Brewster does some lousy stuff to his son, but he doesn't visit upon him every stroke that he himself suffered.

Then again, maybe he visits strokes that cut deeper.

We don't like considering this, but let's consider it anyway: what if there are worse things to do to our children than hit them? Considering the severity of the blows, of course, what if humiliation is worse than hitting? Flesh—provided it isn't left to the Virgil Byrnes school of child discipline—regenerates itself. But the spirit does not. Once we've stifled the spirit in our children it's awfully tough to resuscitate. And what if we desert them—literally, as Sarah Byrnes's mom does when she leaves, or figuratively, as Bo's dad does when he conspires against him in the triathlon? How much more damaging is that than a literal beating? We know this: "My dad leaves bruises on the inside," Bo says (*Ironman,* 47). And as a response to his father's admission that exiling him from the family after the door-slamming incident hurt him more than it did Bo and almost broke his heart, Bo says "It *did* break my heart, Dad. If it had hurt you as bad as it did me, you wouldn't have done it" (*Ironman,* 71). And as to the specific emotional injuries that led to his broken heart, Bo says this:

> Looking back, I'm still astonished at the flood of humiliation and hatred washing through me as I stood facing him, the field mouse before the hawk. I still don't understand it completely, Lar, but one step backward was the abyss, and I made my nine-year-old stand. (*Ironman,* 24)

What is this *abyss* that Bo didn't fall into? It's the loss of self-worth. We lose that and we've lost everything. We have no more *self,* so we can't stand up for ourselves. We're a field mouse, and the whole world is a hawk.

So which is more damaging, a broken arm or a broken heart?

The answer—if there is one—has to be a matter of degree. More important than the answer, though, is the point: both ways of treating children are lousy, and we should prevail upon ourselves—or get someone to prevail upon us—before we give in to the inclination to do either.

This question of whether physical abuse or emotional abuse does more damage to a child is one Crutcher doesn't like talking about for publication. And who can blame him? To suggest that anything we can do to our children might be worse than hitting them brings on an irrational response. Someone is going to say, *Crutcher says it's okay to hit kids!* Here's what Crutcher does say: "If we are to put the treatment of children on a scale, in many cases humiliation is worse than hitting." Hitting is no good, of course, because it makes kids into hitters. But humiliation is *insidious* in Crutcher's view. Children can see the anger behind hitting and understand why they're being hit. But when they're humiliated they aren't able to understand the nature of the attack. The idea of humiliation is to plant self-hatred, Crutcher says. As a causal agent, humiliation is harder to understand than anger, and the effect of it can be deeper and longer lasting.

In the door-slamming confrontation Bo is trying to make clear the circumstances of his behavior, and his dad won't listen. "Even at nine I could take only so much confrontation before locking down," Bo says. "I have forever hated feeling small and helpless" (*Ironman,* 23). *Forever* is the key word here. Crutcher knows—and he wants us to know—that when we sink our hawk beaks into young psyches, the bite goes deep. And if the bite goes deep enough, the psyche is forever wounded. It never heals.

So how does Bo transcend his father's legacy? And—in a case more drastic than Bo's—how does Shelly transcend the brutal, hateful, and "just plain nuts" (*Ironman,* 86) legacy of her adoptive parents? Her father hit her so hard he cracked her eye socket after she told the police her uncle was sexually abusing her sister and her uncle's daughters; her father and mother told her that being a troublemaker was in her genes and that her biological mother was a drug addict and a prostitute and she'd probably turn out the same.

> "You can't know how much that scared me," Shelly tells Bo. "I didn't even know what a drug addict was, or a prostitute, either, but I knew they were bad and I really believed I could make my parents love me if I could just be good enough to prove I wouldn't turn out like my real mom. I watched enough TV to know if you were good at sports you'd never be a drug addict or a prostitute." (*Ironman,* 87)

So Shelly tried to remake herself as an athlete, and she got to be good, particularly at basketball, which was where she took a nearly terminal psychic shot from Redmond. "I *loved* basketball" (*Ironman,* 89), she tells Bo, and she was good. But Redmond cut her from the team. When she showed her rage in practice he realized how willing she was to mix it up, and when he read her records he "decided he couldn't afford to have someone [like her] poisoning the team's morale" (*Ironman,* 92).

How does Shelly elude these forces that are more than powerful enough to make her hate herself and the world? She's angry, certainly, but she's amazingly well considering everything in her childhood that militates against a positive sense of herself.

Shelly—and Bo, and Hawk from *The Crazy Horse Electric Game*—escape to a great degree the negative forces that could shape their lives because Crutcher endows them with the strength to do so. Yes, Mr. Nak's anger management helps Shelly and Bo, and having a friend like Lion helps Bo, and Lakeside School helps Hawk. And we have all read about and seen on TV and maybe know in our own lives young people who have escaped a lousy home life. But the truth is that most of us don't transcend our environment. Most of us aren't strong enough or smart enough to do it, or lucky enough to find the help we need. And here lies one of the most vital—and largely unacknowledged—functions of the storytelling art, and particularly of Chris Crutcher's storytelling art: it shows us what is possible.

These stories are not life. They are like life, but they are not life. They take place in a world Chris Crutcher creates. He creates his world as he knows the actual world is, as he knows it can be sometimes, and as he wishes it would be more often.

Crutcher's stories are a way of striking a blow "for every ragin' beat-up son of a bitch [in Anger Management], and maybe in the world" (*Ironman,* 173).

The odds against an actual-world Shelly surviving the childhood that Crutcher gives Shelly in the book are great. They are worse than great; they're desperate. But Shelly has a chance in the book because Crutcher gives her a chance. He has created her, and he has blessed her with emotional and physical strength, with spirit, and with good friends. He has placed within her the potential not only to endure but to prevail.

Many of us don't prevail, though. For many of us endurance is the closest we'll come. For many of us, as the novelist Harry Crews quotes: "Survival is triumph enough."[2] Crutcher knows this and he invests Bo Brewster with this knowledge. Bo is into the running segment of the triathlon, listening to the tape his friends in Anger Management have made him, and as he pictures them running with him he realizes: "The truth is, their lives will go on—pretty much unchanged—whether he wins or not" (*Ironman,* 173). And then he thinks of Hudge, the profoundly damaged boy whose father burns the backs of his legs with cigarettes to teach him a lesson about punctuality in doing his chores, and says: "What must it mean to Hudge to participate in this? To belong, to have a hand in someone striking a blow for *him*" (*Ironman,* 174). What such an experience means to Hudge is probably beyond capture in words. Imagine the glow in his face as he spray paints a fluorescent orange stripe down the back of Bo's toughest competitor so Bo can keep an eye on him. It touches us to imagine Hudge's face, even though we know he'll go back home after the triathlon is over.

It's an inspiration to watch Shelly and Bo fighting to liberate themselves from the treatment they've received. When we see human beings doing things as monumental as standing up against the forces in their lives that want to knock them flat, we are inspired. It is a real, physical sensation. Just for one moment we feel a breath move through us that's not our own. Some people believe this is a divine breath, which is what *inspiration* means. But it might not have anything to do with divinity. It might be that for one moment, because we've been touched by the heroic potential of the human spirit, our breathing falls in synch with the rest of humanity.

11. *The Deep End:* Crutcher's Adult Novel

Adult novel? Now there's a strange designation. Is that *adult* as in *adult bookstore*? Does this suggest that in 1991 Crutcher took a break from work on his much-admired novels about young people to write pornography? No, the strange designation does not suggest that. *The Deep End* is not pornography. It's a *novel of suspense,* as the cover states.

Among the vital and intriguing questions that arise from the richness of ideas in Crutcher's work, many are more vital but none is more intriguing than this question that arises from outside the work: what's the difference between adult and young adult literature?

The answer has some fuzzy edges, but basically it is this: the age of the focal character. If the focal character is an adult, the book can't be young adult. And who makes these decisions? The publishers of young adult books.

That's all? They go by the age of the focal character? There are a few exceptions. But, yes, that's what they go by.

Let's look at Crutcher's work specifically: Is *The Deep End* more violent, more profane, more explicitly sexual, more sophisticated in subject, style, or theme than his books with teenage focal characters? Not much. It might be a little more violent. But then Virgil Byrnes stabs Eric Calhoune, and that's pretty violent. And it is a little more profane. The F-word is used, but then the F-word is used in *Ironman,* too. And we could probably say it's a little more explicitly sexual. The protagonist, Wilson Corder, has a sexual relationship with Molly Comstock, to whom he isn't married.

But then in *Ironman,* although Bo and Shelly haven't yet made love, Bo seems pretty sure they will in the line "when are we going to have sex?" (*DE,* 84).

The first thing that jumps into a lot of people's minds as the big difference between adult and young adult literature is that YA thrives on a presentation of values, whereas mainstream literature is more subtle and is sometimes even value-negative, angst-rich, nihilistic. This is accurate to a degree, but it doesn't cover Crutcher. *The Deep End* overflows with not just similar information but the same information that his YA novels present: how life works, how people work, the value of the truth, and how we might treat our children so they have the best chance to be happy.

The themes of *misnaming* and relying on expectations are prominent in the YA books, for example, and in *The Deep End* the two themes are joined. Wilson Corder, divorced father of two, is remembering his marriage and the first step he took toward its destruction. *Love* is what Corder realizes has been misnamed; he counted on information that wasn't accurate. He says he shocked himself the first time he cheated on Sarah. He had loved her, literally, his whole life; when they were married he knew she was all he'd ever want. But then one day, after he and Sarah had two children, a woman he barely knew issued an invitation that surged through his groin and short-circuited all meaningful activity above his neck. "To this day," Corder says, "I remain amazed at the power of erotic longing, and how it can displace the subtler feelings of what we come to call love."

> Love. What a trickster that word is. Conquers all. All you need is. Will keep us together. What is this thing called. It adorns either end of a sentence like pearl earrings on the finest lobe, like a pencil-thin gold band on the most delicate finger. I counted on it to keep me free of my baser human instincts, and when it failed, decided it was absent. It took me years to realize it wasn't absent at all, only camouflaged.
>
> It ain't what it appears to be. (*DE,* 57)

This passage reminds us of Sandy Weaver's words to her son Willie in the conclusion of *Crazy Horse*:

> "Our parents, schools, everyone tells us things will be a certain way when we're adults and if they're not that way, we should make them be; or at least pretend. But after a certain point that just doesn't work." (*Crazy,* 210)

Okay, we say, *The Deep End* has that same rhetorical quality we see in Crutcher's YA books and stories. The man has come to some conclusions about living, and he passes that information on in his work no matter how old the focal character is.

But we're not giving up yet. We have it now: one difference between *The Deep End* and the YA books is that there's no teenager on the cover.

That's right, there is no young adult on the cover of *The Deep End*. The images are a boat on water and a teddy bear. Okay, so it could be a teenage teddy bear. But take another look at *Stotan!*: no teenager on that cover, just a swimming pool shimmering as though it expected an infusion of Stotans at any moment. And *Athletic Shorts* declares itself with a pair of—you've got it—athletic shorts. Young adult covers have a distinctive quality about them, but covers are not what distinguishes young adult from adult.

This question of the difference between young adult and adult literature is intriguing, all right, but it doesn't lead us to any illumination about literature because it's not a question about literature. It's a question about business, about how books are packaged and marketed, about how they are displayed in bookstores, and about how our libraries, middle schools, and high schools make choices on the books they buy and recommend.

This is an academic question if you're an academician, but it's a practical question if you're an author, and it's a question about which the author Chris Crutcher fulminates.

Crutcher walked into the B. Dalton in downtown Spokane after *Running Loose* was published. He was embarrassed to be kicking around in there looking for his own book, but he wanted to see it in one of the places where books are supposed to be—on a bookstore shelf. He looked in the teenage section, and no *Running Loose*. No need to check the literature section, of course. He continued to browse, and as he was walking by the section for little kids he saw it.

Crutcher had been in a few bookstores since *Running Loose* was published, but he'd never introduced himself or asked about the book because he didn't want it to seem like he was being arrogant. This time, though, he grabbed the book and walked up to the cash register. "Why in the world," he asked the people, "is this book in a section for first-through-third graders?"

They told him this was the only section where the shelves were high enough for the book to stand up.

"I don't normally say this," Crutcher replied, "but I'm the author of this book, and I'd rather not have it here. I would rather not have it in your store."

Crutcher doesn't get agitated often, but he can work up a big load of steam about the idea of young adult literature existing separate from literature in general. "I would really like it," he says, "if somebody would step up and promote this stuff [which is to say his stuff and other stuff similar in magnitude] as being different, promote it as being not like *The Baby Sitters' Club,* not like *Sweet Valley High,* not like *Dance a Step Closer*. I want my books separated out from that."

> I think the publishers need to create a specific category for books that can be read by adults and youth, books that have both literary and teaching merit.
>
> Few people would disagree that *Fallen Angels* stands up to anyone's standard of good literature. *Ironman* gets powerful and consistent response from adult males who have had power struggles with their own fathers, not to mention those who are having power struggles with their kids. I can't count the number of women who have come to me and said this is a good book for their kid, but they sure wish their husband would read it.

Another thing that frosts Crutcher about young adult literature is that YA books aren't stocked in national bookstores in hardback. "You buy a good book in hardback," he says. "You want to keep it, so you buy it in hardback. After *The Things They Carried* was published in hardback it came out in paperback, and I've got three paperbacks. But I want that book in hardback. John Irving's books I want in hardback."

> People don't get the chance to buy YA books in hardback because they aren't available. I mean I don't know where they're available in hardback. You can order them from the publisher, but they're not in bookstores. If a local bookstore knows you and promotes you, they'll stock the books. But that's it.

Let's get this straight: it's not young adult literature that Crutcher objects to. It's the fact that young adult literature is separated from the rest of literature. And it's not a matter of money. Crutcher has all the money he needs. He writes those books for people to read, but as long as they are placed two aisles back from literature many people who would enjoy them and be touched by them will never even know they exist.

Everybody has a chance to know *The Deep End* exists, however, because it was not marketed as young adult. When the paperback came out you could find it in grocery stores to take home with your milk, butter, and eggs. And when the movie comes out a new edition with a movie cover will be in a rack beside the checkout. Right there with the Carmex and the *National Inquirer*. Now there's *exposure*.

The biggest difference between *The Deep End* and the YA books is probably that it's a thriller. Yes, the concluding third of *Sarah Byrnes* is highly suspenseful, but suspense is not what drives the first two-thirds. Every Crutcher book makes us want to know what's going to happen, but we're not on the trail of a specific mystery. *The Deep End,* however, is a specific mystery from cover to cover. On the novel's opening page we learn that our narrator is a therapist working at a mental health center; on the second page he's reading the newspaper when he recognizes a photo of a girl next to this headline: EASTSIDE CHILD MISSING—FEARED KIDNAPPED (*DE,* 10). The missing child is Sabrina Parker, older sister of Jerry Parker, one of the narrator's clients. The story quotes the child's mother, Peggy, on the difficulties of raising children and the dangers lurking everywhere.

> My heart aches for her [the narrator tells us], deplores what she must be going through right now, but the nature of my job

> requires a certain hard edge of suspicion, and a small insistent voice in my head says there is more, and Peggy knows it. (*DE*, 11)

"There is more, and Peggy knows it." With these words the mystery begins. Peggy knows something, all right, but it's Jerry who has the key, and he is too traumatized by his sister's abduction to reveal it. Corder and Molly work with Jerry to help the police, and malevolent forces work against them. Much is at stake: Jerry's life, Corder's life, the lives of his family members.

The Deep End received excellent reviews. *People* said

> Crutcher . . . writes with heartwrenching realism about the cases observed by Corder, in a tone both empathetic and matter of fact. . . . this multilayered mystery debut [is] remarkable not only for its frenetic final pages but also for a probing of domestic violence that is never condescending.[1]

The *San Diego Union Tribune* found that "Chris Crutcher has produced a dandy thriller, notable both for its impeccable background . . . and its unrelenting suspense."[2]

Kirkus Reviews declared: "the plotting (crucified cat—colleagues' freeze-out—threatened kids—motorcycle chase—apocalyptic face-off with villain from hell) is standard fare, [but] YA-author Crutcher's needle-sharp focus on hurting kids makes this memorably harrowing from the starting gun."[3]

And *Library Journal* noted a quality particularly important to Crutcher. Its reviewer found the characters "vividly drawn, especially . . . the kidnappers—men driven to cruelty by the abuse they suffered in childhood."[4]

This idea of understanding the nature of cruelty is something Crutcher brings up in any extended conversation about child abuse. He knows how torturers and killers are made, and he believes in mercy. Our inclination is to want to hurt such people for the pain they cause, but Crutcher's view is that they've been hurt so much already that there's nothing we can do to hurt them any deeper. He believes we should just put them away where they can't hurt anyone else and where they can't be hurt themselves.

Crutcher uses the analogy of the rabid dog to make his point. As Corder states in *The Deep End*: "when you see a rabid dog coming down the road, it doesn't do a lot of good to picture his puppyhood" (*DE,* 265). The necessity of protecting ourselves from the dog, however, doesn't negate the fact that he really was a puppy and that he didn't give himself rabies. Unless he's an immediate threat, he deserves mercy. And even if he is an immediate threat, he doesn't deserve cruelty.

The idea here is that just because the world is not a merciful place it doesn't mean we can't practice mercy, and maybe if we do practice mercy the world becomes more merciful.

12. *Athletic Shorts*

Crutcher says he "needed a lift" after finishing *Chinese Handcuffs*. We might assume this means he flew to the south of France, arranged a tryout with the Chicago Bulls, or found himself a good therapist. But what he did was write "A Brief Moment in the Life of Angus Bethune." First half one day, second half the next. It was the first short story he ever wrote, and he edited it less than anything else he's ever written.

Angus does not have the world's easiest life: he's "a fat kid with two sets of gay parents (so when he visited his mother, he also visited his stepmother, and when he visited his father, he also visited his stepfather)," and he's named Angus Bethune.[1]

The *lift* the story gives from a *Chinese Handcuffs* level of pain is that in spite of the burden Angus's life is to him, it's also a good life. All his parents are decent people who treat him well, he's a gifted athlete in spite of his size; he's smart, has a great sense of humor, and when he needs a break in the worst way he gets his *moment* with the beautiful Melissa Lefevre.

As all Crutcher heroes do, Angus gets some help with his life. His granddad taught him "to be a dignified fat kid" (*Shorts,* 10). His advice to Angus about people who didn't like the way he looked was to say "Screw 'em." Granddad also took Angus to Polk Street in San Francisco to see some gay people. These people—unlike Angus's gay parents, "working class folks who are with only the person they're with" (*Shorts,* 12)—looked like "they were headed for a Tandy leather swap meet" (*Shorts,* 13). The comparison made Angus's parents seem more normal to him. It doesn't take much thought to realize this is *why* Granddad took him there. Normalcy is desperately important to Angus, as it is to most young people, and to most of the rest of us. This universal quality is one of the reasons the story has touched so many people and one of the reasons it was adapted as a feature film.

Help also came from Angus's father, who taught him to dress comfortably and to give the salesperson his full waist size rather than cut some inches from the truth to save embarrassment.

Additional wisdom comes from Angus's stepfather, Alexander, in a passage that ranks with Crutcher's most perceptive. Angus is dressing for the dance, and he's terrified. Alexander sees this and tells Angus that Superman isn't brave. Angus doesn't get it.

> "He's indestructible," Alexander says. "You can't be brave when you're indestructible. It's guys like you and me that are brave, Angus. Guys who are different and can be crushed—and know it—but go out there anyway." (*Shorts,* 16)

The power here comes not just from the accuracy of the observation but from the experience of the observer. Alexander is homosexual; he knows absolutely what it's like to be different and to live with the potential of being crushed, and out of that experience he has found wisdom and passed it along.

The moviemakers destroyed the power in this scene because they made the grandfather the speaker; they cut the gay parents. The scene falls flat because it doesn't grow out of pain. In the story, Alexander's voice resonates with the experience of pain; in the movie the grandfather's voice is just words.

Crutcher figures the movie "Angus" suffers from two mistakes: cutting the gay parents and making the major characters younger. Losing the gay parents lessens the magnitude and complexity of the story and cuts the potential for humor. Imagine the scene where Angus negotiates the No Kissing Contract with his four parents and presents them with Kissbusters T-shirts. How to bring off such a scene? Crutcher says watch *The Bird Cage* and see how they did it. He believes that making the characters younger in the movie doesn't allow the story the weight it deserves. That is *not* a pun.

One of the reasons Crutcher chooses older teenagers for his focal characters is that they're on the bridge between youth and adulthood, which is a high, shaky, scary place. It's a crossing they must make and want to make, but it's not easy. Lowering Angus's age lowers the stakes. It makes experience that moves from the excruciating to the exultant into something that's just cute.

But, as we said, Angus gets his moment, and so does Melissa Lefevre. Angus has faced down Rick Sanford, whose design it was to elect him Winter Ball King and to humiliate him at the dance, and Angus and Melissa, the queen, are slow dancing in front of everyone. Melissa asks in a whisper if Angus would like to know something about her. She tells him she's bulimic. "[I]t's not always so great looking the way I do, either," she says. "I pay, too." Angus is the only person, except for the people in her therapy group, to whom Melissa has ever revealed this. "I just wanted you to know things aren't always as they appear" (*Shorts,* 23), she says.

Melissa breaks free of her destructive relationship with Sanford, and she frees herself a little from her secret by telling it to Angus. With Melissa's help Angus finds out he can dance by using the coordination he exercises on the football field, and for one brief moment in his life he feels way better than normal.

Sounds like awfully serious subject matter, and it is. But this is also probably Crutcher's most clever, wittiest writing, and Angus might be Crutcher's most engaging narrator. Every line is energized with humor or pain or perceptivity or a combination of qualities that *entertain* us in the best sense of that word. It's not an exaggeration to call "Angus Bethune" a *tour de force.*

Two Pins

One of the things Crutcher likes about writing short stories is that they finish quicker. He doesn't have to wait two hundred pages to find out what happens. He believes the demands of the shorter form have made him a better writer, forced him to cut the fat from the prose, and kept him from getting lazy and trailing off the path of the story. He says this sincerely, but as we think back over his work it's difficult to remember instances of fat, laziness, or trailing off. Maybe just contemplating the short stories he knew he would write between 1989 and 1991 enhanced his skill with the craft.

He likes "the punch, the real impact" a good short story has, and both "The Pin" and "The Other Pin" have such a punch. In "The Pin," the relationship between Johnny Rivers and his dad Cecil is like the relationship between Bo and Lucas Brewster, and Crutcher could have developed it into two hundred pages. Instead of the evolving series of punches that a novel would be, however, he made it the single knockout blow of the wrestling match where Johnny pins his dad in front of a gym full of kids and parents, and his dad reacts by slapping him.

It's vital to the appreciation Crutcher's work deserves that we understand how he achieves such impact: he makes Cecil truly contemptible, makes Johnny's contempt for him truly hateful in the closing moments of the match, teaches both Cecil and Johnny a hard, hard lesson about The Law—"you done it 'cause it was done to you" (*DE,* 35)—then redeems Cecil and frees Johnny of the guilt he feels for his father's pain with the revelation that it wasn't Johnny who hurt his father by pinning him; it was Johnny's grandfather who did the damage to his dad. And there's one other element in the magnitude Crutcher sets up as he creates his conflicts between fathers and sons: the antagonists—Cecil Rivers and Lucas Brewster—are truly admirable in many ways: they're highly disciplined, they're brave, they really do want the best for their children and they struggle to create it, but they don't have the information to know what the best is, and so they do damage where they want to do good.

"The Other Pin" packs a punch, too, but this time it's a comic punch. This is probably the least painful story Crutcher has ever written. Again, however, his hero, Petey Shropshrire—who, along with Johnny Rivers, we remember from *The Crazy Horse Electric Game*—needs help, and Crutcher provides it in the person of Petey's grandfather. Petey is unraveling with worry over his coming match with Chris Byers—that's Chris as in Christine—and Granddad tells him: "You got a problem with Chris Byers, take it to Chris Byers" (*Shorts,* 67). He asks Petey what he thinks being the only girl wrestler anyone's ever heard of is like for Chris, and Petey says he doesn't know. "That's right." Granddad says, "You don't know. An' when you don't know, it's 'cause information's missin'" (*Shorts,* 68). Sounds like Dakota from *Running Loose,* doesn't it? That's because Dakota is always present in some form.

It's his grandfather's admonition that sends Petey to Chris. Petey finds out that Chris is tired of wrestling, and Chris finds out how desperately Petey wants to avoid the humiliation their match will surely bring him. When the two young people get some information about each other, they enact a strategy that saves them both.

Criticism

Athletic Shorts is an extremely popular book, as nearly all the reviews suggested it would be. To dig for the negative criticism and look hard at it, however, is probably more illustrative about the stories and about life in general than looking only at the positive.

English Journal, for example, concluded that the "hard-sell didactic message" of "In the Time I Get" was too big to be stuffed into a short story and that it "reek[ed] of political correctness."[2] Crutcher has nothing but contempt for political correctness, as he implies here in his prefatory note to "Telephone Man," a story about how racism is learned and can be unlearned:

> I have fears in writing a story about racism. In fact, there are a significant number of people who don't understand the simpler truths about bigotry . . . and who don't believe that basic lessons are best taught by reflecting the truth. Those people believe when I use the word *nigger* or *spic* or *beaner* or any other of a million slurs, I am condoning the use of those words. They think kids should not be exposed in print to what they are exposed in their lives. (*Shorts,* 108)

This is a much gentler response to political correctness than Crutcher makes in less-guarded moments.

But just because he feels this way doesn't mean he couldn't make a mistake and allow a sense of political correctness to slip into a story. We won't go into "In the Time I Get" here because we worked it over so hard in chapter 5, but it will be intriguing for the reader to look at the story again and make a judgment on this question.

Another review, in *Bulletin of the Center for Children's Books,* found a similar quality in the collection, except for "Angus" and "The Pin":

> [T]he other stories are panderingly didactic about good kids who discover how good they are, and each gives the reader (this reader, anyway) the disconcerting sense of being patted on the back just for reading it. Crutcher's introductory notes to the collection and stories are unnecessary and exacerbate the self-congratulatory tone.[3]

Other qualities we might hear in those introductory notes are Crutcher's mild relief at being able to express directly ideas that he must present through indirection in narrative and his satisfaction at getting to speak to his readers in his own voice. By 1991, when *Athletic Shorts* came out, Crutcher's books had attracted thousands and thousands of readers. He answered their letters and spoke to them in person when they came up to him after a reading or a speech, but these introductions to the stories offered him as good a method as he'd ever have of talking to all those readers whose words he'd never read in a letter or whose faces he'd never see.

Lionel Serbousek's Big Hurt

In "Goin' Fishin'," Lion's hurt is probably the biggest hurt of all: he loses his whole family to death, and he's left alone in the world. No, not alone. He's without kin. Crutcher wouldn't leave him alone. Lion has friends, and a friend saves him. And because Elaine saves Lion, Lion is freed from his rage to rescue the object of that rage, the young man who killed his family.

There are such things as accidents: a meteor falls out of the sky and drills a house full of us into the ground—that's an accident. But an underage kid, drunk, driving a high-powered boat through the middle of another boat full of people fishing is not an accident. That's the kid's fault. That's murder. And that's a story with a barge load of magnitude. But then again, how many kids drive boats drunk and make it back to the cabin without hurting a soul? Plenty of kids do. And remember, this is the work of Chris Crutcher, so mercy will be granted somehow.

Chances are good that "Goin' Fishin'" is the finest thing Crutcher has written. It can't have the sustained power of a novel because there isn't as much of it, but in terms of the craft of writing stories that have value beyond diversion, as well as artistic value, this piece is superb. He says he believes a short story should be lean and pack a punch, and he has this mauler down to about 0 percent prose fat. He's also evolved about as far as writers get in telling us and showing us what it's like to be human. Lion describes how he felt by sundown on the day his parents and brother were killed like this, for example: "I felt as alone as if I'd been hatched from an egg by the sun" (*Shorts,* 86).

And Crutcher's rhetorical skills are optimum here, too. Early in the story Lion tells us that his dad believed fishing required all the best elements of what a person needed to live a graceful life, and by the conclusion we see that this is what the story is about. Yes, it's about loss and friendship and the ultimate power of chance, but all other themes serve the theme of how to live a decent, graceful life.

Almost four years go by and one day Neal, the guilty and at the same time enormously ill-fortuned killer, shows up at Lion's door wanting to make it right. Lion sees how Neal's life is disintegrating, but still he sends him away. He realizes how vicious he was to Neal, and he says it felt good. Neal's mom calls and tells Lion that Neal is dying—more slowly than Lion's parents died—and that he needs Lion to forgive him. "Won't happen," Lion says. "He killed my family" (*Shorts,* 98).

Lion feels lousy after this, so he goes to work out in the pool. Elaine, whom we also remember from *Stotan!,* shows up and gives him hell about how he treated Neal, who had been their friend. They almost come to blows. She threatens to dump their friendship. In the process of the hot exchange, Lion says, "If I ever quit hating him, I—I—I'll die right with them" (*Shorts,* 101). Then he drops to the bleachers like a rock with the realization of what he said. Elaine reminds Lion of how Lion himself has driven drunk. "What you did was no less stupid than what Neal did. Only thing is, the universe caught him and it didn't catch you." *"Think about it!"* she screams. *"Think about it, Lion! Think about it!"* (*Shorts,* 101–2). This is the same thing Lion's dad always told him.

A week goes by and Lion is seriously worried about losing Elaine's friendship, which has kept him together since that day on the lake. He knows it was his swimming friends who kept him going, he knows what would have happened without them, but he also still hates Neal. He goes to look for him. "I wanted to believe I was doing this because I had come to my senses," Lion says, "but in reality I was learning the price of friendship" (*Shorts,* 103).

Lion finds Neal living among the bottom feeders, one of whom he has become. Lion tells him to pack his stuff. "Maybe you and me oughta go fishin'," he says in the story's concluding line (*Shorts,* 103).

We're reminded of Lion's father, of course, and how he believed that fishing required all the best elements one needed to put together a graceful life, and we feel that Lion has taken a step toward grace and brought Neal with him.

Notes and References

Preface

1. Dave Jenkinson, "Portraits," *Emergency Librarian* (January–February 1991): 68–69.

2. Chris Crutcher, *Staying Fat for Sarah Byrnes* (New York: Greenwillow, 1993), 87; hereafter cited in text as *SB*.

3. All quotations of Crutcher's statements throughout this book that are not attributed to a specific published source come from our talks over breakfast at Pioneer Pies on North Division in Spokane most Thursdays from May through August 1993 or from follow-up phone conversations, unless otherwise noted.

1. Lifeguard

1. Chris Crutcher, *The Deep End* (New York: Morrow, 1992), 11; hereafter cited in text as *DE*.

2. *Children's Literary Review* (Detroit: Gale, 1992), 98.

3. Chris Crutcher, *Chinese Handcuffs* (New York: Greenwillow, 1989), 139; hereafter cited in text as *CH*.

2. Cascade and Beyond

1. Jennifer Larson, "Biography of Chris Crutcher," 1.

2. The quotations from Jewell Morris Crutcher come from my interview with her in July 1993 and from phone conversations throughout that summer.

3. Chris Crutcher, in *Speaking for Ourselves, Autobiographical Sketches by Notable Authors of Books for Young Adults,* compiled and edited by Donald R. Gallo, (Urbana, Ill.: National Council of Teachers of English, 1990), 59.

3. Carpentry on the Keyboard

1. Chris Crutcher, "Limitations on Young Adult Fiction: An Interview with Chris Crutcher," Louisa Smith, *The Lion and the Unicorn* (June 1992): 69.

2. Chris Crutcher, *Something about the Author* (Detroit: Gale, 1988), 31.

4. A Healing Vision

1. Chris Crutcher, "Healing through Literature," *Author's Insights,* Donald R. Gallo, ed. (Portsmouth, N.H.: Boynton/Cook, 1992), 34; hereafter cited in text as "Healing."

2. Chris Crutcher, *Running Loose* (New York: Greenwillow, 1983), 139–40; hereafter cited in text as *RL.*

3. Chris Crutcher, *Stotan!* (New York: Greenwillow, 1986), 148.

4. Chris Crutcher, Greenwillow publicity brochure.

5. Chris Crutcher, "In the Time I Get," in *Athletic Shorts* (New York: Greenwillow, 1991), 127; hereafter cited in text as "Time."

6. John H. Bushman and Kay Parks Bushman, "Coping with Harsh Realities: The Novels of Chris Crutcher," *English Journal* (March 1992): 82.

5. The Adventures of Louie Banks

1. *Kirkus Reviews* (15 April 1983): 461.

2. Frank Ancona, *Bestsellers* (June 1983): 109.

3. Catherine Ecroyd, "Booksearch," *English Journal* (April 1988): 84.

4. *Publishers Weekly* (1 April 1983): 60.

5. Zena Sutherland, *Bulletin of the Center for Children's Books* (May 1983): 165.

6. Trevelyn Jones, *School Library Journal* (May 1983): 80.

7. Christine Terry, letter to Chris Crutcher, February 7, 1993.

8. Alleen Pace Nilsen and Ken Donelson, "Honor Listing Update, 1991: A Lucky Seven," *English Journal* (November 1992): 91.

9. Chris Crutcher, letter "To All Concerned" [in Berlin, Pennsylvania], February 19, 1994.

6. Stotan, *Stotan, All the Way!*

1. Jerry Flack, *School Library Journal* (May 1986): 100.

2. *English Journal* (November 1988): 89.

3. Mary K. Chelton, *Voice of Youth Advocates* (April 1986): 29.

4. *Kirkus Reviews* (1 April 1986): 550.

5. *Bulletin of the Center for Children's Books* (June 1986): 183.
6. John Hambrose, *Bestsellers* (June 1986): 115.

7. Yes, There Is This Much Sadness in the World

1. Chris Crutcher, *The Crazy Horse Electric Game* (New York: Greenwillow, 1987), 207; hereafter cited in text as *Crazy*.

8. Allegory of the Chinese Handcuffs

1. Stephanie Zvirin, "The YA Connection: *Chinese Handcuffs* by Chris Crutcher," *Booklist* (August 1989): 1966.
2. *Children's Book Review Service Inc.* (Spring 1989): 136.
3. Zena Sutherland, Review of *Chinese Handcuffs, Bulletin of the Center for Children's Books* (July–August 1988): 271.
4. *Kirkus Reviews* (15 February 1989): 290.
5. *Voice of Youth Advocates* (June 1989): 98.
6. *Publishers Weekly* (13 January 1989): 92.
7. *Quill and Quire* (January 1990): 18.
8. *The Horn Book Magazine* (July–August 1989): 487.
9. Stephen Schwandt, *The Five Owls* (May–June 1989): 75.

9. Succeeding in Saving Sarah Byrnes

1. John Irving, *Trying to Save Piggy Sneed* (New York: Arcade, 1996), 18; hereafter cited in text as *Piggy*.
2. *School Library Journal* (March 1993): 218.
3. *Publishers Weekly* (March 29, 1993): 56.
4. *Kirkus Reviews* (March 15, 1993): 369.
5. Chris Crutcher, untitled work in progress.

10. Bo Brewster, Ironman

1. Chris Crutcher, *Ironman* (New York, Greenwillow, 1995), 1.
2. Harry Crews, *A Childhood: The Biography of a Place* (New York: Harper & Row, 1978) [unpaged].

11. The Deep End: Crutcher's Adult Novel

1. *People Weekly* (February 17, 1993): 27.
2. *San Diego Union Tribune* (February 2, 1992), "Books," 7.
3. *Kirkus Reviews* (November 15, 1991): 1436.
4. Joyce Smothers, *Library Journal* (December 1991): 193.

12. Athletic Shorts

1. Chris Crutcher, *Athletic Shorts* (New York: Greenwillow, 1991), 5; hereafter cited as *Shorts*.

2. Alleen Pace Nilsen and Ken Donelson, "Honor Listing Update, 1991: A Lucky Seven," *English Journal* (November 1992): 91.

3. Roger Sutton, review of *Athletic Shorts, Bulletin of the Center for Children's Books* (December 1991): 87.

Selected Bibliography

Primary Works

Novels

Chinese Handcuffs, New York: Greenwillow, 1989; Dell, 1990.
The Crazy Horse Electric Game, New York: Greenwillow, 1987;
The Deep End, New York: Morrow, 1992; Zebra 1994.
Ironman, New York: Greenwillow, 1995; Dell, 1996.
Running Loose, New York: Greenwillow, 1983; Dell, 1984.
Staying Fat for Sarah Byrnes, New York: Greenwillow, 1993; Dell, 1994.
Stotan! New York: Greenwillow, 1986; Dell, 1987; Dell, 1988.

Short-Story Collections

Athletic Shorts, New York: Greenwillow, 1991; Dell, 1992.

Secondary Works

Articles

Bushman, John H., and Kay Parks Bushman. "Coping with Harsh Realities: The Novels of Chris Crutcher." *English Journal* (March 1992): 82.

Frederich, Heather Vogel. "Chris Crutcher: 'What's Known Can't Be Unknown'" (interview), *Publishers Weekly* (February 20, 1995): 183.

Jenkinson, Dave. "Portraits: Chris Crutcher: YA Author Bats 4 for 4 on ALA's 'Best Books for Young Adults' Lists," *Emergency Librarian* (January–February 1991): 67.

Jones, Patrick. "Feeling Good about Tough Choices: Booktalks about Teen Stress," *Voice of Youth Advocates* (February 1992):359.

McDonnell, Christine. "New Voices, New Visions: Chris Crutcher," *The Horn Book Magazine* (May–June 1988): 332.

Raymond, Allen. "Chris Crutcher: Helps Teachers Know Kids," *Teaching K–8* (February 1990): 42.

Smith, Louisa. "Limitations on Young Adult Fiction: An Interview with Chris Crutcher," *The Lion and the Unicorn* (June 1992): 69.

Short Stories

"A Brief Moment in the Life of Angus Bethune." *Connections: Short Stories by Outstanding Writers for Young Adults.* New York: Delacorte, 1989.

"Superboy." *Ultimate Sports.* New York: Delacorte, 1995.

Nonfiction

"Healing through Literature." Portsmouth, N.H.: Boynton/Cook, 1992.

Selected Book Reviews

Athletic Shorts

Bushman, John H., and Kay Parks Bushman. *English Journal* (April 1992): 82.

Carol, P. Sissi. *English Journal* (November 1993): 81.

Gallo, Don. *The ALAN Review* (Fall 1991): 34.

Kirkus Reviews (October 15, 1991): 1340.

MacRae, Cathi. *Wilson Library Bulletin* (June 1990): 180.

Mercier, Cathryn, M. *The Five Owls* (September–October 1991): 17.

Morning, Todd. *School Library Journal* (September 1991): 278.

Murphy, Susan. *Journal of Reading* (May 1992): 684.

Nilsen, Alleen Pace, and Ken Donelson. *English Journal* (November 1992): 90.

Publishers Weekly (August 23, 1991): 63.

School Library Journal (February 1996): 70.

Seajay, Carol. *Feminist Bookstore News* (November–December 1991): 22.

Sutton, Roger. *Bulletin of the Center for Children's Books* (December 1991): 87.

Vasilakis, Nancy: *The Horn Book Magazine* (September–October 1991): 602.

Chinese Handcuffs

Belden, Elizabeth A., and Judith M. Beckman. *English Journal* (December 1989): 79.

Blair, Jeff. *Wilson Library Bulletin* (September 1989): 3.

Brough, Randy. *Voice of Youth Advocates* (June 1989): 98.

Brubaker, James M. *English Journal* (October 1991): 94.

Bush, Margaret A. *The Horn Book Magazine* (July–August 1989): 487.

Fakih, Kimberly Olson. *Publishers Weekly* (January 13, 1989): 92.

Kirkus Reviews (February 15, 1989): 290.

Publishers Weekly (January 13, 1989): 92.

Schwandt, Stephen. *The Five Owls* (May–June 1989): 75.
Sutherland, Zena. *Bulletin of the Center for Children's Books* (July–August 1989): 271.
Unsworth, Robert E. *School Library Journal* (April 1989): 118.
Zvirin, Stephanie. *Booklist* (August 1989): 1966.

THE CRAZY HORSE ELECTRIC GAME

Baldwin, Sheila. *English in Texas* (Spring 1989): 9.
Belden, Elizabeth A., and Judith M. Beckman. *English Journal* (April 1989): 87.
Bulletin of the Center for Children's Books (May 1987): 165
The Horn Book Magazine (November 1987): 74.
Kirkus Reviews (May 15, 1987): 793.
Morning, Todd. *School Library Journal* (May 1987): 108.
Roback, Diane. *Publishers Weekly* (May 29, 1987): 79.
Silvey, Anita. *The Horn Book Magazine* (November–December 1987): 741.
Voice of Youth Advocates (June 1987): 76.

THE DEEP END

Kirkus Reviews (November 15, 1991): 1436.
Printz, Mike. *School Library Journal* (September 1992): 289.
Publishers Weekly (November 8, 1991): 50.
Smothers, Joyce. *Library Journal* (December 1991): 193.
Toepfer, Susan. *People Weekly* (February 17, 1992): 27.
Wade, Robert. *San Diego Union Tribune* "Books" (February 2, 1992): 7.

IRONMAN

Chelton, Mary K. *Voice of Youth Advocates* (June 1995): 92.
Gorman, James. *New York Times Book Review* (July 2, 1995): 13.
Hurlburt, Tom S. *School Library Journal* (March 1995): 222.
Kirkus Reviews (March 15, 1995): 380.
O'Malley, Anne. *Booklist* (March 1, 1995): 1240.
Publishers Weekly (February 13, 1995): 79.
Sieruta, Peter D. *The Horn Book Magazine* (September–October 1995): 606.

RUNNING LOOSE

Bestsellers (June 1983): 109
Chelton, Mary K. *Voice of Youth Advocates* (April 1983): 36.
Connor, John W., Kathleen M. Tessmer, Nancy T. Fetz, and Alyce J. Toloui. *English Journal* (December 1984): 64.
Ecroyd, Catherine. *English Journal* (April 1988): 84.
English Journal (February 1984): 106.
The Horn Book Magazine (August 1983): 451.
Journal of Reading (November 1983): 180.

Kirkus Reviews (April 15, 1983): 461.
Kliatt Review (Spring 1986): 6.
Publishers Weekly (April 1, 1983): 60.
School Library Journal (May 1983): 80.
School Library Journal (August 1983): 26.
Sutherland, Zena. *Bulletin of the Center for Children's Books* (May 1983): 165.

Staying Fat for Sarah Byrnes

Del Negro, Janice. *Booklist* (March 15, 1993): 1313.
English Journal (January 1994): 78.
Kirkus Reviews (March 15, 1993): 369.
Lesesne, Teri S. *Journal of Reading* (September 1993): 68
Lockwood, Lucinda. *School Library Journal* (March 1993): 218.
Publishers Weekly (March 29, 1993): 56.
Vasilakis, Nancy. *The Horn Book Magazine* (May–June 1993): 336.

Stotan!

Abrahamson, Richard F. *Journal of Reading* (October 1986): 80.
Bulletin of the Center for Children's Books (June 1986): 183.
Carroll, Sissi. *English Journal* (November 1988): 89.
Chelton, Mary K. *Voice of Youth Advocates* (April 1986): 29.
Flack, Jerry. *School Library Journal* (May 1986): 199.
Hambrose, John. *Bestsellers* (June 1986): 115.
Kirkus Reviews (April 1, 1986): 549.
Nelms, Ben, and Beth Nelms. *English Journal* (April 1987): 83.
Roback, Diane. *Publishers Weekly* (April 25, 1986): 80.
Silvey, Anita. *The Horn Book Magazine* (September–October 1986): 596.

Index

The Author

Terry Davis is author of the novels *Vision Quest, Mysterious Ways,* and *If Rock and Roll Were a Machine*. He teaches in the MFA program at Mankato State University in Mankato, Minnesota.

The Editor

Patricia J. Campbell is an author and critic specializing in books for young adults. She has taught adolescent literature at UCLA and is the former assistant coordinator of young adult services for the Los Angeles Public Library. Her literary criticism has been published in the *New York Times Book Review* and many other journals. From 1978 to 1988 her column "The YA Perplex," a monthly review of young adult books, appeared in the *Wilson Library Bulletin*.

She now writes a column, "The Sand in the Oyster," on controversial issues in adolescent literature for *Horn Book* magazine. Recently she has been traveling the country to lead her "YA Biblioramas," intensive workshops on young adult fiction for teachers and librarians.

Campbell is the author of five books, among them *Presenting Robert Cormier,* the first volume in the Twayne Young Adult Author Series. In 1989 she was the recipient of the American Library Association Grolier Award for distinguished achievement with young people and books. A native of Los Angeles, Campbell now lives on an avocado ranch near San Diego, where she and her husband, David Shore, write and publish books on overseas motor-home travel.